ANTENNA ZONING

FOR THE RADIO AMATEUR

By Fred Hopengarten, K1VR

MW00560812

With Thanks to Contributors
Jim Altman, W4UCK
Greg Becker, NA2N
Ralph Brock, W5MV
Larry Burke, WI5A
Saul Dinman, W1SBD
Steve Fairfax
Steve Fraasch, KØSF
Brent Gourley, KE4MZ
Dave Hoaglin, K1HT
Phil Kane, K2ASP

With Special Thanks to the Following Contributors
Jay Bellows, KØQB
Jeff Briggs, K1ZM
Tim Ellam, VE6SH
Rusty Epps, W6OAT
John Hennessee, N1KB
Jim Idelson, K1IR
Chris Imlay, W3KD
Len Kay, K1NU
Jim O'Connell, W9WU
Dean Straw, N6BV

Production
Supervisor: Michelle Bloom, WB1ENT
Cover Design: Sue Fagan
Composition and Layout:
    Jodi Morin, KA1JPA
    Paul Lappen
Technical Illustrations:
    David Pingree, N1NAS
    Michael Daniels
Proofreader: Jayne Pratt-Lovelace

About the Cover

Front cover photo by Don Robbins, KL7Y. The author is pictured below a 20-meter antenna at KL7Y, Wasilla (near Anchorage) Alaska.

Published by:

ARRL *The national association for* AMATEUR RADIO

225 Main Street • Newington CT 06111-1494

Contents

Foreword

About the ARRL

Introduction—Why this Book was Written
- Times are Changing
- Acknowledgments
- About the Author

1: Principles that will Help You
- Expect the Best; Prepare for the Worst
- Commit Yourself to Win
- Build Your Winning Team
- Always Wear the White Hat
- Commit to a Policy of Full Disclosure
- Eschew a Commercial Use
- Preparation is Everything
- Know Exactly What You Want
- Know the Process
- Know the Law
- Know the Players

2: The Process in a Nutshell
- Preparation, Preparation and Preparation
- Buying a Home
- Evaluating Home/Antenna Sites
- The Purchase-And-Sale Contract
- Getting to Know the Players
- Building Permits
- Your Building Permit Application
- Public Hearings
- Deliberations and Decisions
- Appeals
- Lawsuits
- How Long will this Take?
- How Much will it Cost?

3: Your Winning Team
- You — Do you Know your own Skills?
- Your Supporters

4: Basic Preparations
- Materials You Will Need
- Documents You May Need
- Your Computer

5: Getting to Know the Players
- Types of Players
- Informal Discussions
- Fill Your Notebook
- Zoning Authorities
- Homeowners' Associations

6: Possible Objections
- Preparing for the Permit Application and the Public Hearing
- Structural Safety
- Airspace Safety
- Attractive Nuisance and Child Safety
- Aesthetic Impact
- Zoning Violations—Setbacks, Yards, Etc.
- Interference: RFI or TVI
- Property Value
- Radiation and Emissions Safety
- Alternative Technologies—Internet, Satellites, Smaller Antennas
- Proposed Height Not Required
- Ham Radio is "Just a Hobby"
- Antennas Not Specified in Application
- Not Licensed for this Location
- Lightning
- Noise
- Danger to Birds
- Remote Control
- Two Support Structures

7: Preparing the Permit Application
- Filing the Permit Application
- Format of this Sample Permit Application
- Information Sheet
- Cover Page
- Table of Contents
- Introduction
- Description of the Proposed System
- Why this Height?
- Good Engineering Practice
- Insurance
- Property Values
- Preemption
- Bylaw Section Nnnn Criteria are all Satisfied
- Conclusion

Exhibits and Appendices

8: Public Hearings—Your Big Moment in the Spotlight
Purpose
Advertising
Your Big Night
Substance

What I Bring to the Hearing
Federal Law
State Law
Radio Frequency Interference (RFI)
Nomenclature
Antenna Height
Public Service
Bioeffects or Hazards
Screening
Property Values
Birds
Caselaw.doc

Your Opportunity to Make (Or Break) Your Case
Continuances
Submitting a Proposed Decision and Order
The Viewing
The Press

9: Deliberations and Decisions
If You Won
If You Lost

10: Now, Get the Permit and Build Your Antenna!
The Process

11: Awkward Post-Permit Situations
Construction Problems
The TVI/RFI Complaint
Some Sample RFI Letters
The CB Interference Statute
The Renewal

12: Appeals
Process: Can you Spell *Remand*?
Appeals of a *Granted* Permit
Appealing a *Denied* Permit
Generic Appeal to Court

13: Tower and Antenna Regulation in Canada
Introduction
Jurisdiction in Relation to Radio Communication
The Townsend Report
Legislative Authority for Amateur Radio
Procedures Suggested by Radio Amateurs of Canada
Restrictive Covenants
Case Law
Safety Code 6
Radio Frequency Interference
Conclusions
Footnotes

14: Bibliography
Books
Articles
Useful URLs
Additional Biographic Information

Appendix A: The Law
Common Covenants and Restraints (CC&Rs)
Local Zoning Bylaws and Ordinances
Building Code
State Law
Federal Law Relating to Amateur Radio
Amateur Radio Service — Part 97 — Purpose, Etc
PRB-1
Lessons from the Past
Federal Law Relating to TV Antennas—the OTARD Rule (47 CFR 1.4000)
Federal Law Relating to Cellular Telephone, PCs, Paging, Etc.
Federal Law Relating to FAA Clearance
Federal Law Relating to RF Exposure
Federal Law Relating to Environmental Protection

Appendix B: Drafting a Bylaw, or Redrafting a Bylaw or Ordinance; Drafting a State Statute
In General
The Elements of a Bylaw
Examples
Drafting a State Statute

Appendix C: Lawsuits
Can I Be Sued?
Who Can Sue Me?
Can I Sue to Recover my Legal Fees or Legal Costs?
Full Text of Selected Cases (See CD-ROM)

Index   227

Foreword

We are pleased to offer this new book, written by Fred Hopengarten, K1VR, a prominent attorney in the communications-law field (and a noteworthy contest operator as well). In the last five years a huge body of regulations in the form of ordinances and bylaws has sprung up in towns and cities across the country, mainly in reaction to the increasing number of cellular telephone towers being erected. Hams have sometimes been caught inadvertently in the resulting crazy quilt of regulations.

Fred has written this book to help the ham navigate the thicket of ordinances and bylaws, with the goal of obtaining a building permit for an antenna system. After all—*no antenna, no ham radio!*

In his many years of practice as a communications-law attorney, Fred has seen the full gamut of emotional issues that can arise at public hearings. He goes through them in exhaustive but delightful detail, and explains the best approach to each issue.

Fred's lively, conversational tone minimizes the numbing "legalese" often used by lawyers. Numerous sample letters in Microsoft Word format are on the CD-ROM that accompanies the book. The ham (or his/her lawyer) can customize these letters to suit the circumstances peculiar to each case. The CD-ROM also has a wealth of precedent-setting legal cases and other reference materials, in Adobe Reader PDF format.

Any ham seeking a building permit for an antenna structure will be well served by this book. It is especially useful to help bring your local attorney up to speed on relevant communications issues and case law. Training your attorney in this way can save many hours and many dollars.

One last note: The ARRL Board has made available a limited amount of money to help defray expenses for truly landmark legal cases—ones that can set precedents that benefit all amateurs. The criteria for qualifying for these funds are daunting, as they must be. See the CD-ROM file for details: **ARRL Funding.PDF**.

If you have any comments or suggestions on how we can improve this product, please let us know by returning the handy Feedback Form at the back, or sending an e-mail message to **pubsfdbk@arrl.org** (Publications Feedback).

David Sumner, K1ZZ
Executive Vice President
Newington, Connecticut
April 2001

About the ARRL

The seed for Amateur Radio was planted in the 1890s, when Guglielmo Marconi began his experiments in wireless telegraphy. Soon he was joined by dozens, then hundreds, of others who were enthusiastic about sending and receiving messages through the air—some with a commercial interest, but others solely out of a love for this new communications medium. The United States government began licensing Amateur Radio operators in 1912.

By 1914, there were thousands of Amateur Radio operators—hams—in the United States. Hiram Percy Maxim, a leading Hartford, Connecticut, inventor and industrialist saw the need for an organization to band together this fledgling group of radio experimenters. In May 1914 he founded the American Radio Relay league (ARRL) to meet that need.

Today ARRL, with approximately 170,000 members, is the largest organization of radio amateurs in the United States. The ARRL is a not-for-profit organization that:
- promotes interest in Amateur Radio communications and experimentation
- represents US amateurs in legislative matters, and
- maintains fraternalism and a high standard of conduct among Amateur Radio operators.

At ARRL headquarters in the Hartford suburb of Newington, the staff helps serve the needs of members. ARRL is also International Secretariat for the International Amateur Radio Union, which is made up of similar societies in 150 countries around the world.

ARRL publishes the monthly journal *QST*, as well as newsletters and many publications covering all aspects of Amateur Radio. Its headquarters station, W1AW, transmits bulletins of interest to radio amateurs and Morse code practice sessions. The ARRL also coordinates an extensive field organization, which includes volunteers who provide technical information and other support for radio amateurs as well as communications for public-service activities. ARRL also represents US amateurs with the Federal Communications Commission and other government agencies in the US and abroad.

Membership in ARRL means much more than receiving *QST* each month. In addition to the services already described, ARRL offers membership services on a personal level, such as the ARRL Volunteer Examiner Coordinator Program and a QSL bureau.

Full ARRL membership (available only to licensed radio amateurs) gives you a voice in how the affairs of the organization are governed. ARRL policy is set by a Board of Directors (one from each of 15 Divisions). Each year, one-third of the ARRL Board of Directors stands for election by the full members they represent. The day-to-day operation of ARRL HQ is managed by an Executive Vice President and his staff.

No matter what aspect of Amateur Radio attracts you, ARRL membership is relevant and important. There would be no Amateur Radio as we know it today were it not for the ARRL. We would be happy to welcome you as a member! (An Amateur Radio license is not required for Associate Membership.) For more information about ARRL and answers to any questions you may have about Amateur Radio, write or call:

ARRL—The national association for Amateur Radio
225 Main Street
Newington, CT 06111-1494
(860) 594-0200
Prospective new amateurs call:
800-32-NEW-HAM (800-326-3942)
You can also contact us via e-mail at **hq@arrl.org** or check out *ARRLWeb* at **http://www.arrl.org/**

Why This Book Was Written

TIMES ARE CHANGING

There is a ham across town, on the next block, down the street, or even next door, and when he went to put up his tower no one bothered him. Let's call him *Oldtimer*. He doesn't have a permit and everything is fine. But there are several facts you may not have considered—perhaps legal facts, perhaps physical facts and demographic facts, perhaps ugly but nonetheless real facts.

Legal Facts

Since Oldtimer erected his antenna system, the town bylaws or ordinances may have changed. Since the passage of the Communications Act of 1996, towns all over the United States have aggressively been changing their bylaws or ordinances. Some towns have, thankfully, adopted bylaws that specifically exempt Amateur Radio from their new bylaw, which was designed to deal with cellular telephone and personal communications service (PCS) antennas.

Some towns, however, either (1) forgot to exempt ham radio or (2) specifically intended to make life difficult for the next radio ham to come along.

Don't think they've changed the bylaws or ordinances? Check out *Kleinhaus et al v. Cortlandt*, S. Ct. N.Y., County of Westchester, Index No. 19396/95, (Lefkowitz, J.), March 18, 1996. Kleinhaus, W2XX, contracted to purchase a residence in the Town of Cortlandt in 1993 at a time when the Zoning Code of the Town of Cortlandt had no height restriction applicable to freestanding antennas. Prior to completion of the purchase, the Town amended its zoning laws to provide that in an R-40

(residential one acre) zone the maximum height allowed for structures is two and one-half stories or thirty-five feet (Section 307-17).

W2XX was eventually successful when the Court found "that some of the ZBAs [Zoning Board of Appeals] findings are not supported by the evidence." The ZBA's determination to decline a variance was "annulled as irrational, arbitrary and capricious." The court remanded the matter to the ZBA for further proceedings and the parties were able to work out a compromise. W2XX got permission to erect a 100-foot tower.

However, this whole process cost the Town and W2XX a lot of money—a *lot* of money. The taxpayers of Cortlandt were not well served by the inability of their representatives to compromise earlier.

The purpose of mentioning this specific case is to show that even smart hams can get caught up in undesirable situations when a Town changes the bylaws before they move in. It could also happen to you after you've moved in and before you get around to applying for a permit. I'll get into all the details of the process in this book.

Physical and Demographic Facts

Towns that were once 20 miles from downtown and considered rural may have been built out. Today they may be considered suburban. Where once you had a rougher breed of townsman who felt that what you do on your land is your own business, you may now have a newer breed who uses phrases such as *view shed* to argue that his or her mere ability to see something you are doing on your land is an environmental concern.

In my own town today we have people who moved into homes at the end of a local airport's major runway, and now find themselves like Captain Louis Renault in the film *Casablanca*, who was "shocked, shocked" to discover that there was gambling going on at Rick's Cafe. These folks are surprised to discover that overhead there are airplanes taking off and coming in for landings. Imagine that.

This new breed favors more government intrusion into property rights. Without venturing a guess as to why, it is still possible to observe that such folks are more common in high-income suburbs than rural exurbs. So, as a town becomes more developed, expect tougher bylaws or ordinances.

Ugly, but Nonetheless Real, Facts

It is most saddening to report that America is still not free of pride and prejudice. I was once a lawyer in a case where a well-established ham, himself a descendant of President John Quincy Adams, with an existing 120-foot tower, confided that the applicant for a 100-foot tower in the same town would never have had as much trouble if the ham newer to the town "had a numeral" after his name. For this reason, bylaws or ordinances that are designed to give a lot of control to neighbors (think of such bylaws as equivalent to a neighborhood veto) are far more dangerous to someone who is a minority in town than to someone who represents the majority group in town and goes to the "right" church.

Similarly, I've been involved several times in a city where it would seem that native Spanish-speaking hams get short shrift in that city's building department. You may not like it. I certainly don't like it. But if you don't have several acres of buffer, with lots of trees to protect neighbors from the sight of your antennas, and if your plan calls for going above the tree line, think long and hard about how you can approach the town and accomplish your purpose, despite your minority status. If you've never experienced prejudice, you are lucky. Once you have, you'll understand more about the intersection of law and politics at the town-hearing level.

So, dear reader, it is not your imagination. It *is* more difficult to get an antenna permit today than it was in former times. I have written this book to try to give you a guide on how to navigate the difficult and dangerous shoals of getting an antenna permit in today's litigious and sometimes contentious environment.

ACKNOWLEDGMENTS

I thank my clients—the best teachers a lawyer could ever want for learning his craft, because they keep asking the hard questions. Sometimes those questions were asked out of fear, and sometimes out of wisdom. But they were always great questions.

Thanks also go to K1IR for the idea of writing the book. Finally, here's the answer to my wife's question: This book is what I was doing in front of my computer all that time! I was not just collecting Internet humor.   ;-)

ABOUT THE AUTHOR

Fred Hopengarten, K1VR

Six Willarch Road, Lincoln, MA 01773-5105
Tel: 781-259-0088,
e-mail: **hopengarten@post.harvard.edu**

Since 1990, Fred Hopengarten has acted as a consultant to venture capital firms on communications investments, and as a lawyer in communications law matters—especially those involving land use for dishes and towers. In addition, he founded Strong Signals LLC, a Maine company to own and operate a major communications tower and site near Lewiston-Auburn.

From 1978 to 1989, Fred was President of Channel One, based in Newton, Massachusetts, a company providing equipment and installation services for home and commercial satellite earth stations, as well as temporary downlinks for ad-hoc networks. He installed over 100 downlinks and 15 towers, obtaining building and zoning permits, buying hardware and climbing towers to erect antennas. Beginning as a startup, the company grew to operate private cable TV systems passing 13,000 homes.

Fred has published articles on various aspects of satellite television services in *Communications-Engineering Digest*, *ComputerWorld*, *Dealerscope*, *Pay Television*, *Inside SPACE*, *CQ*, *Satellite Communications*, *Radio-Electronics*, *Cable Television Business*, *CableVision*, *Cable Marketing*, *Broadcasting*, *Cable Television Business*, and the *New England Real Estate Journal*. He has published Amateur Radio antenna articles in *73*, *CQ*, *National Contest Journal*, *DX Magazine*, *QST* (with N6BV) and *The ARRL Antenna Book* (with N6BV).

A frequent speaker at technical and trade events, Fred has been a guest speaker for the Electronic Industries Association, the Satellite Communications Users' Conference, Online Systems, Payment Systems, M.I.T., Boston University, Resource Management Consultants, the Dayton Hamvention and others. He is interviewed frequently for articles, as well as TV and radio shows, on satellite television, mini-cable™ systems, and satellite teleconferencing, and has worked as a consultant to various companies and investors with an interest in the field.

Fred is a graduate of Colby College (AB, economics, Class of '67), Waterville, Maine, where he was also the chief engineer of the college radio station, WMHB. While creating Channel One, he taught, as an Associate Professor, Business Law and Marketing for one semester at Colby. He received his JD from the Boston College Law School (Class of '70). He is a member of the Bar in the District of Columbia (where he was Law Clerk to the Chairman of the Federal Trade Commission) and in Maine. He is also a graduate of the Harvard Business School (MBA, Class of '72).

Hopengarten has held an amateur Extra Class license since 1975, as K1VR. He received his first FCC license in 1956, as WN1NJL. In 1993, he wrote the user's manual accompanying *CT*, a software program for ham radio contesting that is the most popular such program in the world (over 20,000 users). He serves as a Volunteer Counsel for the ARRL, working mainly on zoning matters.

Fred is married to Betty E. Herr, MD, PhD, a physician in a private group practice at St. Elizabeth's Medical Center, Boston. The Hopengartens reside in Lincoln, Massachusetts. They have a daughter and a son.

1

Principles That Will Help You Win

EXPECT THE BEST; PREPARE FOR THE WORST

You are about to embark on a process that will have ups and downs. There are, however, some certainties. The first certainty is that you will run into some predictable questions, to which there are good answers. The second certainty is that your luck will dramatically improve with preparation. But you knew that. The third certainty is that you can benefit from the efforts of those who have gone before you, if you choose to pay attention and learn from their mistakes.

Remember the aphorism: Stupid people never learn. Smart people learn from their own mistakes. Brilliant people learn from the mistakes of others.

COMMIT YOURSELF TO WIN

If you are willing to work hard and prepare, learning from the mistakes of others, you will achieve several things:

- You will find that your early steps aren't as bumpy as you might have feared.
- You will dramatically reduce the cost of legal assistance, should you choose to retain a lawyer.
- You will put on a presentation that gives you the greatest chance of achieving the permit for the project you propose, and
- Heaven forbid, should you be denied after the initial hearing, you will increase your chances of succeeding on appeal.

You should understand that it is common for zoning bylaws or ordinances to include a clause that prevents you

from reapplying for a year, sometimes two, if you are turned down. So if you are not well prepared, you may introduce up to a two-year delay in your project.

There are other reasons for thorough preparation, such as avoiding the feeling of looking like an idiot in a public hearing, missing good DXCC countries, being unprepared for disaster communications and the like.

Some Zoning Boards like to think of themselves as "just your neighbors." They may encourage you to "come on down and tell your story." Unfortunately, while they may indeed be well meaning, civic-minded volunteers, they may not be familiar with Amateur Radio and may not understand what you intend to do. They may also consider themselves as "protectors of the town."

Always remember that this is a complex matter and that it involves both technical and legal issues that may be new to the Board. Be careful. Here are some thoughts you should banish from your mind.

- This application process is *silly* and it could take longer to get the permit than it will take to erect the tower. Banish this thought from your mind because it is true, but depressing. If you dwell on it, you'll never get going.
- This process is expensive and it could cost more than the structure and antennas. Banish this thought from your mind as well, because it is also true, and depressing. There have been many examples of hams who have succeeded in erecting good antenna systems almost exclusively because they conveyed the sense that they were committed to winning (and it showed in their preparation). As a result, Boards and neighbors decided that working with the

ham was a more fruitful strategy than what has become known as the *Nancy Reagan posture*: "Just say no."

Here's an example. Let's say you let it slip during a conversation with the Building Inspector, or a neighbor, that you really want to work something out here because you need the money for the kid's tuition, house payments, a used car, whatever. You are really telegraphing to the Board that they can walk all over you, because you can't afford to take this case to the next level.

I'd much rather say: "Amateur Radio is the most important activity in my life, outside of my family and my duties to God. I've waited through years of living in apartments for this time. I'm fully prepared to spend whatever it takes. Fortunately, I saved up a lot of money for this project. Life has been good to me and it is a thrill that I'll be able to spend whatever it takes to see this project through to completion." (Notice the repetition of the phrase "whatever it takes.") People should understand that you are really, really determined.

Forget political correctness. Let's put it this way: If you are a male, do not let your wife undermine this position. She should never be heard to say the equivalent of: "I just don't know how we're going to get through this, with bills to pay and all." Prepare yourself mentally to win.

BUILD YOUR WINNING TEAM

Not only must you prepare yourself for the project, but you must also assemble your team. Depending on your situation, you may have to brief your wife, the kids, other hams in town, neighbors, hams from the last place you lived and a team of "experts" as well.

Who are those experts? Before this is over, you may need a lawyer, a friend who is really good with a computer word-processing program and a scanner (or a professional secretary), a surveyor, a registered professional engineer, an insurance agent, a real estate agent and, usually at the last minute, a printer. Start thinking about whom you'll ask to be on your team now. It can be difficult to get those folks organized the night before a public hearing, because your emergency is not necessarily their emergency. And sometimes they need clearance from senior management to help you, or at least to help you in a hurry.

ALWAYS WEAR THE WHITE HAT

Conceptually, you should be thinking about how to wear the *white hat* at all times. This reference comes from the old cowboy movies. You could always tell the bad guys—they wore black hats. The heroes always wore white hats.

So Who Wears a White Hat?

- Good citizens who have prepared a permit application that complies with the bylaw or ordinance (or meets standards even better than the bylaw or ordinance)
- Public-spirited citizens who stand ready in times of natural disaster
- Homeowners who show they have considered the interests and concerns of their neighbors
- Applicants who have consulted with neighbors before showing up at the hearing
- Careful people who are going to build something that won't hurt anyone.

And Who Wears a Black Hat?

- Applicants who come in shouting "my home is my castle"
- Applicants who haven't really figured out what they are asking of the Board
- Applicants who haven't consulted with their neighbors
- Applicants who haven't thought their plans through very carefully
- Applicants who give off vibrations that they are haphazard people who are really capable of building something dangerous.

COMMIT TO A POLICY OF FULL DISCLOSURE

In preparing your permit application you may be tempted to glide over some detail. Perhaps it is a tiny detail. Perhaps you want to skip over something because you really haven't made up your mind. Attempting to hide something at the hearing is a *bad* idea. It is not what the wearer of the white hat would do.

Here are some examples of things that were not disclosed in permit applications that became embarrassing during the public hearing. There is no need to fall into these traps. The disclosure may not look good, but there is usually a convincing explanation for the issue. There is, however, never a good explanation for not disclosing some things in the first place. As your application will likely receive close scrutiny, you'll get caught. So before the examples begin, here's the basic rule: Spell it out and then explain it away.

- Example: Disclose who owns the property and assure the Board you have permission to build. If, for some reason, the land is in the name of your wife, a trust, your parents, a landlord, and so forth, include that information together with some sort of affirmative statement that you are applying with the permission and good wishes of the owner. You are the real party in interest. Don't let the Board get hung up on who owns the property, causing a delay to the next meeting until you show up with that permission.
- Example: Disclose all distances. *All distances.* Sooner or later, someone is going to ask. You are far, far better off if you say: "Please refer to Exhibit __, on page __, where you'll see that the distance to the property line is __ feet." The truth is that these things don't fall over and injure people. If you build according to the building code, it won't fall over. That is decidedly preferable to being asked to come back in two weeks, or next month, with the dimensions requested. So be sure to show the distances from every part of your house to the property line, from the proposed structure to various property lines—and adjacent homes or detached garages too!

Also measure the distance to the overhead electrical power line. I've seen many hearings held until the applicant provided a map that made sense. One last tip for situations in small yards (which may be, for this purpose, defined as half an acre or less): Learn the turning radius of any antenna you've thought of erecting. (By the way, to avoid confusion, always express the turning radius as a radius, not a diameter.)

ESCHEW A COMMERCIAL USE

What does that mean? It means that most radio hams shouldn't even think about a commercial use. Avoid the thought!

It is most likely that readers of this book live in a single-family residential district, where commercial uses are either forbidden or limited to "traditional home-based businesses." The latter phrase has always meant spinners and weavers, doctors, dentists, educational tutoring, carpenters, certain other tradesmen, and so forth. (Curiously, it is surprising how many ordinances appear, on their faces, to forbid activities such as selling insurance or writing software.)

Another possibility for permitted activities is certain forms of farming. Farming means that you may have a tree farm, a small patch of vegetables or corn (some ordinances even permit a farm stand without further permit in a residential district), again without a special permit.

An eight-foot whip antenna, to use one example, whether used for a commercial repeater or pager or used for ham radio, will not change the character of a neighborhood. But legally, there is a world of difference, because one is a commercial use and the other is an ancillary use of a residence. If the real reason you are erecting your ham radio antenna-support structure is to rent it out for a commercial use such as a cellular telephone antenna, then you may find yourself wearing the black hat. You will not be entitled to the special exemptions that amateurs receive with respect to RF emissions, environmental matters, setbacks and so forth.

My advice: *Don't do it.* Erecting a commercial antenna is a different ordinance, a different set of state and Federal laws. It is a separate book. It may well be no more obtrusive, and it will certainly be more lucrative, but it isn't Amateur Radio. You're the one wearing the white hat, remember?

PREPARATION IS EVERYTHING

The classic expression is apt: "If you don't know where you're going, any road will take you there." This means you must know what you want, know what you need (note the distinction between what you *want* and what you *need*, and remember to apply it to a neighbor who objects), and how you intend to accomplish it. After you've made those decisions, many of the steps involved fall out easily.

KNOW EXACTLY WHAT YOU WANT

If you are vague on your desires, many decisions become difficult. Here's what I suggest as an example of a level of specificity for your goal:

I Want: 130 feet of Rohn model 45G, with Phillystran guys at three levels.

I Need: 121 feet, comprised of 110 feet of sections and 11 feet of mast, with guys at three levels.

Now you can create a model of your backyard and move the structure around until it fits. Discover the several places it fits,

since there may be more than one spot. The manual way to discover the best place for the structure is to create a drawing of your plot on graph paper, to scale. Add in the buildings on the land (house, garage, shed, etc). Add the setbacks required by your town. You now have what is commonly called "the building envelope." Using the same scale, cut out a triangle, which is equivalent to the space "occupied" by a structure with three directions for guy wires. Now you can move that triangle around until you find sites that fit.

The more modern method is to use a computer to do your layout. I'll talk about that later in the book.

KNOW THE PROCESS

Before you submit your application, you must learn the process. Now you may be one of those exceptionally lucky individuals who live—or move—some-place where there are no regulations on antenna structures. Or you may live in a town where you may *by right* put up a system that is, say, less than 120 feet high.

On the other hand, you are probably reading this book because you are not one of those fortunate people! You must learn how to navigate through the shoal waters of your own town's regulations, ordinances or bylaws. This can be tricky, since every town or city runs things a bit differently. In general, your process will involve some sort of public hearing held before a Planning Board, or Zoning Board, or perhaps a Zoning Board of Appeals. Different towns have different names for these bodies.

However, the hearings you will probably run into are open, public meetings. This is true everywhere in the USA. So, even before you've begun to assemble your own application, find out when your Board meets and attend at least two meetings.

If your town is small and there are only a small number of people in the room, you may be asked: "Is there anything we can do for you?" Don't be a fool and blurt out: "Yeah, I'm here to find out how to put up a tower." The local reporter could mention this in the weekly newspaper, or it could hit the local rumor mill and put the neighbors on alert. Nothing good will come of it. Some people who hear the news will immediately assume that what you are going to propose to build is commercial, very big and very ugly. It is somewhat natural to assume the worst and fear the unknown.

Instead, should you be asked why you are there, reply simply with a variation on one or two of the following:

- It's kind of you to ask. I'm new in town and I wanted to learn how things work here.
- Actually, I've never been to a meeting of the Board of Appeals, and I've always wanted to see one or two.

It is rare for the Board to pursue the matter after such responses. But, since you may be nervous if inexperienced in such matters, here's how to handle the next round, should it come.

- Q: Are you planning to come before us?
- A: I haven't got anything worked up, but if I decide to seek a permit, I'll certainly be better off for having come this evening.

- Q: What kind of project did you have in mind?
- A: We just moved in. I don't have anything specific yet. I've never attended one of these meetings and I was curious.

Or, for the longer-term resident:

- A: I've lived here six years, but I've never seen one of these meetings. I figured that if I ever need to come here, I'd better learn what you are interested in hearing from applicants.

In other words, you don't have to tell them details at this point. It is unlikely that you will be pressed. And don't be so suspicious. They're just curious about why you are in the room, and trying to be neighborly. They are not mad at you yet. Don't give them a reason to be aggravated. Be pleasant, and smile.

KNOW THE LAW

Arrrrgh. I can't tell you how many times hams have called and said: "Well, before I bought the house, I went and talked to the Building Inspector, and he told me it would be no problem. So I bought the house, moved in and now I've got a problem."

So here's lesson number one: Don't take your medical advice from the teenager at the cash register in the drug store. And don't take your legal advice from the Building Inspector, or from the sweet lady at the counter in the Building Department who says: "You don't have to buy the whole zoning ordinance; I could just photocopy the relevant section."

Wrong. Buy the bylaw or ordinance. And if you are going to retain counsel, buy two copies: one for you and one for

Fig 1—As long as there have been hams, they've dreamed of big antennas! From June 1916 *QST*, entitled "After Reading 'QST'."

your attorney. If you don't provide your attorney with a copy of the local bylaw, s/he's just going to charge you for the time the paralegal spends getting it. While it is true that there are services available to lawyers (and anyone else who wants to spend the money) that sell CD-ROMs filled with the zoning bylaws of every municipality in the state, it is hard to bring the CD to a planning board meeting and pass a relevant section across the table. The typical cost for a bylaw or ordinance is $3 to $20. If it is expensive to purchase a copy of the bylaw or ordinance and if it is short enough, you may photocopy it for your lawyer. Generally, there is no copyright protection for a public law.

What could you find in the bylaw or ordinance that you might not get from the Building Inspector or Secretary to the Board?—Definitions, effective dates, cross-references to exceptions, a zoning district map, and so forth. You and your lawyer need the original bylaw. Don't accept anyone's word about what it says.

Don't even accept the word of a friendly ham who already lives in the town and who has his own antennas up in the air. He may not have kept up with changes instituted since he erected his antenna system. He may, God forbid, have never even applied for a permit. Don't laugh, I've seen both. A ham license is not a license to practice law.

KNOW THE PLAYERS

It is not crucial that you know the members of the Board personally. One of the blessings of America is that, by and large, we have better government than we deserve.

The Board may pay special attention to a gray-haired town father or mother with encyclopedic knowledge of town history. The Board might rule against you for any number of reasons. But you probably cannot obtain the good will of Board members starting now. Spend your limited time on preparing a terrifically thorough presentation, not schmoozing with Board members.

However, you should make a courtesy call on the Secretary to the Planning Board, the Secretary to the Board of Appeals and the Town Planner (if there is one). And, as mentioned above, you should attend meetings of the Planning Board and the Board of Appeals to see what kinds of questions pop up over and over again. Here's a clue: Boards always want setbacks, distances, construction details, scaled drawings, the names and addresses of abutters and so forth.

When you make such courtesy calls, do not ask: "Can I get a permit to erect my ham radio antenna system?" Instead, the correct question is: "What information does the Board need to properly evaluate my application for a ham radio antenna system?"

Be Nice, and Flexible

After you've made your courtesy calls, you will return to start assembling your application. After it is assembled, you'll be back to ask if you've included everything necessary for an evaluation. As a citizen of the town, and as a decent human being, it is always to your advantage to be nice—even if you feel that the Town is out to get you.

Yes, even paranoids have enemies. And the Town may indeed be out to prevent the installation of your antenna system. Even so, be nice and show respect. You could be dealing with these people for up to two years (if it drags out, and sometimes forever if the town has a renewal of the permit process.)

Remember, most local elected officials try very hard to be reasonable and fair with all applicants. Never forget that they are human beings too. Nobody appreciates someone who swaggers into meetings with a "know-it-all" attitude.

As someone very wise once said: "Therefore be wise as serpents and harmless as doves." And don't forget that most officials are willing to consider alternatives. So be sure you are willing and flexible too.

2

The Process in a Nutshell

Let me warn you now: If you do it right, this is going to be a grueling process. The majority of the burden will fall on you, the applicant. In a contested case, a lawyer will probably be a necessity if you want the permit to put up your antenna system.

PREPARATION, PREPARATION AND PREPARATION

Everyone watches TV programs about lawyers. They always show intense discussions with the client and exciting courtroom scenes. TV shows never portray the hours and hours of preparation, poring over documents and creating documents. Nonetheless, the magic to getting a permit lies in *both* preparation—creating your application and appendices, *and* live action—encounters with planners and the code-enforcement officer, as well as decisions made during the public hearing, if a public hearing is necessary. Sadly, much of the time in today's contentious environment, with people up in arms about cellular towers, a public hearing is indeed necessary.

The best way to promote the cause of winning a permit is to prepare a *terrific application*. Do it right and the hearing can be easy. In this chapter I will assume that you are buying a home in a different town, but even if you already have a home and are just starting the process of applying for a permit to construct an antenna system, read on.

BUYING A HOME

Selecting a Real Estate Agent

If you are like most people, you will select the most common form of real estate agent, an agent with listings in the paper. As you think about this, remember:

- The real estate agent is not *your* agent, but rather the agent of the seller

Meaning to you: Nothing you confide to the agent will remain confidential. So, unless this is really the boondocks, don't talk about your plans to install a really big antenna system. If the agent thinks a particular neighborhood could revolt when you announce your plans for an antenna system, you may not be shown every possible home. You may be shown homes in areas of town that the agent considers more *industrial* or somehow more *appropriate*.

- The real estate agent does not know enough—or doesn't want to learn—about antenna-related issues.

What am I really saying here? I'm saying that there are a lot of real estate agents around—some are great; some aren't so great. You have very specific requirements that you know best. For example, you don't want to be near a hospital—they are notorious RF noise generators that do not quiet down at night—a fact of great relevance if your enjoyment includes operation on 160 meters. You also don't want to be in a valley, or halfway down the side of a hill.

Unless the agent clearly understands the facts you are relating, you could waste a lot of time being shown homes that are totally unsuitable for a radio ham—because the lot is too small, because the home is located within a development with covenants, conditions and restrictions (CC&Rs) that will prove intolerable, because there is a giant hill between the house and Europe (or, if you live near the West Coast, that hill will be between you and Asia), and so forth. Life is too short to deal with a real estate agent who won't listen well.

Here's a test that has proven useful for others.

- Ask the agent to tell you the direction from this house to the local high school. If you get a nervous laugh and an answer to the effect that he or she was never much good at science or math, forget it. Find another agent.
- Ask the agent for the distance from the house to the nearest serious hill. This will flesh out the agent who doesn't own a USGS section map or the agent who can't scale out distances from a map. You don't want that agent. (I've never yet found a real estate agent who could actually do the trigonometry to tell you the angle to the hill.)

So who do you want as a real estate agent? You might find a really savvy agent, but it is rare for anyone to be as good as *you* are at the process. Begin by arming yourself with local maps, local USGS section maps (for elevations), and the bylaws or ordinances of communities you are willing to consider.

Never ever trust the word of a real estate agent on the question of what the local bylaw or ordinance says. *Almost never* trust the word of a real estate agent on the question of how close the house is to an interfering hill or mountain (you probably don't want anything higher than 2° to 5° above the horizon between you and Europe or Japan). Again, you will be your own best agent.

There is one possible exception: The buyer's agent. This person works for you, and not the person selling the house. He or she owes a duty of loyalty to you. But you may have to pay this agent whether or not you buy a house through him or her. Nonetheless, check it out. If your time is just not available, this may be your answer.

There is another strategy: Hire a local (really local) ARRL Volunteer Counsel. Such a lawyer may well have had experience with various local towns and bylaws. Let him/her guide you away from trouble and toward happiness. Then use a smart real estate agent of any stripe (buyer's or seller's).

What to Tell the Real Estate Agent

Tell the real estate agent that you have special land requirements in mind and house questions are secondary. Remember this: It is always possible to enlarge or remodel a house. It is very hard to improve a piece of land that is unsuitable for ham radio due to interfering hills, bad homeowner's association bylaws and so forth. It is almost impossible to enlarge or remodel a piece of land.

Don't tell the real estate agent that you want to erect "some really big towers." This may frighten her/him. Although you say "125 feet," the agent may somehow end up envisioning "1250 feet." The seller's agent owes you no duty of fidelity or confidentiality. You would obviously never tell the seller's agent how much you are really willing to pay for a house. That information will find its way to the sellers. In a like manner, avoid detailed discussions about your Amateur Radio plans.

Here's a checklist that you may just wish to hand over to the real estate agents with whom you work. [This is on the CD-ROM as filename: **House Hunting Guidelines.DOC**.]

Dear Agent:

House Hunting Guidelines

Please show me houses that are either at or near the top of a hill, atop a plateau or in a generally flat area. I want to see houses that offer more land than would normally come with a house in my price range.

Do not show me houses that are near industrial plants, hospitals, highways, AM radio stations and major cross-country high-tension lines. Do *not* show me houses that are in a valley (no matter how pretty), down by the river (if it looks like a valley), at the bottom of a hill or on the side of a hill, or in new developments of what was once farmland where there are few trees.

Sincerely,

Joe Ham

EVALUATING HOME/ANTENNA SITES

It was a while ago, but *QST* once published an excellent series of articles on selecting a site for DXing. The author was Paul D. Rockwell, W3AFM. "Station Design for DX," parts I through IV were published in *QST* from September 1966 through December 1966.

Part I—September 1966, page 50
Part II—October 1966, page 48
Part III—November 1966, page 50
Part IV—December 1966, page 53

There are three other articles on "Station Design for DX" authored by Clarke Greene, K1JX, published in the October and December 1980, as well as the January 1981 issues of *QST*. Reprints of these seven articles appear on the accompanying CD-ROM.

Recent editions (17th and later) of *The ARRL Antenna Book* have included detailed statistical information on the range of elevation angles needed to communicate from a host of worldwide transmitting sites to important receiving locations around the world. See Chapter 23, **Radio Wave Propagation** and Chapter 3, **The Effects of Ground**.

An innovative computer program called *YT* (Yagi Terrain analysis) is included with the 18th and 19th Editions of *The ARRL Antenna Book* to analyze the effect of irregular local terrain on the launch of HF signals into the ionosphere. You will need detailed topographic maps for your transmitting location to provide the terrain data for the *YT* program. In the USA, you can get information on how to obtain the appropriate topographic map for your area by calling 1-888-ASK-USGS or checking **http://mapping.usgs.gov/**.

Free topo maps may be found at **http://www.topozone.com/**, although navigation to find a particular location is frustrating because of the relatively slow server speed, especially when zooming or shifting the map center. The smoothness or "seamlessness" when changing from one topo map to an adjacent one is not perfect either. (But what do you want for free?)

Fig 2-1 shows a screen printout from the *YT* program for the K1VR QTH in the direction of Europe, an extremely important direction for long-distance work from New England. You can see that your local terrain can sometimes radically modify the antenna elevation response, compared to the response over flat ground. Nowadays, the prudent ham checks out a prospective location using such software tools to make sure the terrain really suits his needs!

Note in **Fig 2-2** how the hill located some 9000 feet in the direction of Europe affects the antenna performance. In fact, the antenna at 100 feet in height is just barely able to launch a direct signal over the top of this hill. Diffraction effects allow some signal to "sneak over" the top of the hill. The terrain data toward Europe was taken from a government USGS 7.5-minute topographic map.

Note very well that at VHF or UHF the terrain would

block line-of-sight signals trying to get to repeaters in this direction. Enough height is crucial for local VHF/UHF emergency communications.

Conclusion

In the very important direction toward Europe, this location is partially blocked by a hill. In order to achieve minimally acceptable results on the HF bands, a tower height of 100 feet is necessary. A height of 150 feet would actually be far preferable, but K1VR was sensitive to the desires of his neighbors and compromised on a height of 100 feet. This kind of analysis can contribute to developing the amateur's case for the need of a particular height.

THE PURCHASE-AND-SALE CONTRACT

Using an Attorney

To a layman, the "offer" or "purchase and sale agreement" may seem like the easiest portion of the house-buying effort—a portion the amateur can handle himself. Actually, it is the portion of the effort for which you will likely pay *much less* than you think is required, but for which you will get *much more* than you realize. One often-overlooked possibility is that once you submit an offer, and it is accepted, you have a contract. If you discover a bylaw problem at this point in the discussions, you may have to kiss your "earnest money" goodbye.

Here's a story combining several recent cases. I don't do real estate conveyancing, but I have a friend who does (and to whom I recommend prospective ham purchasers of property). I did all the "antenna law" work and (as it involved three towns,

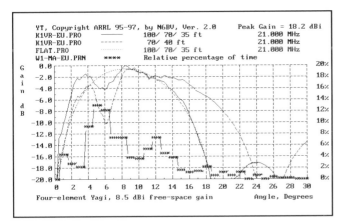

Fig 2-1—Plot from *YT* program showing the 21-MHz response for stacked 4-element Yagis at the Massachusetts QTH of K1VR. The solid curve is for a stack of three identical Yagis at 100/70/40 feet. This is compared to the response (dotted curve) for an identical stack of Yagis, but over flat ground to show the effect of the local terrain. Also overlaid on the plot (using asterisks) is the statistical range of elevation angles for the path from Massachusetts to all of Europe. At the peak elevation angle of 5° the K1VR stack has 14.3 dBi of gain, about 2 dB less than the flatland stack of Yagis. At an elevation angle of 6°, the difference is almost 3 dB, equivalent to one-half of the transmitter power. Consider the situation if only two antennas are deployed, with the top one at a height of only 70 feet. This is shown by the dashed curve. Now the deficit at 6° is almost 9 dB. This is equivalent to a mere ⅛ of the transmitter power!

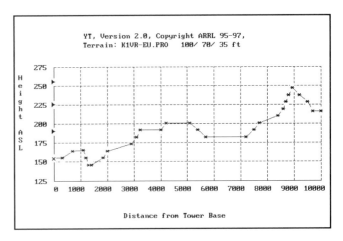

Fig 2-2—The reason why the K1VR antenna system has some problems in the 5° to 6° elevation-angle range is the hill about 9000 feet away from the base of his tower in the crucial direction toward Europe. The top antenna (shown by the top rightward facing arrow) is at 100 feet on the tower (at 255 feet above sea level, since the tower base is at 155 feet above sea level). It is just barely able to "peek over" this obstruction. The 60-foot high antenna must look into the side of the hill and the response suffers correspondingly.

including meeting the Building Inspector in each town to clarify interpretations of tough questions) and charged about $2,000. It was an unusually large amount of work for such a matter, but the ham was moving from the West Coast and couldn't really do any of the footwork himself.

The client now has a permit for the tallest antenna-support structure ever erected in his chosen town, and we never had to go through hearings of any kind. My lawyer friend, who did the conveyancing work, charged $750 (but should have charged about $1,250, since it took longer than anticipated). But the client got about $4,000 shaved off the purchase price when the conveyancer found some problems that the purchaser was willing to fix himself.

So the client (remember, this is a composite story) paid about $2,750 total, saved $4,000 and got the antenna system of his dreams. Since the client was working with lawyers who know their way around, we even introduced the client to a bank that (1) would close sooner than the one he found and was going to use, and (2) would match the very best price (mortgage interest rate) he found. His other bank was giving him a hard time on one element of his financial picture, while our recommended bank did not make a fuss about that element. For the latter service, there was no charge. All of these expenses, by the way, were a tiny tiny percentage (<0.5%) of the home's purchase price.

Note the picture I am painting. Using a lawyer early can save you money, time and grief. Of course, as an attorney you'd expect me to say that.

Making an Offer on A Home

Real-estate agents have been known to urge buyers to quickly sign an offer to buy a home, before you have a chance to retain a lawyer to represent you. As explained previously, don't forget that an *offer*, once accepted by the seller, is a *contract*.

Below is some wisdom in the form of documents prepared from the work of Jim O'Connell, W9WU, and John Swartz, WA9AQN. W9WU is an ARRL Volunteer Counsel as well as a senior litigation attorney in Illinois. He is the lawyer who succeeded in getting radio hams within a town declared a class, for a class action, in the *Borowski* case. John Swartz is a real estate, bankruptcy and commercial lawyer with Giffin, Winning, Cohen & Bodewes, Springfield, IL. Both have granted permission to use their ideas, but neither one is your lawyer—so you can't sue them if something goes wrong!

These forms below may prove useful for the "do-it-yourselfer," or for his/her attorney. These additions to the purchase-and-sale agreement are designed to give you and your attorney time to research the local bylaws or ordinances, and to force the seller (or the seller's attorney) to hand over relevant documents, and to give you (or your attorney) time to review them. You are free to negotiate the number of days necessary to do this. [These forms are on the CD-ROM as filename: **Addenda to Real-Estate Offer.DOC**.]

(For Existing Construction)

Addendum to offer to purchase between Buyers and Sellers, for the purchase of property at

_____

This offer is contingent upon there being no limitation imposed by any municipal or local unit of government having jurisdiction over the erection by Buyer upon the property of a system of antennas and supporting structures not less than _____ feet in height suitable for use by Buyer in the Amateur Radio Service as authorized under 47 CFR, Part 97. The acceptability of any such limitations shall be in the sole discretion of the Buyer. Buyer shall have twenty-one (21) days from the signing of this agreement to determine if there are any such limitations imposed which are unacceptable to Buyer, and declare this contract void. Seller shall thereupon return any funds deposited hereunder.

This offer is further contingent upon inspection by buyer and buyer's attorney of the applicable covenants, conditions, restrictions of record, homeowner's association rules (if any), or other documents restricting the use and occupancy of the land and premises in order to determine whether such documents contain any restriction which would prohibit buyer from erecting and maintaining his Amateur Radio antennas and supporting structure not less than _____ feet in height on the property. Within fourteen (14) days of the signing of this agreement, seller or seller's attorney shall furnish to buyer's attorney a spotted survey showing all improvements, restrictions and easements, and a copy of the existing title policy or other documents showing such covenants, conditions or restrictions of record as well as copies of any homeowner's association rules and regulations affecting the property. Buyer and buyer's attorney shall have fourteen (14) days thereafter to inspect the documents to determine whether the restrictions or conditions therein are acceptable to buyer. Should easements, covenants, conditions, restrictions of record, homeowner association rules or regulations exist so that buyer's installation of the aforementioned antenna and support structure may, in buyer's sole opinion, be inhibited or precluded, at buyer's option this contract shall be deemed null and void, and all obligations of both parties cancelled and all deposits refunded promptly.

_____
Buyers

_____
Sellers

Date: _____, 200_

(For New Construction/Subdivision where the builder/developer still owns the lots)

Addendum to offer to purchase between Buyers and Sellers, for the purchase of property at

_____

A. Buyer has informed Seller that Buyer is a licensed Amateur Radio operator, and Seller warrants that no covenants, conditions, restrictions of record, homeowner association rules or requirements presently exist or have been or will be recorded prior to closing, which would or which may be construed to restrict or prohibit Buyer, from and after closing and delivery of the premises, from installing and maintaining Amateur Radio antennas and support structure not less than ____ feet in height on the property. Seller further agrees that no such covenants, conditions or restrictions of record will be imposed by Seller or his transferees or assigns in any plat of subdivision or Planned Unit Development agreement affecting the property recorded hereafter. Seller agrees to provide Buyer, within fourteen (14) days of the signing of this agreement, and again ten (10) days prior to closing, with copy of the recorded plat of subdivision and all other documents showing all covenants, conditions or restrictions of record, homeowner association rules or regulations running with the land or affecting the property. Should such covenants, conditions, restrictions of record, homeowner association rules or regulations exist on either date such that Buyer's installation of the aforementioned antennas and support structure may be inhibited or precluded, then at Buyer's option this contract may be deemed null and void, all obligations of both parties canceled and all deposits refunded promptly.

B. Seller further agrees that, to the extent Seller is the owner of property located within 300 feet of the subject property, Seller will provide Buyer with a statement that Seller, as owner of adjacent properties, has no objection to the granting of a building permit for an Amateur Radio antenna support structure by the local municipality.

C. Seller also agrees that, to the extent that Seller controls any Architectural Committee, Homeowner's Association or similar committee from which permission is required for construction of the Buyer's Amateur Radio antennas and support structure, that Seller will grant or cause to be promptly granted such permission upon application by Buyer.

D. Seller further agrees that this offer is contingent upon there being no limitation imposed by any municipal or local unit of government having jurisdiction over the erection by Buyer upon the property of the system described in paragraph A, above. The acceptability of any such limitations shall be in the sole discretion of the Buyer. Buyer shall have twenty-one (21) days from the signing of this agreement to determine if there are any such limitations imposed which are unacceptable to Buyer. If there is such a limitation, then at Buyer's option this contract may be deemed null and void, all obligations of both parties canceled and all deposits refunded promptly.

E. The promises and covenants by the Seller contained in Paragraphs A through D hereof shall survive the closing of this transaction, notwithstanding the delivery of the deed by the Seller.

_____
Buyers
_____
Sellers

Date: _____, 200_

[Caution: This document was prepared in consideration of the laws of the State of Illinois. Real estate law varies among the states. You should consult an attorney prior to entering into any real estate transaction. If you mess it up, you'll have only yourself to blame.—*James C. O'Connell, W9WU.*]

GETTING TO KNOW THE PLAYERS

Fix Any TVI/RFI First

RFI should be irrelevant to your application for a permit to erect and maintain a ham radio antenna system. However, the existence of RFI will color the proceedings and inject negativity—against you, the applicant. Of course, the truth is that the higher the antenna, the *less* likely, not the more likely, there is to be interference. However, that's not the way most neighbors might feel about the subject. Remember, you want to wear the white hat here.

This is not an engineering text, so see **http://www.arrl.org/tis** for some good information packages on various aspects of RFI. The *ARRL RFI Book* (**http://arrl.org/catalog/6834/**) is another good source of help for all types of RFI problems.

BUILDING PERMITS

Building Permits are Not Special Permits

Let me define here some terms you will encounter as you proceed further on this adventure. Your city or town is likely to require a *Building Permit*. Absent some special circumstances, a Building Permit can usually be granted by a *Building Commissioner* or a *Building Inspector*.

In some municipalities, however, you may need to seek the grant of a *Special Permit*, *Special Exception* or a *Conditional-Use Permit*. For convenience, let's group these special types together and call them *Special Permits*. You may also encounter the *Variance*. All such grants are not the same thing as a straightforward Building Permit. (Take a look at **http://www.freeadvice.com/law/592us.htm** for further insight into the specialized terminology used in these matters.)

Information on the exact type of permission you must get is either contained in the local ordinance, state law or both. In general, the difference between a Special Permit and a Variance is that a Special Permit may be granted if you meet the conditions set out in the ordinance. By contrast, a Variance, again governed by the law of your state, may be considerably more difficult to obtain and will "run with the land" (meaning that it applies to your plot of land forevermore).

Normally, a Variance requires that the *Board of Appeals* or *Planning and Zoning Commission* (whatever may be the name of your local body) find that there are special conditions relating to the land before a Variance can be granted. What is "varied" (changed), in the circumstances of an amateur radio antenna system application, is normally a yard, setback, height, or other dimensional regulation.

Put simply, if your bylaw or ordinance says that you need a Special Permit to erect an Amateur Radio antenna system over 75 feet high, and must meet certain conditions to get this Special Permit, you are seeking a discretionary permit, but the rules are generally clearer. If your bylaw simply forbids what you want to do, because it will be too close to a property line, or too tall, to name two examples, then you need a Variance before a Building Permit may be granted.

Even after obtaining the correct grant, however, you will still have to deal with the Building Inspector, who can, in his or her discretion, make things easy (read: less expensive) or hard (read: more expensive) for you. Be respectful. Get and post the permit. Get the proper inspections along the way. Do things right.

It is not weird or unusual for the system to require you to apply for a Building Permit that the building inspector then denies, before you go to the Board of Appeals. After a win at the Board level, granting a Special Permit, you return to the Building Inspector for the actual Building Permit.

One common question I hear is: "What if I have an attorney draft a Variance application and represent me before the review board? What should I expect to pay the lawyer for these services?"

My response is, first, try to avoid a Variance application if at all possible. Conditional-Use Permits, Special Permits or Special-Use Permits are generally easier to obtain. Construction as *a matter of right* is best!

Always remember that no lawyer can guarantee results. You will be best off if you do your own legwork. Move in. Meet the neighbors. Charm them. Get a sense of who is going to give your trouble and who won't care. Get letters of support, or at least letters of indifference. Then apply for the permit. Figure that each evening meeting of a Planning Board or Board of Appeals that your lawyer attends will cost you about $500 to $750 (hourly rate times hours, and he gets travel time too).

YOUR BUILDING-PERMIT APPLICATION

Retail Politics

Once you have your proposal—your permit application— ready, it is time to show it to the neighbors. This is retail politics at the "door-knocking" level.

Former Speaker of the House, the late Thomas P. O'Neill (known as "Tip") (D-MA) relates this story in *Man of the House: The Life and Political Memoirs of Speaker, Tip O'Neill, with William Novak* (NY: Random House, 1987), (a very entertaining book, by the way) at page 26:

> The second political lesson I learned from my first campaign came from Mrs. O'Brien, our elocution-and-drama teacher in high school, who lived across the street. The night before the election, she said to me, "Tom, I'm going to vote for you tomorrow even though you didn't ask me to."
>
> I was shocked. "Why, Mrs. O'Brien," I said, "I've lived across from you for eighteen years. I cut your grass in the summer. I shovel your walk in the winter. I didn't think I had to ask for your vote."
>
> "Tom," she replied, "let me tell you something: people like to be asked."

The wisdom of that statement is remarkable. It is paralleled in the old salesman's maxim: "Always ask for the order." The thought also applies to antennas. "Everyone likes to be asked."

Canvas the Neighborhood

How much time do you have to soften up the neighbors? It might take six months to meet them first, and then to go back on a second occasion to discuss your project. If you don't have the time, or could never generate the nerve to go calling twice, you might be forced to condense the "meet and greet" and the "briefing" into the same meeting.

Eventually, though, you will need to put together a good printout of your whole permit application, in a nice presentation folder and pack up preprinted letters for each of the neighbors you are going to visit. It is okay to bring around a fat envelope carrying these things, because you want to convey to neighbors that you are going to speak with the entire neighborhood, as best you can. (There will always be people with whom you simply cannot get in touch, since they may be away for the season, traveling, in the process of divorce, or whatever.) You want to be seen as "trying to work with the neighborhood."

You should bring along three separate versions of a letter and let the conversation flow. As you head for *the close* (the point where you ask the person what he or she thinks of your proposal), remember that you have these three alternatives in your envelope.

Alternative 1 (for "Friends of the Project"):

I have no objection to the granting of a Special Permit [Special Exception, Variance] to him, and I encourage the Board to do so.

Alternative 2 (for "Neutrals to the Project"):

I do not object to this project.

Alternative 3 (for "Grumpy to the Project"):

[Name of ham] has reviewed the alternatives with us. The woodsy site he proposes is the most favorable to us from an aesthetics perspective.

or The woodsy site he proposes to use offers favorable screening to me as an abutter.

or The [woodsy] site he proposes is the least objectionable site.

[The accompanying CD-ROM has full letters ready for your use.] When the time comes to reach into the envelope and pull out a sheet, pull out the version of the letter that this neighbor is most likely to sign. If you have to guess, always choose the version that requires the neighbor to be *less* favorable (if in doubt between grumpy and neutral, hand over the grumpy version). The most important thing is not whether the person signs Alternative 1, 2 or 3, but rather that the person signs something that is not an objection.

It is not necessary to leave a copy of the permit application with each person. If that person turns out to be an enemy, you want inertia to be on your side. An enemy can always go to

Town Hall and pay for a photocopy of any permit application, but it is amazing how seldom that occurs.

Mostly, people just show up and complain on general grounds. The less they appear to know what they are talking about, the better off you are. For example, if an opponent really gets the wind in his sails, he might give the impression that you are going to erect the Eiffel Tower, when you plan on a support structure that never exceeds 18 inches in width.

Another mistake opponents make that can make them look bad is to bring in a photograph with a hand-drawn tower that is way out of scale. Your own scaled photographs or drawings will look much more reasonable in contrast. Don't be the first to give an enemy all the details to study each night and get heartsick over.

So bring the application and try to take away a signed letter. Note, however, that even a presentation to an enemy is a good idea, because you will want to represent to the Board that, as best you could try, you've spoken to each neighbor—"even the ones who are here tonight to oppose me."

Petitions

Instead of asking someone to sign a personalized letter, you may be thinking: "Wouldn't it be easier to just ask for a neighbor to sign a petition, with other names above it?" The answer is: "Of course!" The problem is that for the very reason that you think getting a signature on a petition is a good idea, a signature on a petition carries less weight. It is always easier to get signatures on a petition than to get letters. Because it is easier, there is a tendency for Boards (and elected representatives too) to consider petition signatures as less valuable. However, there are ways to make the obtaining of individual letters almost as easy as obtaining petition signatures.

How to Obtain Favorable Letters

Start with the Easy Ones

Go to a CD-ROM or the Internet version of ham radio license information. Check out **http://callsign.ualr.edu/callsign.shtml**. Print out your whole town. If your town is too big, look up only the surrounding neighborhood using your ZIP Code. In the United States, about one out of every 400 persons is a licensed radio ham, so even in a town of 4,000 people you should find about ten hams. These are the first people to whom you should go. But what do you want from them?
• Town background
• "G-2 on Neighbors" (originally a World War II term—think of it as "good gossip.")
• Analysis of your proposal
• Favorable letters, and
• Allies

Town Background

If you are new to the town, discussing your situation and desires with other hams in town will elicit information on previous experiences that hams have had with the town in erecting antenna systems. For example, it can be hard, if not impossible, to find previous applications for antenna systems. The town record-keeping system is just not indexed that way. It is indexed by property.

You might discover that a ham moved in seven years ago, applied for an antenna system, received a permit, erected it and moved away last year, just before you moved to town. So you wouldn't know about the existence of this precedent by driving around town looking for towers. Yet the file, found under that residence address in the Planning Board, Board of Appeals, or Building Department office, could prove very useful.

While prior administrative decisions in land-use matters seldom create a legal precedent (because each piece of land, and each neighborhood, is different), the use of such a file is the story it tells. Here's an example of a good use to which an old file may be put. There are towns that measure the structure's height to the top of the antenna-support structure, not to the top of the mast. There are towns that want both.

The file may show (read the minutes of the hearing, if available) if a prior applicant was represented by a lawyer. That lawyer may still be around, and, should you choose to hire that lawyer, you'll pay for less time in bringing a lawyer up-to-speed on amateur radio. The prior applicant paid for that education!

The file may tell you what kind of objections seemed to concern the Board, what additional information or documentation the Board required and what kind of restrictions, if any, the Board put on the permit. Use prior files to be sure that your application covers all of the ground that the Board wants covered.

Finally, the file can provide a basis for arguing that Western Civilization as we know it will not come to an end if a Amateur Radio antenna system is erected! If you want to be really thorough, you could use a prior antenna situation to create proof that real estate values do not fall when an antenna is installed. Just go to the assessor's office and look up the assessments for that house and the neighbors. You can even enter those assessments into a spreadsheet, before and after the erection of the antenna system, to show that values did not go down. In other words, prior files can be very helpful.

G-2 on the Neighbors

Other hams in town may have some knowledge of who your neighbors are, what causes they have been active in, if they have children, and so forth. Use the hams in town to get a read on your neighbors so that you'll know whom to approach first when the time comes to getting letters of support.

What you will want is momentum, *the big mo*. If you have six letters of support in your pocket, it is easier to get the seventh. So after obtaining a letter from any ham in town who will write one (it does not matter if the ham lives on the other side of town, so long as he is a resident of your town), it becomes part of your arsenal ("I have several letters of support already and I was hoping that you'd sign one too.")

Though the Board might give a letter from a ham across town less weight, it will still show that you've been out there trying to sell the project and that you are trying to work with the town and the neighbors. Remember, Boards do not like controversies. What they really want is a hearing where the proposal is unopposed, or where opposition is muted and the ham seems to have done his homework.

Analysis of Your Proposal

Of course, your application proposal is a brilliant solution to your antenna problems. You know that. However, you'd be amazed how useful it can be to have another ham look at the situation too. Is the structure really in the best place? Are your guy wires really oriented to minimize visibility? They'll be less visible against a background of trees. It always helps to have another set of trained eyes look over ("vet") the proposal.

Favorable Letters

You definitely want the most favorable possible letters from the other hams in town. You may find a ham who is a "town father" and who is well known to the Board. You could get really lucky and find a ham who formerly served on that very Board. You might find a ham who is in charge of the town's Civil Defense and who can write a letter for you on town stationery (don't laugh; it has been done).

Generally, however, it does no good for the ham to identify himself as a ham in the letter, unless he can write a letter that says, in effect, "You may recall the hue and cry at the time that I applied for my permit. It was predicted that Western Civilization as we know it would fall apart. I am pleased to report that, since then we, as neighbors, have reconciled and that despite dire predictions, no television interference has occurred—and property values have risen."

Unless you get a letter from another ham in town that says such things, leave off his ham radio affiliation, as it will only be used against him, as in "Well, harrumph, he's another ham radio operator, so you'd expect him to be insensitive to the *real* issues."

Allies

Courting the other hams in town can also be useful for the purpose of developing allies. The best kind of ally is one who reviews your application with you, provides G-2 on the neighbors, and shows up at the hearing. But there is also the question of lobbying.

You'd be amazed. It happens. There is going to be a period of weeks, sometimes months, between the point where you reveal your plans for the first time and the evening of the hearing. You could discover that a ham in town is the brother of a member of the Board considering your application. You could discover that a ham is married to your next-door neighbor's sister. Whatever. The point is that a strategic word put in here or there could prove useful. For all of the above reasons, try to find and make friends with the other hams in town.

Now Go to the Neighbors

Again, start with the ones you suspect, based on prior intelligence, will be the most inclined to sign favorable letters. This generally means the ones least able to see your house and antenna system. What you are looking for here is the *steamroller effect*. Get the hams on your side, and then get the more-distant neighbors on your side.

If your experience with a neighbor has been minimally favorable, as you pack everything up, putting your application back in your envelope or briefcase, putting away the letter that the neighbor just signed and heading for the door, pause at the door and ask: "Who do you think I should talk to next?" Then ask: "What should I know about him/her/them?"

You'd be amazed at the responses you'll get when you are no longer taking notes. It will prove very useful when you approach the next neighbor.

Now you know what the difficult questions are going to be and you've had a little practice in making these presentations. You'll be better off now handling the nearby neighbors. Remember, if the closest neighbors don't object, few Boards will refuse your permit because some wacko from the other side of town stands up and makes irrelevant and possibly illegal noises about electromagnetic fields.

PUBLIC HEARINGS

It is highly likely that there will be a public hearing, unless you are applying for a permit as a matter of right, just like applying for a permit to renovate your bathroom. If you are applying for a Conditional-Use Permit, a Special-Use Permit or a Variance, you will be faced with preparing for a public hearing, and this necessitates planning and contact with the neighbors.

The Viewing

It is likely that the Board (the permit-granting authority) will want to come by your place to have a peek at the situation. This is not trespassing. Clean up your place and welcome the visit. Coffee and donuts is unnecessary and will likely be ignored. The visit may last only five minutes.

DELIBERATIONS AND DECISIONS

Before the public portion of the meeting is closed, you may submit a proposed decision, which may be ignored, or may prove useful, depending on whether or not the Board is going to grant your application. After that, if your state has an open-meeting law, you may sit in on the deliberations, even take notes, but say nothing.

APPEALS

If your town bylaw limits all antennas to 35 feet, or if there is some other reason that the Building Commissioner (sometimes called a Building Inspector) cannot issue you the permit you have requested, you will appeal to the Board of Appeals, the Planning and Zoning Commission or whatever it is called. This is another reason to own your own copy of the whole zoning bylaw, as the appeal process will be spelled out in the bylaw.

Keep your eyes open, however, as the Building Inspector may recommend that you apply for an appeal in the form of a request for a variance, a request that may be difficult or impossible to obtain, while your best action might be simply to appeal a decision of the building inspector on the grounds that s/he is wrong, or that Federal law supersedes. In other words, the exact form of your appeal is a legal question, with very real consequences.

LAWSUITS

Lawsuits take a while, cost serious money and have an uncertain outcome. Seek advice about all of your alternatives short of a lawsuit before commencing one. This is especially true because the most common outcome of a lawsuit by a ham who wins it is that the ham is returned to the same original Board, with instructions from the court. If it becomes necessary to file a lawsuit, the information in the Appendix and CD-ROM will save you a lot of money.

HOW LONG WILL THIS TAKE?

It will probably take three months to a year to get through the Board level and back to the Building Inspector. Add another one to two years for a lawsuit, a win and return trip to the Board. While you could be done in six months, it is not unheard of for this time frame to be three years.

HOW MUCH WILL IT COST?

The certain answer to this is: More than you want to pay! You can rely on the fact that few hams like the requirement imposed by local law to go through the hearing process. Fewer still like retaining a lawyer for the hearing process. No one likes retaining a lawyer to appeal the matter to a court.

Cost is measured in the hours required. Lawyers do not generally take such cases on a fixed fee. I've never heard of it happening. Of course, if the fee were high enough, one supposes that lawyers would be more flexible.

Very roughly, the application process may cost as much or more as the structure and erection. Very roughly, an appeal can run from $3,000 to $20,000 in the year 2000.

3

Your Winning Team

YOU—DO YOU KNOW YOUR OWN SKILLS?

You are about to embark on a program of assembling a construction proposal, convincing your family, lobbying your neighbors, presenting your proposal to a public meeting and defending yourself against unwarranted attacks. Are you really good at all those things? To do it well, you must be part landscape designer, civil engineer, writer, photographer, graphic designer, salesman, lawyer and humble neighbor.

As a landscape designer, you will be selecting the spot on the property that puts the antenna system in the least visible place. Ask yourself if you could move the structure so that it will not be directly in line with the view from a neighbor's kitchen window. You don't want your neighbor thinking about you every time he or she washes dishes!

As a civil engineer, you will be trying to locate the structure so that guy wires go in the right places (which means not landing in the middle of your swimming pool), and thinking ahead about such questions as "How will I get the concrete in here?"

As a writer, you will be assembling a terrific written proposal that covers all the ground, has a beginning, middle and end and asks for what you need.

As a photographer, you must get good, usable pictures—pictures that will reproduce well after scanning and permit you to tell a story. They must also be pictures that show what people will recognize and that fairly represent what is going to happen.

As a graphic designer, you will be assembling a proposal that is a sales document and law brief, all wrapped up in one cover. You'll be selecting photos and deciding when to put two or four on a page and when to put just one. You'll be deciding how to present a map of your neighborhood, being sure to show tree lines.

As a salesman, you'll be arguing persuasively for what you intend to do, presenting yourself door-to-door in a way that will leave even people who oppose you saying that you dealt with them fairly.

As a lawyer, you will be marshalling all the Federal and state law that benefits you, especially Federal law on the limited preemption of local zoning for antenna systems that favors hams, and the total preemption of RFI/TVI, including telephone interference.

As a humble neighbor, you will always remember that you must live in the neighborhood after this is all over, that your children must go to school with the kids of those who opposed you, that you must worship with those who fumed at you.

If you lack any of the professional skills just mentioned, ask a friend for help or hire a professional. If you assume that you can submit a messy, disorganized application—missing required information and necessary arguments—yet the Board will still see the merit of your application anyway, you are dreaming. This almost guarantees that you'll have to retain a lawyer later to straighten out the mess. So start right now to arrange for services that require skills that you lack.

YOUR SUPPORTERS

Family

As discussed in Chapter 1, **Principles That Will Help You Win**, make sure your family is prepared, so that they don't raise unnecessary red flags in casual neighbor-to-neighbor discussions over the back fence or during a town or a Zoning Board meeting.

Other Hams

It will prove useful to know about other hams in town, whether or not they are active and whether or not they have antenna systems. They may be able to tell you about antenna systems you may not yet know about. They may be able to give you tips on dealing with town personnel. Other hams may be a good source of information on how others have fared in this process, what the Boards like to see and hear, how to get a favorable letter from the local Civil Defense people, emergency management agency or police chief and so forth.

To locate other hams in your town, try:
http://www.arrl.org/fcc/fcclook.php3 or
http://ifsclinux.ifsc.ualr.edu/callsign.html.

Your Local Club(s)

Ask around. There may be a local radio club that you don't know about. It may not be based in your new town but it may cover and serve your new town. How many members does it have? Does it have a TVI committee? Does it have public-service activities? Answers to these questions could prove useful later.

Your Assembled Experts

Before deciding to do it all yourself, take a long hard look at what needs to be done. If you can't do something yourself, ask friends or hire someone who can. If you live in a contentious and expensive suburb, expect resistance. If you live deep in the woods, away from historic districts, on a large lot, with a bylaw that appears to guarantee the success of your application—and you like to gamble—rejoice. Help may not be necessary.

On the other hand, since you want to wear the white hat throughout the permit process, experts will prevent you from making a mistake that may later be interpreted as an attempt to "sneak one by" the relevant Board.

Your Attorney

The ARRL Volunteer Counsel Program

The ARRL Volunteer Counsel (VC) Program has several goals. It was developed to provide a better means of tracking and, when necessary, opposing local ordinances and statutes that might have a detrimental effect on the Amateur Radio Service and League members.

The second goal is to compile and maintain an up-to-date list of attorneys capable of representing amateurs involved in antenna or RFI disputes. Amateurs who need the services of an attorney to deal with local opposition to their radio activities frequently call ARRL Headquarters.

The ARRL does not expect a VC to represent an amateur free of charge. When HQ makes referrals, the point is made that VCs make a living practicing law and amateurs should not expect free or reduced cost legal representation. Volunteer Counsels are asked, however, to provide an initial consultation *gratis* so that the amateur may knowledgeably decide what further steps to take.

For the latest version of the list of ARRL Volunteer Counsel, e-mail: **reginfo@arrl.org**, or go to the ARRL web page **http://www2.arrl.org/field/regulations/local/vci.html**.

What to Expect of Your Attorney

Selecting an attorney is one of the scariest things you may do. You may find the following document interesting. I use it whenever I hire another law firm or lawyer. Perhaps you will find it useful also. See the CD-ROM, filename: **Attorney Fees Letter of Understanding.DOC**.

To: Law Firms
From: Fred Hopengarten
In re: Billable Hours, Invoices and Expenses

Hiring a law firm is one of the scariest things that I do for myself, my business partners or my investors. It is tantamount to opening one's pocketbook and saying: "Here, how much do you want?"

Legal services are necessary from time to time, however, and therefore it is important that everyone understand the rules of the game. I hope that this document will explain those rules as we (my partners and I) see them.

Activities Not for the Benefit of the Client

We have a distinct distaste, and decline to pay, for activities that are performed for the benefit of the firm, and not for the benefit of the client.

One example is a conference of several attorneys for the purpose of merely deciding the scheduling of work among them. The client should not be paying for time spent while one attorney says to another: "No, Alice, you'll have to attend that deposition, as I have a hearing in Oshkosh that day." We have seen invoices in which the firm attempted to bill us for both the speaker and "Alice" for that conference.

Another example is a situation in which a second attorney must be involved merely for a ceremonial occasion. In our view, the client should not pay for a second attorney to attend a court session when his or her attendance is required principally to move the admission of the primary attorney.

Or, for instance, a loan closing may require the partner in charge of the relationship of the bank to be present when the bank-lending officer is present. Yet the partner's time is really to cement his relationship with the bank, and not to do any substantive work. That's a sales expense, and does not inure to the benefit of the party who may be called upon to pay the bill from the bank's law firm.

Yet another example is the situation in which an attorney simply must take an emergency telephone call during a deposition. Such things happen in this life. Yet we'd be mightily distressed to learn that both clients were billed for that time.

If an attorney goes to, let us say, a land court to check on several matters in one trip, we expect that the trip will be apportioned, both as to time and expenses, not billed to each client separately.

We also object to being billed for time spent by an attorney in contacting us to suggest work that he might do, to soliciting approval for such work (we regard such activities as an attorney's sales expense), discussing billing matters (a collection expense), or entertaining us or our employees (in general, we'd all be better off at home with our families, thereby lowering the divorce rate).

At billing rates such as $100 per hour and up, we expect that no lawyer will bill us for time spent making photocopies, getting directions, preparing bills, organizing a file chronologically and so forth. These matters are properly handled by the lawyer's secretary, for which no additional charge should be made. In this regard, merely moving such matters into the hands of a paralegal, despite the fact that the paralegal has a much lower billing rate, does not satisfy the criticism. Such functions are properly overhead charges, not client charges.

I also get upset about overtime charges for secretarial help when the attorney was simply involved in someone else's matter during the regular business day/week. For that matter, I don't expect to be billed for secretarial time in any event, expecting that it is part of the attorney's hourly rate overhead. If it is secretarial or clerical work, we do not expect to see it on the bill.

Quality Control

In the course of the past 20 years, I have sometimes been told that certain time was necessary on our matter for purposes of quality control. Since I absolutely hate to pay for a lawyer reviewing the work of another lawyer, may I suggest the following guidelines?

• If time is spent reviewing work of a junior attorney, where a principal use of the review is to evaluate the quality of the junior attorney's work with a view toward the question of partnership, it is inappropriate to charge the client.

• If the time is spent with the expectation that something can be improved a scintilla, then the benefit is likely not worthy of the cost.

• If the reviewing attorney finds significant things to change, then the attorney who did the work has done an inadequate, perhaps even faulty, job, and it would be inappropriate to charge the client for the faulty workmanship of the junior attorney, even at a lower rate. If the master plumber must rip out the work of the apprentice, should apprentice time be charged?

Presentation of Invoices

We will not pay invoices that are non-specific (as in: "For professional services rendered"), unless the matter has been taken by the law firm on a contingency, in which case, I assume that a very specific agreement on fees has been made.

We require presentation of the invoice in what some call "insurance company format." This means that we want to see the name (or initials in the case of attorneys well-known to us) of the attorney, the date on which work was performed, the nature of the work (time slip detail is adequate), the amount of time, the billing rate for that attorney, and the extension (amount of time, times billing rate).

For almost all law firms, merely correcting the spelling of time slips will permit the immediate presentation of a bill, so we do not believe that this requirement is burdensome.

Increases in Billing Rates

If an attorney has been given a raise, and the billing rate for that attorney has been raised, we require that we be notified of that increase in billing rate reasonably *in advance.* Furthermore, if it is likely that the billing rate will be raised during the course of a matter, we consider that to be a very serious matter, as we might well choose a different attorney to represent us.

I hope you will not be offended when I tell you that I was once invited to retain a lawyer whose billing rate was $90 per hour, only to discover that, during the course of the matter (only 6 months later), that lawyer's billing rate was raised to $125, a 38.8 per cent increase. Frankly, we considered that to be a "bait and switch" billing tactic, and the resulting discussions were distinctly unpleasant for all concerned.

Expenses

If you're going to invite someone from our firm out to eat, and have the meal appear later as an expense, please let us pay for it in the first place. If you need lots of photocopies of a document, please let us arrange it. If you need printing, we'd like to arrange it. In our experience, law firms, feeling that such items are on the client's nickel anyway, are rarely the smartest buyers of such services.

Which brings up Federal Express. This fine company has done a good job of convincing the legal profession that it is the only way to go. Not so. We get fine service from the U.S. Postal Service with Express Mail, at 75 per cent less cost. In addition, ordinary UPS is almost always overnight service within our region, at 20 per cent of the cost of FedEx. Purolator and Emery can also save money and deliver fine service.

FAXing does not necessarily solve the FedEx problem, by the way. The most efficient way to move a document from your word processor to us is to send it as a file by e-mail. This gives us the document in a form that we can immediately edit, digitally, and return. If you, or your office manager, cannot manage to figure out how to use a modem and e-mail, let me know RIGHT NOW. I'll buy one and install it for you. They cost less than $39 in 2000, and, in the course of a relationship, it will save us A LOT of money, in FedEx tariffs and messenger fares, or even telephone charges for FAXs, if I teach you, or your secretary, to use it TODAY. If you cannot handle electronic mail, including attachments, or scan documents for computerized editing, please let me know today, as this is truly essential.

We'd also like it (assuming that there is no extra expense) if you'd learn to make copies for us on two sides of paper, saving filing space and shipping costs.

Thank You

Obviously, if we didn't have confidence in your firm, we would not have asked you to work on our behalf. Please see that all attorneys who work on our matters see this memorandum. Thanks for helping us out.

That's the letter I always convey to law firms hired for personal or business use.

What to Expect from Your Attorney: The Retainer Letter

By contrast, when I'm hired as a lawyer myself, I send out a retainer letter to my client. You should ask for one. Some states require that such a letter be presented to all clients. My retainer letter, and that of K2ASP, is found below. In addition, I send out advice to clients on how to deal with lawyers after the decision to hire one has been made. Here are those documents, which are on the CD-ROM as filenames: **Hopengarten Retainer Letter.DOC** and **Kane Retainer Letter.DOC**.

Dear **

Thank you for having the confidence to retain me as counsel with respect to various legal issues arising in connection with your desire to erect and maintain an Amateur Radio support structure (the "Matter"). I appreciate the opportunity to serve as counsel to you in this matter, and I look forward to working with you on other matters as well. This letter confirms the terms and conditions of my work for you.

Although you presently are retaining me only with respect to the Matter, the following description of billing policies and scope of engagement is intended (in the absence of a later writing confirming alternative arrangements) to apply as well to any future service that I may provide to you on other matters.

I have established a separate invoicing account for you and intend to bill you occasionally. You will be charged for time, generally calculated to the nearest tenth of an hour, plus costs incurred on your behalf other than routine office expenses, including but not limited to, travel, international long distance phone calls, photocopies of more than a routine number, overnight mailing, and any recording, filing, registration or professional service fees and court costs. My current hourly billing rate is $____ per hour. This rate is subject to a small annual increase, and I would be happy to provide you current rate information at any time upon your request. Though results cannot be guaranteed, I will make every effort to have all work done in the most cost-effective manner consistent with good professional practice.

As an ARRL Volunteer Counsel, there is no charge for the initial hour of our consultation.

You have agreed to pay me $1,000. This fee is non-refundable and represents your fee for my guidance in the field of Federal law on antenna-support structures, even if I do no further work for you. If I do further work for you, I will not charge for the early hours of the engagement until all of the retaining fee has been applied; then I will begin billing at the full rate of $____ per hour, plus disbursements. The retaining fee will be applied to both my hourly rate and costs.

I want you to be clear as to what I am agreeing to do for you. I am a member of the Bar in the District of Columbia and in the State of Maine, and familiar with the Federal law of pre-emption with respect to antenna systems, as well as ancillary related law in several jurisdictions. I am not a member of the bar here in Massachusetts. Should local litigation counsel be required, we will talk about whom to select for that purpose, as, in my experience, local counsel can often make things happen that no one else can, and, as is my standard practice, I will act as a consulting attorney to the litigation attorney.

I hope this letter satisfactorily describes our relationship. If these terms are acceptable, please sign this letter and the enclosed duplicate, and then return the duplicate copy to me along with the retainer. Your signature will acknowledge that you have read the letter carefully and consent to its terms, and that you have retained one fully executed original of this letter for your files.

If you have any questions about this letter or my services, please do not hesitate to call me.

Sincerely,
Fred Hopengarten

Client:
Date:

Dear *.*

It was a pleasure conferring with you [Conference Details]. I have enclosed our standard hourly fee agreement that the State Bar requires when legal services are rendered of a possible value of $1000 or more, to protect both the client and the attorney.

Please initial each page, sign one copy on Page 2 (as I have done), return one copy in the enclosed envelope and retain the other for your files.

I would also ask that you sign and return three copies of "Designation of Attorney" statement. At times I have run into other parties and attorneys who require such written designation.

I thank you for your consideration in hiring us to do this project, and I look forward to the next phases.

Sincerely,
Phil Kane

— Agreement —

ATTORNEY-CLIENT FEE AND REPRESENTATION AGREEMENT

(Hourly Fee)

This document ("agreement") is the written fee contract that California law requires lawyers to have with their clients. We (Philip M. Kane d/b/a Communications Law Center) will provide legal services to you ([Client Name]) on the terms set forth below:

1. CONDITIONS. This agreement will not take effect, and we will have no obligation to provide legal services, until you return a signed copy of this agreement and pay the initial deposit called for in Paragraph 4 below.

2. SCOPE OF OUR SERVICES. You are hiring us as your attorneys, to represent you in connection with the matters listed on the Schedule of Details attached. We will provide those legal services reasonably required to represent you. We will take reasonable steps to keep you informed of progress and to respond to your inquiries.

Our services will only include litigation of any kind, whether in court, in administrative hearings, or before government agencies or arbitration tribunals, as specified on the Schedule of Details attached. If other litigation is required, a modification of this agreement will be necessary.

3. YOUR OBLIGATIONS. You agree to be truthful with us, to cooperate, to keep us informed of any developments, to abide by this agreement, to pay our bills on time and to keep us advised of your address, telephone number and whereabouts.

4. DEPOSIT AND FEES. You agree to pay us an initial deposit of $[Initial Deposit] by [Initial Deposit Date]. Of the initial deposit, $ [Initial Fee] will be our minimum fee, paid in exchange of our agreement to represent you. The minimum fee is non-refundable, but our hourly charges will be credited against it. The remainder of the initial deposit, as well as any future deposit, will be held in a trust account. You authorize us to use that fund to pay the fees and other charges you incur. Whenever your deposit is exhausted, we reserve the right to demand further deposits, each up to a maximum of $ [Deposit Cap]. You agree to pay all further deposits within [Deposit Days] days of our demand. Except for the minimum fee, any unused deposit at the conclusion of our services will be refunded.

5. LEGAL FEES AND BILLING PRACTICES. You agree to pay by the hour at our prevailing rates for time spent on your matter by our legal personnel. Our current rates for legal personnel (and other billing rates) are set forth on the attached Schedule of Details, which also provides for periodic increases.

6. COSTS AND EXPENSES. In addition to paying legal fees, you agree to reimburse us for all costs and expenses including, but not limited to, fees fixed by law or assessed by public agencies, telephone toll calls (including TELEFAX and Electronic Mail), messenger and other delivery service fees, process server fees, postage, in-office and outside service duplication and copying charges, mileage at 25 cents per mile, investigation expenses, consultant fees and other similar items for which we bill you. You authorize us to incur all reasonable costs and to hire any investigators or consultants reasonably necessary in our judgment.

7. STATEMENTS. We will send you periodic statements for fees and costs incurred. You will pay any outstanding balance due within fifteen (15) days after the date of each statement. You may request a statement at intervals of no less than thirty (30) days. Upon your request we will provide a statement within ten (10) days of request.

8. LIEN. If your matter relates to recovery of money or monetary damages, you hereby grant us a lien on any or all claims or causes of action that are the subject of our representation of you under this agreement. Our lien will be for any sums due and owing to us at the conclusion of our services. The lien will attach to any recovery you may obtain, whether by arbitration award, judgment, settlement, or otherwise.

9. DISCHARGE AND WITHDRAWAL. You may discharge us at any time. We may withdraw with your consent or for good cause. Good cause includes your breach of this agreement, your refusal to cooperate with us or to follow our advice on a material matter or any fact or circumstance that would render our continuing representation unlawful or unethical. When our services conclude, all unpaid charges will immediately become due and payable. After our services conclude, we will, upon your request, deliver your file to you, along with any funds or property of yours in our possession.

10. DISCLAIMER OF GUARANTEE. Nothing in this agreement and nothing in our statements to you will be construed as a promise or guarantee about the outcome of your matter. We make no such promises or guarantees. Our comments about the outcome of your matter are expressions of opinion only.

11. EFFECTIVE DATE. This agreement will take effect when you have performed the conditions stated in Paragraph 1, but its effective date will be retroactive to the date we first performed services. The date of this agreement recorded below is for reference only. Even if this agreement does not take effect, you will be obligated to pay us the reasonable value of any services we may have performed for you.

Dated: <Date:>

Philip M. Kane d/b/a   [Client Name]
Communications Law Center [Client Officer]

_____

SCHEDULE OF DETAILS

A. IDENTIFICATION
Client: [Client Name]
[Client Address Line1]
[Client Address Line2]
[Client Telephone]
Matter: [Matter Info]
Reference: [Number/Matter]
Litigation Included: [Litigation Covered]

B. HOURLY BILLING RATE FOR LEGAL PERSONNEL
Rate Schedule: [Rate Schedule]
Attorney: $ [Attorney Rate]
Paralegal: $ [Paralegal Rate]
Law Clerk: $ [Clerical Rate]

C. STANDARD CHARGES
We charge in units of one-tenth of an hour (6 minutes).
Minimum charge for in-office consultation is one-half hour (30 minutes).
Minimum charge for appearances at depositions, hearings or trial is three (3) hours.

D. RATES SUBJECT TO CHANGE
The rates on this Schedule are subject to change upon 30 days' written notice. If you decline to pay any increased rates, we will have the right to withdraw as your lawyers.

Where Will It Hurt?

Believe it or not, lawyers are pretty efficient writers. But they are horribly inefficient at travel and hearings. On the other hand, there is little they can do about that. It takes what it takes to drive somewhere. Upon arrival, the course of the evening is out of the lawyer's control. It could stretch out for more than four fours from time of arrival to the end of the hearing, and may even require sitting through the decision. Then your attorney must drive home. It is your obligation to pay for all of that time. Between driving, waiting, the hearing and the decision, you could pay for a lawyer's time from 5 PM to midnight. That's seven hours.

You need to be calibrated.

Hours	Rate ($/hour)	Bill for the Hearing ($)
7	130	910
7	150	1050
7	175	1225
7	200	1400
7	250	1750
7	300	2100

Now you need to ask yourself if it is worth it. If you are going to live in this house for 10 years, and your total legal bill comes to $8,000, that's $800 per year. You could get lucky—perhaps you'll live in the house for 20 years with a legal bill of $2,000, coming out to only $100 per year. On the other hand, if you move to another house where the zoning ordinance may be more accepting of ham radio, the move alone (the truck and movers, plus hanging new towel holders when you arrive) could cost you $10,000 to $15,000. This is before looking at questions such as points, closing costs, the fees of real estate brokers and so forth.

So applying for an antenna-support structure in a town where the application is likely to be contested is not for the faint-hearted. On the other hand, as you can see from the instructions to clients above, dramatic amounts of money (except for the evening of the hearing) can be saved.

Finally, please accept this advice. Winning at the hearing level, at almost any price, is less expensive than losing, appealing, winning, re-applying and re-appearing for a new hearing. So what's the secret? Prepare thoroughly and well for the first hearing, and do as much work as possible yourself.

Registered Professional Engineer

In general, it should not be necessary to hire a Registered Professional Engineer. However, if you should be so lucky as to have a PE (the usual designation) available to you, there are several elements in which such a person might be involved, where the seal lends credibility to your application. This is not to say that another person, perhaps even you, might not produce the right kind of information.

It is, however, undeniable that if you show up with a panel of experts, ready to exhaust the evening (and the Board) with expertise, you are limiting the battle to areas where opponents will feel that they have the most legitimacy in commenting and the greatest likelihood of persuasion.

Should you feel that the use of a Registered Professional Engineer will be useful to you, or perhaps required, you may begin your hunt at **http://www.arrl.org/field/regulations/local/vcei.html#search**.

What does this mean in real life? It means that if a member of the audience stands up and foolishly says that the RF energy from your antenna system is going to make beepers go off or sizzle eyeballs for a radius of three miles, you can quite correctly cite:

1. The *Broyde* case, and others, to show that the Board should not even consider the issue. See CD-ROM, under filename: **Broyde v. Gotham Tower.PDF**.

2. Your own printout of the Harker (University of Texas) Web site program, or the K1TR program *Pwr_dens.EXE* on the CD-ROM, or your worksheets from W1RFI's book *The ARRL RFI Book,* or his January 1998 *QST* article "FCC RF-Exposure Regulations—the Station Evaluation."

However, while you could quite correctly do all of the above, introducing your friend, the so-and-so Professor of Physics at Local University, who has prepared a study that is signed over his name, complete with PhD, academic appointment (on academic or consulting firm letterhead) and that nice round seal can be very persuasive. If he is prepared to respond to any questions, the Board may quickly decide that RFI and EMF issues need not be considered intensively.

If you don't have such a friend, you don't have such a friend. If you do, however, and he owes you one, this is the time to take advantage of the friendship. A PE can be used (according to the fields in which he or she feels comfortable) to:

- Produce maps showing where the wetlands start and where the buffer zone starts,
- Produce an exhibit on propagation, showing why the height you've requested is required,
- Produce an exhibit on RF safety,
- Produce an exhibit showing a proper grounding plan, or
- Produce an exhibit showing that all of the proposed construction is safe and consistent with the state building code.
- A PE can also answer and dispose of the question: "Won't this structure attract lightning?"

A PE can also be especially handy if for some good reason you are not following manufacturer's installation drawings exactly. Note that the Building Inspector allows construction all the time built without the seal of a PE. After all, we're not talking about a skyscraper here, a building that could endanger thousands. It's just an antenna system in the back yard! Any Building Inspector, after reviewing the manufacturer's specifications in view of the variation you propose, should be able to make the decision without a PE's seal.

Seals

Welcome to the world of PE seals. There are *wet seals* (where the seal is applied to your drawing), and *dry seals* (where you submit a copy of a drawing that had a wet seal at one time). Obviously, a dry seal is cheaper (the price of a photocopy) and no liability attaches to that copy.

A support-structure manufacturer may provide you with drawings bearing dry seals. It could be free or there might be a charge. The manufacturer's PE may not, however, be licensed in your state or the seal may not show that he is licensed in your state. The dry seal will only apply to the standard drawing in the catalog, and will specify standard conditions (which you may or may not meet). If you can get through the process with no seal, or only a dry seal, so much the better.

This is a subject for discussion between you and the Building Commissioner, when you go to ask: "What kind of documentation will I need to get through this process?" During that conversation, be sure to ask: "If I'm following the manufacturer's installation instructions, do I need sealed drawings? If yes, will you accept a dry seal?" The reason you want to proceed with no seal, or a dry seal, is that you will save a lot of money.

On the other hand, if you are doing something unusual, you may want to hire a local PE, especially if you need a good understanding of how to install the base and anchors in your own special circumstances (normally circumstances in which "normal soil" conditions do not apply—such as sand or swamp). If normal conditions do not apply, the Building Inspector may want your plans to bear a wet seal, for your benefit and to protect the public. For money, you can always find a PE who will review or create, modify as necessary and provide a wet seal for your project.

There is an additional question of whether or not your Building Inspector cares to note the specialty of the PE, whether the PE's seal indicates the specialty and whether the specialty is relevant. Finally, there are "in-state" and "out-of-state" seals. What does that mean?

Let me speak from my experience in Massachusetts. Often an ordinance is vaguely written. For example: "Applicant shall submit a sealed drawing showing…" or "Applicant shall submit a drawing bearing the seal of a registered professional engineer showing…" This clearly means that a stamp must be on the drawing.

There are engineers who have taken and passed the examination to become a Registered Professional Engineer (PE or RPE) in electrical engineering. They are qualified in electrical engineering. They have not qualified in mechanical engineering. But this doesn't end the discussion. Assume that the seal notes the specialty. In my view, a PE in electrical engineering could easily certify that a HyTower will perform safely as a freestanding antenna. To the casual observer, looking only for a seal of any kind, that may be enough.

Many PEs have seals that do not indicate a specialty. Few Building Inspectors, especially those looking at an antenna (as opposed, for instance, to a high-rise building) will inquire behind the seal. One strategy: The PE could write you a letter saying what he is certifying and seal the drawing. The applicant might submit only the drawing. If the applicant is later asked for the meaning of the seal, simply produce the letter.

Some states have broad laws. A PE may take the exam, practice in one field, but have broad "sealing" rights. This is akin to the fact that an MD may theoretically treat any disease, even though she is qualified only in a specialty. For example, my wife is a board-certified and wonderful psychiatrist (MD), with a PhD from Yale in pharmacology. She is great at working with modern psychotropic medications.

But God help the patient if she were ever to perform surgery. Yet her license does not prevent it. Similarly, a lawyer may tackle any legal problem, once s/he has passed the bar exam. I like to think I am a good lawyer, with a reasonable understanding of business too. But God help the client if I were ever to do any criminal defense work.

Thus, broad qualification is not uncommon. The burden is on the professional to limit his own exposure to risk of malpractice. So you may find an individual with a seal from your state (or from elsewhere), who will seal your drawings and thereby end some nonsensical requirement that a town drafted without understanding of the issues involved in antennas. There is no harm in asking.

Finally, there is the question of whether or not your Building Inspector will require a seal from a PE licensed by your own state. It turns out that engineering is way ahead of law and medicine in this regard, permitting—in effect—multi-state practice. As best I understand the Massachusetts statute, a Professional Engineer need only register with Massachusetts if he regularly practices here or maintains an office. This is not true of doctors and lawyers, who must be locally licensed first. (Actually, lawyers can practice within a state if the state work is ancillary to a project involving Federal law, but that's another story.)

So there you have it. Bottom line: Make the Building Inspector your friend. He has within his power the ability to make it hard for you to meet the requirements of the building code (by requiring, worst case, a wet seal from an in-state specialist) or to make it easier for you to meet those requirements (by accepting, best case, a dry seal from an out-of-state PE who is not necessarily a mechanical engineer).

I hope you've enjoyed this discourse on seals, the product of some learning in the school of hard knocks.

Surveyor

Many building codes require the submission of a scaled drawing showing the boundaries of the property, location of all significant structures, setback lines, distances to neighboring structures and so forth. Most lawyers can tell you from hard-won experience that neighbors may not agree on where the property line is located. Sometimes (the most common example is when the ham has a mobility problem), getting out there to do the measuring yourself can be a problem. Sometimes it can be really important to know how the land slopes (to justify additional height), or where trees are located (to assure neighbors that their views of your antennas will be obscured by these trees). This is exactly the kind of work that surveyors do. Here are a few real-life examples.

One ham accidentally put his guy anchor a foot or two onto a neighbor's property. It was totally innocent but it happened. Though he later removed the first anchor and installed a new anchor, three or four feet closer to the structure (to allow a margin of safety this time), he was mercilessly attacked as someone who could not be trusted to do anything right.

Another ham hoped to put his support structure as close to the back right-hand corner of his lot as possible. This meant putting one guy anchor as deep into the right-hand corner as possible, so that the two other guy wires, spaced at 120°, would stay out of the grassy area of his backyard. Everyone agreed that the really big tree in that corner was planted on the corner (many years ago), but no one was sure of the angles for the property lines from there. If you make a mistake of 5° at the corner, you are way off (as measured in feet) when you get to the other side of the yard 200 feet away. While your survey map from the mortgage paperwork may be adequate for drafting the property map, it could be very important to hire a surveyor to lay out a valid property line.

This works the other way too. I once had a neighbor install an Invisible Fence™ that went inside my own property, cutting 50 of my buried radials for vertical antennas in the process. It seems that she thought she knew where the property line was located, and the installer just assumed it would do no harm to install the "fence" (a buried wire) a few feet further into the woods. Between the two of them, the error amounted to 27 feet!

Surveyors are a lot less expensive than lawyers. Ask someone in the wood-fence business how he assures himself that he's not installing "over the line." You could get a good tip or two.

In general, you do not need a surveyor to install a ham radio antenna, but you may well need the information that a surveyor can provide. If you have a friend in the construction business who owns a laser-sighting device, a device that will help you lay out a straight line in the woods, it is time to renew that friendship!

Eventually, you'll have to produce a plan for incorporation in your application. Since it can affect placement of the antenna, this should be one of your early steps in the planning process. Remember that it is far easier to assure yourself of those property lines before the snow starts to fly!

Real Estate Agent

As you will see elsewhere in the book, a real estate agent is not necessarily an appraiser. However, there are real estate agents who are also appraisers. Asking a real estate appraiser to perform a study for you is going to cost you the appraiser's fee. In the end, the Board may accept or reject the evidence of the appraiser. It may even reject the evidence of the appraiser if it is unopposed. You never know.

Nonetheless, if you are concerned that the "real estate values will fall" argument will come up, and if you have a friendly real estate agent upon whom you can call, several strategies become available.

Testimony

You may invite the real estate agent to speak at the hearing. This should be a short piece of testimony. If you assemble all the numbers, the agent may also be convinced to say that the study you have assembled from public data correctly states the situation, as the agent understands it.

A Letter

Even if the agent has agreed to appear, you can prepare a letter to be printed under the agent's letterhead that succinctly states your position. This serves two purposes:

1. If the agent is unable, for whatever reason, to appear the night of your hearing, the testimony is still entered. Remember your hearing could be continued to another night before the agent has an opportunity to speak.
2. The process of reviewing the letter you have prepared for the agent will keep the agent on-track and succinct, and will reassure the agent about exactly what is being asked.

Here's a sample letter you'd like to receive from the real estate agent. [This is on the CD-ROM as filename: **Real Estate Agency Assessment.DOC**.]

[On Real Estate Agency Letterhead]

Date

Town of Friendlyville
Board of Appeals
Town Hall
Friendlyville, MA

To the Board:
In re: **Application of Joe T. Ham**

I have been asked to comment on the question of whether or not the presence of a visible Amateur Radio antenna system, nnn feet tall or less, has an impact on the value, selling price, or speed of sale of a neighboring home.

I have been a licensed real estate [agent/broker/representative—as appropriate] since _____(year) _____, having participated in sales exceeding $_____ in value. [Allow real estate person to toot his or her own horn. It's good for business.] I am familiar with the market in Friendlyville. I have examined the spreadsheet of assessor's values attached, assembled by the applicant, and believe them to fairly represent town records.

There are many elements in any given transaction, and it is possible that an anecdote may be produced to show that a particular buyer was discouraged by the nearby presence of an antenna system. Yet it is my experience that the spoken reason and the real reason for deciding against a purchase do not always coincide.

It is my professional opinion that the existence or nonexistence of a visible Amateur Radio antenna system nnn feet tall or less has no impact on the value, selling price or speed of sale of a neighboring home.

Sincerely,
Name

Attachment: Assessor Valuation Spread Sheet

Basic Preparations

MATERIALS YOU WILL NEED

Bound Notebook

Anyone who has ever done lab experiments will tell you that a bound notebook can be very helpful. On the day you decide you want an antenna system, start keeping a notebook. As you learn the names of people from your neighborhood (as well as the names of spouses, children, dogs, and the "cousin who is a ham") and as you take notes on what those people say to you, you could wind up with a lot of pieces of scrap paper. You may forget to date or file each scrap. Use a bound notebook and paste or tape these miscellaneous pieces of paper into it. This way, even if you don't date a particular entry, it can be placed in time approximately by what comes before or after it.

This is the voice of experience talking. Buy an expensive ($5) bound notebook—not a drugstore 99-cent notebook. Most good notebooks have a pouch in the front (or the back), where you can temporarily store pieces of paper that you intend to file or paste into the notebook later on. Even if you are a whiz with your Palm Pilot or equivalent PDA (personal digital assistant), there is no easy way in the field to put a business card or a map into your PDA.

This whole process is going to stretch out over a number of months and will involve names of owners, tenants, wives, children, hams, town officials, as well as telephone numbers, to-do lists, documents needed, maps to obtain, and so forth. You will need a good notebook!

Furthermore, if you want to draw something out for someone and keep a record of what you showed that person, draw it in your notebook and show it to him. You might even ask him to initial the drawing once you have finished your explanation. This avoids the ugly claim: "When the applicant came to my house and explained what he was going to do, what he drew out for me was very different than the application now in front of you. If I had known then what I know now, I never would have signed that letter saying I have no objection."

Looseleaf Binder and Section Dividers

A separate three-ring binder for other 8.5 × 11-inch papers will be a good idea too. Along the way, you'll be collecting a lot of documents that won't conveniently fit in your bound notebook. One good way to keep them organized is to punch them and tuck them into your three-ring binder. Don't forget you'll need a three-hole punch too. Here's a list of section dividers you may find useful.

My House Documents
Topographic Map (also try **http://www.topozone.com**)
Plot Plan
Neighborhood Map
Photos
Letters
Other

Local Law
Bylaw
Building Permit Application Form
Special Permit Application Form
Other

State Law

Building Code
State Equivalent to Federal 47 CFR § 97.15(b)

Federal Law

RFI Preemption
EMF Law
Zoning Preemption
Case Law

Miscellaneous Issues

Reproduced below is a handout from several Dayton Hamvention lectures I have given over the years.

DOCUMENTS YOU MAY NEED

Experience has shown that it is useful to collect the following documents before applying for a permit for your "antenna-support structure and appurtenant antennas." Please don't call it a *tower*, since Federal (and some state) laws protect *antenna structures* (the words found in the law). There is no need to muddy the waters by using a different description of the project.

Include As Background

- An original, recent, copy of your town's zoning bylaw or ordinance, and any amendments not included in the printed, compiled text. *Do not*—repeat, do not—rely on statements by the Zoning Enforcement Officer, or his/her secretary, as to what it says. The printed ordinance is where you will find height and setback rules. Do not settle for a photocopy of what someone tells you is "the relevant page." Source: The Town Clerk, or the Secretary in the Planning, Zoning or Building Department.

- An original, recent, copy of your town's Wetlands Protection bylaw or ordinance, with a wetlands map, and any regulations issued by the Conservation Commission. This is where you will find information on jurisdiction and application procedures. Source: The Conservation Commission.

- Two copies of any form used by the town to apply for a Building Permit, Special Exception/Permit or Conservation Commission proceeding. (Two copies allow for the possibility of an error requiring you to start again.) Source: The Building Department or Conservation Commission.

- If a 110- or 220-V ac line will be run out to the base of the tower, whether for a winch (for a crank-up tower) or just a place to plug in a soldering iron or light, include two copies of any form used by the town to apply for an electrical permit. (Again, two copies allow for the possibility of an error requiring you to start again.) Source: Your town's Building Department.

- The requirements of your state or local building code dealing with *windload*. In other words, will the Building Inspector require your proposed structure to withstand 50 mph winds with 1 inch of radial ice? Or 30 pounds per square foot of windload (which translates to 83 mph)? You need to know the exact requirements so that your application will match them. Source: State or local building code, found at either the Building Department or the town library.

- The USGS topographic (7.5 minute) quadrant map showing your location. It may prove useful by showing that you need more height to overcome a particular line-

of-sight path because of a nearby ridge. Source: a local camping/hiking/bicycling store or Government Printing Office (GPO) store or 1-888 ASK-USGS. Usual cost: about $5. Commercial software is available from **http://www.delorme.com/** (DeLorme Map) and **http://www.topo.com/** (National Geographic). Also see **http://www.topozone.com/** (free!).

Include As Exhibits

- A *plan* showing the lots and streets in your neighborhood. This will orient the Board. It is best if this plan also shows where homes are located on the lots. It may also be helpful to add distances to those homes. Source: Your town's Planning and Zoning Department, or the Assessor's Office. This is often called an *assessor's map* or a *tax map*.

- A *plot plan*, showing the outline of your house and the site of the proposed antenna-support structure. Add distances from the antenna-support structure to the lot lines. Normally, this would be the distance to each side-lot line and the distance to the rear-lot line (three measurements). Be sure that the two distances, from side-lot line to structure and from structure to side-lot line, add up to equal the actual distance from side-lot line to side-lot line! Consider including the *tree line* to show where views are screened. Source: Mortgage papers normally include a plot plan, which should be adequate, unless you've added to your house. To add trees, scan the plot plan and use a computer drawing program.

- A copy of your FCC Amateur Radio license. Though not required, it would be better if it shows your address as the place where you intend to erect your antenna system.

- The specification sheets from the manufacturer of your antenna-support structure for your brand and model. If possible, it should specify model number, height, load it will bear (weight expressed in pounds and maximum windload in square feet at a certain windspeed, or pounds per square foot of air pressure).

- The construction plans for the base and erection of your antenna-support structure (including guying, if appropriate). The more it looks like a draftsman's or architect's rendering, the more effective it will be. Try to get a version with a dry seal of the manufacturer's Professional Engineer printed on it.

- The specification sheet(s) for any proposed antenna(s), showing weight (expressed in pounds) and windload (expressed in square feet).

- The specification sheets for your rotator, showing weight (expressed in pounds or kg).

- If you are moving the antenna system from a prior site, include a photograph (or slide that is suitable for color photocopying) in the application. *Suitable* means a photo that demonstrates that an amateur radio antenna system doesn't create aesthetic blight! One frequently used view is taken from the street in front of the house, at high noon, since it will show less reflection off the aluminum.

- A letter of permission from the landlord (if the applicant is not the homeowner).

- A copy of your homeowner's general liability insurance policy, or at least a *cover sheet* from your insurance agent stating your coverage (which may include an *umbrella* policy).

- Letters of support, or at least letters that express "no

opposition to the grant of a permit," which you have drafted and the neighbors have signed.

- A printout for your station, using a worst-case analysis of the RF safety computer program found at **http://n5xu.ae.utexas.edu/rfsafety/** This will show compliance with Federal regulations in this area.

Great Impressions Help Deliver Great Decisions

You will never make a great impression with a hand-written scrawl on a town form, nor with an application that does not permit the Board to understand what you intend to do. This is major-league selling and all of the modern tools of selling will prove helpful:

- Including color printing
- Including a Cover Page and a Table of Contents
- Including an Executive Summary
- OCR-scanning forms so you can fill them in on your computer
- Reproducing photographs and labeling them for greater understandability
- Creating Plot Plans with dimensions in different colors
- Shading in trees on the Plot Plan
- Accompanying spreadsheets, charts and graphic explanations

A Picture is Worth 1,000 Words (or a Word is Worth a Millipicture)

A triband Yagi can be truthfully described as either 2 square feet of aluminum, or something that looks like an empty H made of thin tubing with outer limits of 24 by 35 feet. When you say that a tribander is but some pencil lines against the sky, and nothing more than an overgrown TV antenna, a photo will support your statements and really help.

When your opponents liken your proposal for a 100-foot structure to a ten-story building in a residential area, a photo will really help if it shows you and a car standing behind, and completely visible through, an antenna-support structure of the same make and model that you are proposing.

When opponents claim that there will be a dramatic contrast between the steel structure and the softer forest background, a photo showing a similar structure almost invisible against a forest background will help, especially to forestall a silly requirement, such as having to paint your antenna structure forest green.

Film is inexpensive. Take a tip from commercial photographers and take *lots* of photos. This dramatically improves your chances of getting a shot or two that will really prove helpful. Be sure to note the camera (and the lens) you use. This will avoid claims that a photograph does not fairly represent the situation. Here are a few tips:

- If possible, take the photos you intend to use during the winter. This eliminates the possible complaint at a contested public hearing that you purposely took your photos when all the leaves were still on the trees and that the proposed antenna system will be more visible when the leaves have fallen.

- While you and I might think that antennas are rather majestic, do not stand to the southwest and take the photos at 3 PM. This will be the one moment in time when your photo might show a glint. Such a photo does not fairly present an antenna system, which is more normally gray against a gray sky, not bright and shiny.

- As you go around town to take photographs, do not photograph brand-new antennas or brand-new steel structures. While such pictures might enhance the majesty of the antenna system, they do not fairly present the normal situation. After only a few months of exposure to the weather, both aluminum and galvanized steel take on a dull, non-reflective finish. Photograph things that have been up more than six months.

- It is highly likely that your town has a tower for police, fire or Department of Public Works communications. Find out how high such a structure or such structures may be, for purposes of comparison, and take photos. This will show several things:

  1. It demonstrates that people have been basically ignoring such a structure for years, even though it may be in a very visible public place.

  2. It shows that the metal does take on a dull finish, just as you say.

  3. It provides a ready example of what a VHF ground plane or vertical looks like. Emphasize that such antennas are especially useful in emergencies. This is another opportunity to play the emergency communications angle, especially if you are active in Civil Defense or another emergency communications service.

- Finally, remember to label any photos submitted. Think about making the labels work for you. For example: "Photo shows antenna system at Applicant's previous location. Taken on February 12, 2000. Note that structure and antennas have a natural, dull-gray finish."

Your Camera

If you remember nothing else from this section, let me hammer home that *film is cheap*. This is especially true when you compare it to legal costs. So go buy three rolls of 200 or 400-speed color film. At 24 pictures per roll, that comes out to 72 pictures. This ought to be enough for any antenna-support structure project. After you've taken the necessary pictures, develop two copies of each. This adds one to two dollars per roll for developing and may seem like a waste at the moment. But when you have three days before you are supposed to file your application and you spill coffee on the one photo you were counting on using, you'll be glad you made two.

Photo Perspective

When you take your photos, always take them horizontally—with the camera's long length parallel to the ground. This is called a "landscape view." Putting it another way, the ground should always be on the bottom, the six-inch

(A)   **(B)**

Fig 4-1—At A, photo of Sander Idelson, KB1FPU, in normal perspective. At B, Sander photographed in "Jolly Green Giant™" mode. (*Photos courtesy Jim Idelson, K1IR.*)

side, of a 4 × 6-inch photograph. Why? Because this makes the photo a *fair representation*. It puts the shot in context. A normal person standing and looking at an antenna system has a wide field of vision—this is why hockey and basketball players can see passes coming at them from the side while looking ahead. A narrow "portrait" field of vision is not representative of reality.

If you fear that someone may try to cheat and put forward a photograph that is not a fair representation of an antenna system, you can prepare for this. You can make it plain to the Board that your opponent is cheating by taking just two pictures to show what is fair and what is unfair. Start with a photograph of a ten-year old child (or any child about four feet tall) taken while you and the child are both standing. Now lie down on the ground so that the camera is three feet away from the child and look up. Take the picture. When it is developed, the child will look ten feet tall. Bring these two pictures along to the hearing and hold them in reserve. If necessary, you can thoroughly discredit an opponent who tries to present an unfair perspective of an antenna system. See **Fig 4-1**, which shows two perspectives of Sander Idelson, KB1FPU, the son of Jim Idelson, K1IR.

The camera you want has a zoom lens, so that you can frame the photo you want. Do not start thinking about camera techniques that might mislead the Board or a court. Remember, the test of whether or not a photo is admissible in court is whether or not it fairly represents the scene. You do not need to misrepresent anything.

A Digital Camera

If you have a digital camera, that's nice, because (1) you have the chance to see the photo immediately after you take it, permitting you to take another if you don't like the image you've captured and (2) it saves the scanning step, should

you decide to bring the photos into the document instead of simply pasting them onto a page. If the photos are originally digital, or scanned in, adding a scaled proposed structure, or a red dot in a circle showing where the Yagi will be, becomes easier.

A Color Photocopy Is Worth the Cost

When discussing the contrast between your proposed antenna system and other structures in the neighborhood, it can be difficult for you to make an effective argument using black and white photocopies. After all, one gray item in the photocopy may well resemble some other gray item. For example, let's say you have a red car behind a gray lattice tower. In black and white, the structure may look like it blocks the car. In color, the antenna-support will hardly be noticeable. And for those of us who are not color blind, life is in color.

There was a time when a color photocopy might have cost $2 to $3 per page. When multiplied by the number of copies of the application you will be preparing, that would have been significant. Since 1999, color photocopying has become a lot less expensive. By the way, if you are wondering how many copies to print, here's a way of thinking about it:

Recipient	Number of Copies
Members of the Board	5
Town Planner	1
Secretary to the Board	1
Building Inspector/Commissioner	1
Neighbors	10
Your lawyer	1
Your file	3
Total:	22

If the application has 30 pages and you print using your own ink-jet printer, for which the variable cost is 10 cents per page (including color), then a rough estimate of your reproduction cost is:

22 copies × 30 pages × $0.10 = $66

If you use a commercial shop such as Kinko's or Alphagraphics, assume that only 8 of the pages use color.

22 copies × 22 pages (BW) × $0.10 = $48.40
22 copies × 8 color pages × $0.75 = $132

Total $180.40

Thus you will get a lot of punch for a lot less than the cost of two hours of a lawyer's time. Use color printing when useful. In addition, ask for tips from your printer or copy shop on paper, covers, and other elements to make your presentation professional looking.

Copy of Local Zoning Bylaw

Lesson Number One, discussed previously, dealing with local officials is to get your own copy of the local bylaw or ordinance. This is *not* the three-volume set on the shelf of the Building Inspector, the one that sells for $300. That's the Building Code for construction in your state. What you want is the zoning ordinance or zoning bylaw. It probably has 7 to 120 pages, depending on how intrusive zoning may be in your jurisdiction. In 1999, a copy of the Land Use Ordinance for Oahu, Hawaii, was $8; in Kitsap County, Washington, it was $9. They tend to top out at about $21 or so.

You must have your own copy of the whole bylaw, and not just the one page that the clerk tells you "covers this topic." Why? Among other reasons, you will want to read the *Definitions* section, usually in the first section. You will want to read the section on height in your zone (height may be different in each of an industrial, rural, farming, residential two-family, or residential single family district—if your town has such districts).

You will also want to read any new section covering *Wireless Communications Facilities*. This may have been added after the Communications Act of 1996 came into law. You specifically want to see if hams were exempted from this section, which ordinarily covers cellular telephone antenna-support structures. You will also want to read the section covering setbacks. That's to start.

If it appears that you will need a Special-Use Permit, Special Exception or Variance, you will want to have the section with the criteria covering such grants, as well as the section that tells you how to apply and what to include in the application. As you can see, a single-page photocopy of the "ham radio" section simply will not serve you well in most cases.

Copy of Relevant State Law

Should your state be one of those that has incorporated a version of Federal 47 CFR § 97.15(b) into its own set of statutes, you will want to have a printout to include in your application or to hand to a Building Inspector or a Board

member. You will find a list of state with such statutes at **http://www.arrl.org/field/regulations/statutes.html**.

Manufacturer's Specifications and Installation Requirements for Your Tower

You don't have to include the entire instruction manual for your antenna-support structure. The Board just wants to see that what you propose is made by a reputable manufacturer, one who publishes real specification sheets with installation plans that can be reviewed by the Building Inspector. There is one specification that the Building Inspector will probably, and correctly, insist upon seeing—the allowable wind loading at the windspeed requirement for your county and site.

If you are contemplating a Heights tower (and you might take a look anyway because it is interesting), check out **http://www.heightstowers.com/engspecs.htm**. This is included on the CD-ROM as filename:
Heights Tower Systems Specs.PDF.

Specification sheets for Rohn 25 and 45 series of towers are included on the CD-ROM as filenames:
Rohn 45G Sections.JPG
Rohn 45G Guying.JPG
Rohn 45G Base.JPG
Rohn 25G Sections.JPG
Rohn 25G Guying.JPG and
Rohn 25G Base.JPG. Also check out:
**http://www.rohnnet.com/CommPro/Towers/
  Towers.htm**.

Long Tape Measure

It will be necessary for you to include the distances from the proposed structure base to the lot lines, to your house, to neighboring houses and to the street. These can be painful to measure using a 10-foot, or even a 25-foot, tape measure. A 100-foot tape measure sells for $14 to $20 at your local big-box hardware store. Tape measures that are 300 feet long are also available. Buy one now to use in your application process. (You'll need one later anyway to measure the lengths of elements for your 20-meter or triband Yagi, won't you?)

Handheld Compass

Actually, this is a trick question, as you do not need a compass to prepare an excellent application. But you will need it later to construct your system. For the moment, everything you need is on your Plot Plan and the neighborhood Assessor's Maps available from town hall. Look for the arrow pointing north.

How to determine True North is a topic that could easily take up an entire lunch hour, or more, since there are so many ways to do it. It will become a necessary step in the installation of your system. But it is not a necessary step in the preparation of your antenna-system permit application. Your Plot Plan and map will have everything you need, which simply is an arrow indicating the direction of north.

Inclinometer

An *inclinometer* is a device used to determine the angle

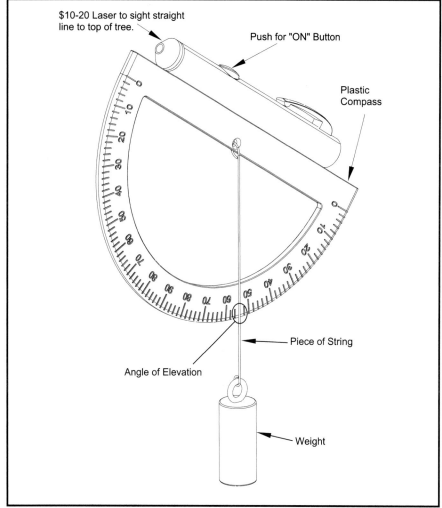

Fig 4-2—A simple laser-aided inclinometer to measure tree heights. Measure the angle using the inclinometer and measure the distance to the tree using a 100-foot tape measure. The height of the tree is calculated from:

Height = Distance × tan(Angle)

tree. Measure the distance from where you are standing to the tree, using the 100-foot tape measure recommended above, and you've got all the necessary factors to determine, with just a little trigonometry, the height of the tree.

Add a laser pointer, and you can also prove what hand waving and shouting will not. If you tape the laser pointer to the straight edge of your compass and aim it, you can thus dramatically end any argument about whether or not you've sighted to the top of the tree, above the top, or below the top. See **Fig 4-2**.

You haven't lived until you've sat through an argument between a neighbor and an applicant about the height of a tree. It is a pretty silly way to spend your time and an inexpensive laser pointer will accomplish what hand waving will not, as both parties can go to the site and look for the red dot. I've seen classroom laser pointers for as low as $8.95 on sale and a commercial version of a laser angle-measuring device is available from **http://www. mcmelectronics.com/** at **http://www. i-mcm.com/Search/search4-frame. jhtml?_DARGS=%2Fcommon %2Fprodsearchform.jhtml**.

There is no need to irritate the volunteers who sit on Boards with such arguments. The facts are what the facts are and they should be presented as such to the Board. After that, you can argue about the implications.

YOUR COMPUTER

You are embarking on a process in which you are asking people who are not familiar with ham radio to approve the erection and maintenance of a structure that they may never have seen. Further, they are being asked to approve this construction in the face of what may be vehement opposition. Many zoning bylaws or ordinances put the burden on you, the applicant, to demonstrate that the proposal is not inconsistent with a single-family residential area.

Have no fear—you can do it. However, you must be thorough and completely understandable. Nowadays, the process of preparation will almost certainly involve a computer. You will need a computer with word-processing software and enough RAM to handle the scanning of documents as well as photographs. In addition, the ability to receive and send a fax through your computer would be useful (although a good quality fax can always be scanned in).

You will also need a modem for visiting FCC Web sites, the MSN TerraServer Web site, **http://www.topozone.com/** and so forth. A good quality inkjet or laser printer will be

to the top of a tree. It can be particularly helpful if you live in a neighborhood that is not generally level. It will save a lot of math homework, not that the math is really difficult. Any ninth grader should be able to help you with the trigonometry necessary for an antenna system application.

But if you want to see if a Yagi will be visible from a certain spot at a given height, an inclinometer will make it easy. Also, the inclinometer will permit you to accurately detail the height of the trees in your yard, as well as the trees in a neighbor's yard, should the question ever arise about whether or not an antenna will be visible from the neighbor's backyard.

You can buy a ready-made inclinometer. The last one I bought cost about $80 and had a nice liquid-dampening system. Or you can make your own from a plastic compass, a piece of string and a weight.

Sight along the straight edge of the compass toward a treetop. Allow the weight to hold the string straight down. Pinch the string and you've got the angle to the top of the necessary, along with good-quality paper. A color printer will be useful for maps, your license (the application looks more official in color), photographs that you've scanned (documenting a balloon test, an anti-climbing device and so forth).

If you are a computerphobe, get used to the idea that this application is going to have several drafts. It will be a better application, with a higher chance of success, if you make it a professional presentation. You are going to need a word processor with a spell checker.

Since it is highly likely that you already own a computer with a word processor of some sort, boot it up right now and create a document called: TIMELINE.DOC. From now on, whenever you send a letter, receive a letter, make a phone call, receive a phone call, file anything, or whatever, you will enter it as a short note in your notebook and in your TIMELINE document. Trust me. Some day this could make your life a whole lot easier. It becomes especially relevant as the paper piles up. It becomes crucial if you must find documents or prove dates. Make those entries simple. For example:

6/2/2001: Filed building permit application.
6/3/2001: Filed map that I failed to include yesterday.

Oh yes, it is always a good time to remind you that any papers filed in town hall should be filed in duplicate, and time-stamped there. You should keep a copy of the stamped version—to prove the date on which something was filed. This becomes important if they try to change the bylaw on you, once it becomes obvious that you intend to go forward with your plan. It could also be important if the town takes no action at all, and you must later prove the passage of time. Don't feel nervous about asking anyone to time-stamp something. The administrative staff at your town hall does it every day, for no charge. It is routine.

Word Processing Software

Many word processors include templates for various types of formal reports. Such templates can help make your presentation look more professional. One of the most professional things you can do is to include a Table of Contents and an Executive Summary.

Ideally, you will have a word processor that is capable of inserting scanned images into a document. If not, you can simply use any word processor and put all the exhibits at the end, numbered. Be sure to include a page listing all the exhibits at the beginning of the exhibits section, to reduce repetitive thumbing through the document in search of the proper exhibit.

Where possible, create your proposal and send it as an e-mail attachment to friends. Gather their comments and incorporate improvements they suggest.

Images and Image Editing

A document scanner will be very helpful. It will be helpful if you can add comments, arrows, dimensions and so forth, electronically, when you incorporate scanned images into your presentation.

Working with Numbers (Spreadsheets)

To perform an analysis demonstrating, for example, the lack of impact on house values due to the presence of existing Amateur Radio antennas, you will need spreadsheet software. The CD accompanying this book has several such spreadsheets in Excel (*.XLS) format. A great deal of thought went into the study design. See if one of them works for you.

Drafting Software

If you are going to create your own Plot Plan, or if you intend to demonstrate how a neighbor's view will actually be screened by nearby trees or an existing house, you may need software that allows you to draw and keep things in perspective. See **http://www.imsisoft.com/** to check out their freeware *TurboCad* program, Version 5.

Showing Your Antennas on Photographs

You may discover that mathematically you cannot fairly insert an antenna or support structure because $1/4$ inch tubing, or Z-bracing, is simply too small and even one-pixel-wide lines would be too fat. This may require you to exercise some judgment about whether or not you wish to attempt to insert a steel tower or aluminum antenna in a photograph. One alternative is to simply use a red dot to show the height of the proposed antenna and to explain the situation with a footnote.

It is also possible, perhaps likely, that your antenna may not even be visible, since trees will block it. In such a case, the use of a red dot on the photo to show the height of the proposed system, where the dot is plunked down on a tree, will show the Board that the proposed system will be blocked from view.

In any event, this is an example of a situation where you may wish to have a scanned photo and insert the dot (with a circle around it or an arrow pointing toward it to help the reader spot it). Fortunately even the simplest scanning software today allows you to achieve such an exhibit.

One thing may surprise you. Scan in your FCC license and reproduce it in *color*. It is unlikely that anyone will comment on it, but it is very effective at reinforcing the idea that you have an official FCC license. A copy of a useful article on this subject is reproduced on the CD-ROM with the file name **Photo Simulation.PDF**.

5

Getting to Know the Players

TYPES OF PLAYERS

As you proceed down the road to applying for a permit for your antenna-support structure, you may encounter opposition. Many hams immediately regard this opposition with hostility and suspicion. Some suspicion may be justified; some may not be justified. In no event will hostility help you.

Rethink the situation. Don't be so ready to believe that opposition to you represents a conspiracy. There's usually a far more innocent explanation—usually related to *a lack of knowledge*. If you experience opposition, it is most likely to be based either on a fear of the unknown or on a conviction that there will be a negative impact.

A fear of the unknown is often expressed as a negative impact. It is not uncommon to see opposition to antenna systems that will be visible neither from the neighbor's house nor from the street. So the first line of defense is always to explain what you are going to do.

Objector Type A: Fearing the Unknown

This is an opponent who is basically fearful of your system. He may never have actually looked at your plans and is probably best characterized as fearing the *unknown*. He's against it because he doesn't know what it is.

Today, when people hear the word *tower*, they think a heavy steel cellular or microwave tower—18 feet wide at the base, 4 feet wide at the top—with a crow's nest at the top and dishes up and down the tower. They are not thinking about a support that is only 12 to 22 inches on a face, constructed as a lattice ("see-through"), with guy wires no

bigger than $1/4$ inch diameter and with a Yagi antenna on the top that has no element bigger than 1.5 inches in diameter. If you'd like to keep legal expenses low or avoid them entirely, it's your job to talk to your neighbors about what you propose.

- If you don't talk to them, they'll assume the worst about your *project*.
- If you don't talk to them, they'll assume the worst about *you*.

Many an amateur has had bitter remarks addressed against him at a public hearing that began with: "Mr. Chairman, the first I ever heard about this proposal was when I received the registered letter telling me about the hearing this evening."

Boom. You are off to a bad start with the Board. Why? Boards of Appeals, or Planning Boards, are made up of volunteers—people who like to think of themselves as community-oriented folks who just want to keep their town a nice place to live. They like to think of the public hearing as "just an opportunity to discuss the proposed project with your neighbors."

This is often a delusion, since a Board of Appeals is a quasi-judicial body working with vague, sometimes impossible-to-discern standards (such as "shall not have a negative impact on the neighborhood"—note the double negative). These vague standards mean that it is impossible for you to put together a package of presentation materials that is ever a 100% guaranteed, slam-dunk winner.

In addition to being uninformed about your specific

project, your opposition may be uninformed about Amateur Radio in general, and/or they may be uninformed about engineering in general. I once faced a neighbor opposing a project on safety grounds who simply claimed, "You can't predict what Mother Nature will do." If that claim were entirely true, you could never build an acceptably safe bridge, house or office building, never mind an Amateur Radio antenna system.

In other words, until you've met with them, you don't know how well informed neighbors may be, nor how intelligent. You just don't know, one way or another.

Effective Strategies

There is only one effective strategy with an uninformed neighbor. *Inform* him or her. This gives you a chance to clear up any misconceptions. Sometimes you can do that. On the other hand, after being informed, you may discover that the neighbor is no longer uninformed and negative. The neighbor may now just be plain old negative.

Objector Type B: Convinced of Negative Impact

Sooner or later you will meet people who are opposed to what you intend to do. You may become convinced that the neighbor will never listen to reason. And you may be right.

Nonetheless, you must always treat each person you encounter with *respect*, and keep your promises to that neighbor. Putting it another way, never make a promise you can't keep. For example, you may not be able to promise that your neighbor will never be able to see your antennas. You may not be able to promise that your neighbor will never have TVI or RFI. You still can do something positive in the face of such opposition.

There are neighbors who just need to vent a frustration that they cannot completely control the neighborhood and what other people do on their own properties. These are people who would be happy to tell you, if it weren't impolite, that you've chosen the wrong color to stain your house or that you routinely leave your garage door open and it makes the neighborhood look unkempt. There is a chance that, some days, months or years hence, this neighbor will accept your invitation to come by for iced tea or perhaps a stronger beverage.

There are neighbors who hate Amateur Radio. I remember one such old man who no doubt had a bad experience with TVI in 1953 or so, when shielding on both the TV and transmitter was not yet what it would later become. He died, of natural causes I hasten to add, still harboring that hatred of Amateur Radio caused by the interference he had suffered on his TV almost fifty years before.

Fortunately, both Amateur Radio transmitters and television receiving systems (including cable TV) are getting better. Printed circuit boards with good ground planes, toroids, shielding and filtering have helped TV sets. Commercial manufacturing, shielded enclosures, coax, and filtering have helped Amateur Radio transmitters.

Sadly, some hatred may never be overcome. There are neighbors who hate you. This is hard to talk about in modern society, but I have personally seen bias against radio hams who were Hispanic, and bias against a radio ham who was Jewish. It happens.

There are neighbors who truly believe that your transmissions may cause cataracts, or cancer, or headaches or whatever. And there are neighbors who truly believe all manner of other objections, such as "It will lower property values." Such beliefs are routinely nonsense, but there can be no doubt that they are firmly held. For this reason, in the absence of the ability to build "as of right," you should rejoice that you have a forum where the Board must obey the law.

You are not simply at the mercy of a requirement that you get permission from all of your neighbors. There are societies like that: Bermuda and England may come close. But despite the decline in property rights, Americans have not lost all property rights. I just hope you won't vote for any candidates who want to increase the invasion of your property rights.

Effective Strategies

- Vote for candidates who believe in property rights. Well, that's a good long-term goal anyway!
- Talk to every neighbor you can, whether or not you believe that you can convert him or her. Even if your neighbor is unalterably opposed to your proposal, or won't commit one way or another (and you should treat all "maybes" as "no"), you may still learn the basis for the opposition by simply asking: "What is it that bothers you about this proposal?" Thus you can better prepare for the public hearing, if there is one, or the next cocktail party, if that's the only forum.
- Prepare, prepare, and prepare your presentation and exhibits some more. Make it thorough, correct and neat.
- Prepare your family, your experts, yourself. Gather the documents you may need; learn what the law says and what it does not say; assemble your exhibits; take your photographs; practice your answers. Pretend you are about to embark on a political campaign and you know that you are going to be interviewed by tough reporters.
- Think about the questions and practice your answers. For example, the Federal order known as PRB-1 (47 CFR §97.15(b)) is not an absolute and complete preemption. But neither is it a "balancing test." It states that the town must accommodate you. So be prepared to say why you need to do what you propose to do. Work those questions and answers until you could answer each of the hard questions during a 20-second elevator ride without mumbling.

With good preparation, you'll be OK.

INFORMAL DISCUSSIONS

At some point you must settle on a plan and begin to shop it around, or else this idea you treasure is never going to happen. Before you submit the plan and start the time clock (where notice must go out, the Board must meet within so many days, a decision made within so many days, an appeal filed within so many days and so forth), you should take your ideas out for an informal *test drive*.

Talk With Your Family

You are about to embark on a multi-month process. In the end, an offhand remark, an accidental slight or some other small matter could have a substantial influence on the outcome. He who is careful will more likely succeed than he who is careless.

Brief your family before anyone else. It may be politically incorrect, but to be brutally upfront, this most often means briefing your wife.

There is one principal goal: No bad quotations. For example, your wife obviously must not say: "Oh yes, I know Henry is applying to put up a really big ugly tower, but that's Henry. I just go along with him."

Such a quotation could be incredibly damaging. It will be shoved up your nose at some point and that point will probably be during the public hearing. It will happen something like this: "Finally, Mr. Chairman, I've spoken to the applicant's wife. Even *she* doesn't believe that the applicant's description of the proposed tower is benign. She once described it to me as big and ugly."

So here are some lines that your wife must memorize.

- "Well, actually, I've seen many of these installations and they are benign. After a while, you won't even notice it is there. People just don't look up. If they did, most likely they'd see all those big telephone poles."
- "I know that anyone can dream up imaginary horribles, but they are only imaginary."
- "I have no concern whatsoever about interference to TVs, beepers and so forth. We don't have any of those problems in our house. Besides, if they ever did pop up, my husband would do most anything he could to eliminate a problem. But more importantly, the higher the antenna, the less likely is interference. If you don't have any problems now, while the antenna is closer to the ground, there's no reason to believe that problems will arise when it is higher."

And so forth. You absolutely must practice these, and other, responses, since the subject will certainly come up at the supermarket, chance school meetings and so forth. It is inevitable.

By contrast, here are some examples of lines that could hurt you:

- "My husband has cleaned up most of the interference problems around the house and he's promised to get around to the rest later." [The bite: "Not even the ham's own house is free of interference."]
- "Yes, we have one child with only one ear, but some [the right answer is *all*] of the doctors told me that it was completely unrelated to ham radio." [The bite: "We can't even be sure that his own child hasn't been harmed by his transmissions."]
- "My husband has dreamed of erecting one of these antennas all of his life, and we hunted long and hard to find a town that had ordinances that permitted us to erect it." [The bite: "What he's really saying is that he looked long and hard to find a town with weak ordinances so that he could install the equivalent of a toxic-waste dump."]
- "He really needs this antenna system. In order to communicate now, he has to go to a friend's house three miles away." [The bite: "Why can't he continue to do that? He doesn't need an antenna system in our fair town."]

Perhaps there is really only one choice here. It is unlikely that your wife will have the same familiarity with the issues, or have practiced the correct responses as much as you have throughout your life. Ask her to say: "I'm completely familiar with what my husband intends to do. There is really nothing to be concerned about and I feel completely comfortable with the proposal. But if you have questions, I know he'd be delighted to respond to them. Shall I have him call you?"

Talk to Other Hams in Town

There are several reasons to talk with other hams in town. These are covered in some detail in Chapter 2, **The Process in a Nutshell**. Your goals for talking with other hams in town are:

- To gather G-2
- To get reassurance on how to handle any inquiry from your neighbors
- To receive letters of support from them
- To ask for their support and attendance at the public hearing.

Talk to Your Neighbors

Much of this is also discussed in Chapter 2. Set these goals for your talks with neighbors:

- So you can say you've done it
- To gather G-2
- To allay fears they may have about:
  1. TVI/RFI
  2. Setting off their beepers
  3. Setting off their alarm systems
  4. Accidentally opening their garage doors.

Talk to the Building Inspector—The First Visit

The Building Inspector (also known as a Building Commissioner) is usually a busy man, or nowadays a busy woman. If you walk into a Building Inspector's office and assume any female there is a secretary, you can only hurt yourself. Ask.

It is not uncommon for a Building Inspector to have only one hour a day in the office and to spend the rest of the day on the road. Even in the dead of winter, when you'd think that the building season has subsided, Building Inspectors could be busy catching up on a backlog of wood-stove inspections. (I've seen this problem in my practice.) So be prepared before you go to see the Building Inspector. Your appointment could be very short—perhaps five minutes. Plus, there may well be three guys in work boots out in the hall waiting behind you.

Those three guys in work boots in the hall are local contractors who work with the Building Inspector all year round. They have relationships with him. They buy him a bottle of scotch at Christmas. They drink coffee with him on cold mornings on site. They may even be in the room with you while you are making your presentation. It can be unnerving, especially if you thought you'd have a few private moments with the Building Inspector. So be prepared.

The Building Inspector looks at stairs, walls, roofing and so forth, all week long. He may or may not be familiar with the bylaw that controls the antenna system you wish to erect. Moreover, if my experience is any guide, he may not be inclined to tell you that he doesn't have *your* bylaw or ordinance, building code and state statute memorized.

So here are a few suggestions that will be well received by your Building Inspector.

- Bring the relevant bylaw, ordinance, building code and state statute sections with you. This is why we have photocopying machines, paper clips and little sticky notes.
- Walk the Building Inspector through the relevant sections in a rehearsed sequence in under *one minute*.
- Then turn to your list of questions, because the thing he's thinking is: "Why are you here?"
- Ask the easy questions first and get rolling.
  1. Example: "If I use only low voltage (24 V dc for the antenna rotator) will I need to pull an electrical permit?" [The answer is: No. But you should ask since it is an easy question and starts you off.]
  2. Example: "I just want to put up this antenna system as an accessory structure. If I provide all the distances on a scaled drawing will you require a survey?"
  3. Example: "Do I have to show the houses on adjacent properties or can I just show the distances?"
  4. Example: "When is an application considered *filed*? When I hand it to you, or after it has been "circulated" to any necessary Boards or Departments?"
- Then, after you have his attention, dive right into the open-ended questions.
  1. Example: What kind of documentation from the antenna-support manufacturer will you need? Will you accept a catalog "spec" sheet? Factory drawings?
  2. Example: "Will I need a signature from any other departments, such as the Board of Health, the Fire Department or others?"
  3. Example: "Are there any changes in the relevant ordinances now being considered by any board or committee?"
- Save the difficult questions for the second meeting.
  1. Example: "I can put up a less-visible structure (much less bulk than a self-supporting structure), if you'll let me put the guy anchors between the setback and the property line. What do you think about that?"
  2. Example: "Is a PE seal necessary?" (If the answer is yes: Will you accept a dry seal from the manufacturer?)
  3. Example: "Has anyone else that you remember in town ever applied for a permit for an Amateur Radio

antenna system? Could I see that application, please? (If you see one, whether or not it was successful, pay the exorbitant per page photocopying fee (it could be 25 to 50 cents a page) and take home a copy. It's well worth it.) How did it come out? Is he still living there? Is it still up?"

Remember, you can read the rules in the rulebook. The purpose for meeting with the Building Inspector is to learn the answers to questions that are *not* addressed in the bylaws or building code. You want a little local lore, history and practice. You are trying to demonstrate to the Building Inspector that you are knowledgeable about the law on the subject, that you know what you are doing with respect to good construction practice, that you can be trusted and that you won't try to "pull a fast one" (surprise him).

Here are some examples of informal rules that you could learn in a visit, ones that you won't learn in the rulebook or over the phone.

- Some towns have not modified their bylaws or ordinances to meet the requirements of state or Federal law. For whatever reason (inertia, opposition to Federal interference in local zoning, whatever), the bylaw may be clearly illegal. An absolute prohibition against an Amateur Radio antenna more than 50 feet high (the case in Weston, Massachusetts, for example) would be one example. I once asked the Town Attorney if this meant a ham couldn't even put up a wire dipole at 70 feet between two 80-foot trees and she said, "Yes—that dipole would be a zoning violation!" Clearly, this bylaw shows no accommodation to Amateur Radio communications needs.
- In another town, however, where there was just such an absolute prohibition against Amateur Radio antenna systems over a certain height, I went to visit the Building Inspector. I was pleased to learn that he and Town Counsel were aware of the fact that their bylaw was illegal. They had decided that they would grant a building permit as a matter of course to anyone for an Amateur Radio antenna system up to 60 feet high, requiring a full hearing and special permit process only for antennas above that height. (How anyone could obtain, and how they could grant, a Special Permit process without an authorizing bylaw remains a mystery to this day.)
- In another town, the bylaw had a real oddity. It permitted antennas as a matter of right up to 20 feet above the house if they were attached to the house. This town had a lot of three story houses, so the effective right was to build up to about 55 feet above grade. However, a freestanding accessory structure could only be constructed to a height of 35 feet. Upon inquiry, the Building Inspector told me that if the client would run a steel wire to support feed lines from the house to the antenna support structure, he'd consider the structure to be "attached" and would grant a permit as a matter of right up to 55 feet.
- Here's another special case. One Building Inspector told me to calculate a triangle for the uppermost guy wire as it entered the setback area. His bylaw required that

accessory structures in the setback area be less than 12 feet tall (where the original idea was to accommodate basketball nets). What he wanted was that the *average* height for that portion of the guy wires that was within the setback area not exceed 12 feet. This permitted us to move the guy anchors into the setback area.

- In yet another special case, the Building Inspector simply would not permit intrusion into a 5-foot setback, but he was happy to permit guying through a solid live tree, especially when told that a different ruling would result in cutting down the tree, because it was where the guy wires had to land.

Finally, there are times when the rule is clear, but you must know if it applies to you! Here's an example. In one town, the windload requirement was controlled by the easily read definitions of Zones A, B or C. The lowest windload requirement occurs when you are in Zone A, thickly forested and otherwise protected by rolling hills. But the question was, given the client's proximity to the sea, which zone was he in for this purpose? The answer to that question determined how we would propose to guy the structure (three sets or four, $^3/_{16}$- or $^1/_4$-inch EHS guys).

So, prepare your questions, prepare your presentation, and show some respect by showing up during announced office hours or by appointment. Then, grab your answers and leave! You can be friendlier on the second visit.

The Second Visit to the Building Inspector

If time and circumstances permit, you may go back to the Building Inspector for a second visit. This time you should have a good idea of what you want to do, where it is going and so forth. The objective of this visit is no longer to get a feel for the rules, formal or informal but rather to nail down, thoroughly and firmly, the *process*.

Bring your draft permit application and lay it out on the table. Walk the Building Inspector through the application. Your principal questions this time are: "Am I providing everything you (or the Board of Appeals) will need to make a decision? Have I left anything out? Is there anything else you need to see to make a decision?"

Don't bother asking if you'll get the permit from the Board. He has a feeling but is unlikely to tell you what his guess may be. After all, the Building Inspector is supposed to be a neutral, an employee of the town. He has an obligation to be helpful to the Board, which is why he'll be helpful explaining what you must include in your application. But he is unlikely to have a reason to guess at the outcome. At this point, he doesn't know whether there will be any opposition, so his guess isn't worth much anyway. Don't bother asking. It is the sign of a rookie.

Talk to the Secretary to the Planning Board, or to the Town Planner

You will want to:

- Learn what the Board wants to see
- Learn when (day and how often) they meet
- Learn how crowded their calendar is and
- Learn when they decide.

Your town may have a Planning Board, which is different from a Board of Appeals. The Planning Board normally works on issues such as suggesting future changes in the zoning bylaw or ordinance, working on strategies for traffic calming and reviewing (in a somewhat formal, yet somewhat informal way) proposals that will next go to the Board of Appeals for zoning approval.

When you go to the Planning Board, you are out in the open. Your name will be on the agenda; the local newspaper may cover the meeting; the meeting is probably a public meeting (meaning that anyone can attend) and your neighbors will learn what you are planning (which means that they can start to organize against you if that's going to happen). However, it would still be wise to go see the Secretary to the Planning Board or to the Town Planner.

If your town is big enough to have a Town Planner you should approach this person with caution, yet you should also approach this person. Why? Because the Town Planner is likely to be a professional, is more likely than a volunteer to subscribe to professional publications, and may well be the only person with whom you can discuss such questions as "What has the Board looked upon in the past that is similar?"

Here is a list of questions to bring to the Town Planner:

- What bylaws do you think apply?
- What information will the Board of Appeals need to make a decision?
- What does the Board, as a rule, prefer in the way of siting?
- Who are the current members of the Board?
- What's the procedure here in this town?
- What's the timing involved? How many weeks after I apply will I likely be on the agenda? Do they tend to decide that night, or later? How long will it take the Board to issue an opinion?
- Have there been other Amateur Radio antenna proposals before the Board in the last decade or two? Do you think the Board appreciates the difference between a cellular-telephone antenna system and a ham radio antenna system? Are there examples of ham radio antennas in town?

There are Town Planners who will play it straight and give you the scoop on how to make your application so that it will receive fair consideration. There are also Town Planners who will be horrified at the prospect that someone would want to put up a ham radio antenna system. So don't reveal anything to the Town Planner that you don't want revealed at a later date to the Board of Appeals—such as your height strategies, if you have any. It is highly unlikely that the Town Planner will give you any reliable feel for the outcome of the proceeding. Even if the Planner did, you shouldn't rely on it.

The Town Planner is always a better resource than the Secretary to the Planning Board, but you want to become friendly with both, if your town has one of each. Note that you may be asking the same questions of both the Secretary to the Board of Appeals and the Town Planner. Don't worry about seeming repetitive. Only you know that you've asked the questions before. Each person will answer those questions in a slightly different way and that difference in perspective may prove useful.

If there is no Town Planner, there is no harm in asking the above questions of the Secretary to the Planning Board. However, you may not get answers in as much depth. Also, the Secretary to the Planning Board is less likely to have a degree in Town Planning and subscribe to professional journals, which is why the position pays less. But watch out—there are places where the Secretary is the real power. All this only proves what your mother told you while you were growing up: "Be nice to everyone."

Talk to the Secretary of the Zoning Authority

The secretary to the Board of Appeals may be new or lack understanding of the issues. However, now and again you get lucky and the secretary is a long-service employee who can help you effectively assemble your application. She doesn't do this just because you have asked her to be on your side. She does this in response to an appeal along the following lines: "I don't want to waste the Board's time, so I was wondering if you could review my application to see if I've included everything the Board needs to consider to arrive at a decision."

Learn when (the day of the week and how often) they meet. As a separate question, the Secretary will tell you about the Board's schedule. Be careful, since it may vary. For example, here's a schedule that is fairly typical, at least in New England:

- Fall—the second Tuesday of each month, or every other Tuesday
- No meeting in December, or only one meeting
- Spring—the second Tuesday of each month, or every other Tuesday
- Summer—no meeting in July or August.

As you never know (these Boards are comprised of volunteers), *ask.* Learn if the calendar is crowded. Your application may come up in a week, or it may take six or eight weeks before agenda time is available. Since this affects your planning for meeting with neighbors, your printing schedule, your travel plans and so forth, be sure to gather as much information about the calendar as possible. In an ideal world, you will have a chance to attend two meetings before yours comes up. You'll learn a lot about how to present—and how *not* to present a petition.

Learn when they decide. Some Boards pause, talk it out and vote, right then. Others will decide at the end of the evening, hoping that, despite an open-meeting law, many of those present will have gone home. Then they'll be able to decide in relative tranquility—with nobody seething in the audience when a Board member expresses something out loud that reflects a misunderstanding of the evidence.

Still others make no decisions that evening, preferring to meet perhaps on Saturday morning to make all decisions and assign the decision writing. If you have an open-meeting law, but don't know when and where they meet to decide, you can't be there.

FILL YOUR NOTEBOOK

Once you are out there talking to people, you must keep notes, in the bound notebook described in Chapter 4. You must keep details of discussions—including dates, times and who was present. Here are some reasons from real-life experience why you must do this.

- The Building Inspector tells you that, in his/her view, the height is the height of the support structure and not the structure plus mast. If he or she has a change of mind later, you don't want to be accused of "trying to slip one by." You can avoid this predicament by simply reminding the building inspector that you were following his or her instructions from your conversation on a given date.
- You make notes when visiting a neighbor to explain the proposal to both the husband and wife. At a later date one of them claims that all of this is news and you never came by to visit. (The truth is more likely to be that they weren't excited back then but now they are.) If you have notes on the date, place and time, as well as the fact that both were present, they will back off. Your notes can help to refresh their memories.

Identify Supporters and Opposition

If you keep notes, you are more likely to capture information that could prove useful later. For example, you may learn that a ham moved after having put up a large antenna system. You may be able to obtain photographs from that ham to show that such an antenna system once did exist and that life as we know it in Western Civilization did not end. Further, the antenna system was removed once the ham moved away. This is particularly useful to remind all concerned that a ham radio antenna system is not as permanent as the construction of, say, a really ugly house, a commercial building or the proverbial toxic waste dump.

Identify Specific Objections

Another reason for keeping notes is to capture specific objections. Someone may say to you: "But I'll be staring right at it from my dining room table!" It may be that this is not true, but you can be certain that you will hear this objection again at the public hearing. Having recorded the objection in your notebook, you can be reminded later to take a photograph showing that, if true, (1) the actual angle of view does not permit a sight line to your proposed structure, or (2) the view is blocked by trees (even in the winter!). Without photos, on the evening of the hearing it will be your word against his and a Board may assume that the long-term neighbor knows his property better than the newcomer ham.

ZONING AUTHORITIES

What you are about to read is based on experience. You know deep in your heart that surgeons are different from psychiatrists, don't you? But you also know that they've got some characteristics in common too, right?

Well, the people who take positions as Building Inspectors, members of Planning Boards, and Boards of Appeals have some common characteristics too. Getting these feelings and descriptions past my editor was difficult, but here we go.

Building Inspectors/Commissioners/ Code Enforcement Officers

Somewhere along the line in their lives, most—but not all—Building Inspectors, Building Commissioners or Code Enforcement Officers (to use three common titles) have been contractors. Or else they supervised construction in the military. By and large they are *regular guys*. (I've met just one who is a woman, and, as you would expect, she knew her stuff too.) As long as you want to talk about a paragraph in the building code or a drawing, they are friendly and, in my experience, pretty rational.

But they also hold their jobs at the pleasure of the Board of Selectmen, the City Council or Mayor. They know which way the political winds blow. Sometimes they will decide something your way just because it makes sense. Sometimes they really don't want to make a decision at all and will turn you down. This is not because you are wrong, but because with something that may prove controversial they think a civil servant shouldn't make a decision. The Building Inspector may feel that a Board of townspeople can better reflect the town's wishes and that the Board should be making such a decision.

Whatever happens, Building Inspectors deserve your respect. They earn it by calling the shots as they see them, when they can. Always treat them with respect. If it is possible, this means you should call and ask when the Building Inspector has office hours and whether or not s/he takes appointments. Some do and some don't.

Treating them with respect also means that when you meet with the Building Inspector you should be ready with a list of questions all tied to a paragraph in the bylaw or building code, or with questions that have to do with what s/he finds acceptable in construction practices.

Showing respect means that if you leave promising that you'll check something out and get back with an answer, you'd better keep your word. Remember, you'll have to deal with the Building Inspector before any hearing on your permit, during the course of the hearing and after the grant of a permit. Then s/he will make inspections and issue your final certificate of use.

In other words, you've got a lot of interactions with the Building Inspector ahead of you. Be nice.

Planning Boards

Planning Boards may be appointed or elected. However, the method of selection does not matter with respect to the type of person who generally serves on a Planning Board. Planning Boards are generally dominated by people who always wanted to be city planners, people who are working their way through the system and may soon serve (or have just served) on the Finance Committee or Conservation Commission. They're on their way to Selectman or Councilman. This Board often attracts architects and lawyers.

There is one thing about them of which you can be certain. They are on the Planning Board because they like to *plan*. They have a vision about what the town should look like in 20 years. They just *live* to control developers!

In my experience, you cannot predict the actions of a Planning Board. Sometimes they have members who are diehard environmentalists and sometimes they just look at the law—then they look at what you propose and say OK, or Not OK.

Zoning Boards

It is common in small towns for lawyers to serve on a Board of Appeals or Zoning Board in order to please the town fathers—and to pick up local real-estate work. Some lawyers are motivated to become powers in town, so that they can get trust, estate and divorce business. Such lawyers may have no inkling at all about what the issues are, but they are lawyers and therefore may be inclined to think they know it all. (In this respect, they can resemble engineers!)

The blessing about lawyers, engineers and architects is that you can sometimes get them to read a statute, case or at least a paragraph of an FCC ruling. The pain administered by such people is that when attempting to write a tight opinion (while not getting paid) they can be pretty sloppy with the facts. If some fact is misstated in the decision, sometimes you've just got to *paper* the file (write a letter pointing out the factual error) and get on with life. This is exactly what you should do when they blow it but yet you can live with their errors.

HOMEOWNERS' ASSOCIATIONS

What kind of person serves on the Homeowners' Association Board of Directors? At the start of the development the Board is likely the developer, his wife and the construction foreman. The developer normally keeps control of the Board until the development is almost complete. After all, he doesn't want the Board to start passing regulations that would increase his construction costs.

For example, while the developer controls the Board, he can keep a dumpster on site throughout construction and leave trash or building materials around a building lot. A Board, on the other hand, could decide to pass an association rule that dumpsters must be emptied at least every two weeks (or worse, weekly), the premises must be policed each evening at quitting time and building materials must be stored out of sight or under tarpaulins.

Eventually, however, the Association will be turned over to the owners. So what kind of person volunteers to serve on the Board? One type is the person hoping to pick up business: an insurance salesman, office-supplies salesman, lawyer, estate planner, stockbroker and so forth. Another type is the person with a desire to assure himself or herself that the development will be tidy—that garage doors will not be left open, that teenagers' cars won't be parked on the lawn and that the entire development will strongly resemble the town in the movie *Pleasantville*.

Yes, you could say that this person has a need to control others. You don't want to tangle with this person, as s/he totally loves to control others. S/he is not your friend. *Laissez-faire* personalities do not take these posts!

The blessing of Homeowners' Associations is that they sometimes (but not always) have small budgets and cannot afford to spend money on litigation or lawyers. But watch out; you may run into some "free lawyering," at least on the advice and guidance side. Lawyers seldom volunteer to litigate free of charge. It is just too much work.

One other warning: Even if you believe that the association may be unable to afford litigation, there may be a clause somewhere that permits a neighbor to undertake litigation to enforce a CC&R and perhaps even recover those costs from you if successful.

If you are about to make—or have already made—the mistake of buying into a development with a Homeowners' Association, or worse yet, an Architectural Review Board, do your best to discover as much as you can about the finances of the Association or Board. It could determine the outcome of the tussle that is sure to develop. There—you've been warned.

6

Possible Objections

PREPARING FOR THE PERMIT APPLICATION AND THE PUBLIC HEARING

If you pay attention to this chapter, you will find good answers to the types of objections commonly raised at public hearings. In many such situations, the Chairman will turn to the applicant and say: "How do you respond to that?" To avoid rambling, and to respond directly, you may wish to make out 4 × 6-inch index cards with your own responses.

You *must* avoid rambling—If you take several minutes for each response, the Chairman will soon stop calling on you. I suggest you print out the sample "Answer Cards" from the CD-ROM, filename: **Answer Cards.PDF**. These are formatted for pasting on 4 × 6-inch index cards.

Before beginning your preparations for battle, take a moment to consider the poem that appears elsewhere on this page.

STRUCTURAL SAFETY

If someone stands up at a public hearing and says that your structure could fall over and damage his house or injure his children, you can pretty much bet that the real objection is one of aesthetics. However, this does not mean that you can simply ignore the question or the problem. On the contrary, this is a question that you *must not* ignore. The proper approach is to sympathize with the concern and address it. Here's how to sympathize:

"Mr. Jones has expressed the fear that my proposed structure could damage his house or injure his child. He has every right to be concerned. I am very concerned about those same things."

An Amateur Radio Tower
By Marvin Wilson, VE7BJ
(Originally appearing in the bulletin of the Point Grey Amateur Radio Club)

Why do people get upset when one puts up a radio tower? A few things in its favor...

It Doesn't

Squeal its brakes
Screech its tires
Blow its horn
Roar its motor
Slam its doors at ungodly hours
Shine its headlights in your bedroom window
Nor does it backfire.

It Doesn't

Drop leaves that you have to clean up
Grow branches over your house
Drop fruit or nuts that block your downpipes
Block your view like a tree or building
Grow roots that damage your walk or driveway
Nor do its roots plug your drains.

It Doesn't

Bite you
Bark or meow
Leave deposits on your property
Dig up your garden
Scratch on your door
Widdle on your trees
Nor does it dig up and scatter your garbage.

It Doesn't

Have boisterous parties
Or play loud music
Or have swimming parties through the night
It doesn't ring your phone (accidentally?)
Nor does it ride bikes across your lawn.
It's just quiet and has nothing to say...

And here's how to respond: "For that reason, please note that:

- The proposed location was chosen so that should the structure ever fall, it would be stopped by the tree line before ever reaching the ground.
- The proposed construction exceeds the requirements of the building code, and, it is important to note, the building code already has safety margins built-in.
- The construction will be under the supervision of the Building Inspector, whom we trust with the supervision of all other forms of construction in town, including the schools, churches, the hospital and so forth.
- I have no objections at all if the Board would like to add a condition to the Special Permit that the construction must meet the requirements of the state building code and be constructed subject to the reasonable supervision of the Building Inspector.
- Because the proposed construction will be built in accordance with the building code, and supervised by the Building Inspector, you can expect that it will be as safe as any house."

[Note: This isn't really giving anything away. With or without such a condition in the Special Permit, you are never going to be exempt from the state building code or supervision by the Building Inspector!]

- "Failures as a result of construction are so rare that the homeowner's insurance industry doesn't even charge extra for the risk. This is proof positive that an antenna system in your back yard is safer than letting your teenage son drive!"

[Note: Humor in highly charged situations is always helpful, but don't try it if you are uncomfortable at attempting humor in a public presentation. If you are uncomfortable, it will show and the humor will fall flat. And it's probably not a good idea to use this particular joke if the neighbor has a teenaged son in his household… But you did your homework and know who your neighbors and their children are, don't you?]

- "I have children of my own, and I don't intend to put them at risk by the construction I am proposing."

Remember, neither Federal nor state laws that favor ham radio will ever exempt you from building-safety requirements and meeting the provisions of the state building code. Health and safety will override, as they should.

At this moment, you are in front of the Board asking for permission to put this structure in a residential area. Possible building-code violations can always be dealt with later. Even after you have constructed your antenna system, the Building Inspector has the right to come onto your land (since he has police power) and can see if something is unsafe. If he finds that something is indeed unsafe, he can always remove or repair it, applying a lien on your house and land to repay the town for any expenditure.

Conclusion: Treat safety as a big issue. But it is a Building Inspector issue. It is not a use issue that belongs before the Board of Appeals.

AIRSPACE SAFETY

Occasionally someone will rise during the public hearing and ask two different kinds of questions that have to do with airspace safety. Roughly, those two questions might be:

- "Will this thing be painted orange and white and be lighted?"
- "Don't you have to get permission from the FAA first?"

What's really going on here in the painting-and-lighting question might be that the questioner is expressing an innocent and curious question, a question that may be totally reasonable in the context of a neighborhood. However, the questioner might also be trying to throw gasoline on the fire of "it's ugly and not appropriate for a residential neighborhood." Let's look more closely at this painting-and-lighting question.

You probably don't live really close to an airport and you probably don't intend to erect a tower greater than 200 feet tall. So, for almost all Amateur Radio situations, the short answer is that you aren't required to paint and light. Your public position is that you don't intend to paint and light.

See 47 CFR § 97.15 (b-d), reproduced on the CD-ROM, filename: **FCC Part 97.PDF**. Note especially § 97.15 (c), which offers a complete exemption from prior FCC approval and FAA procedures if "[a]n amateur station antenna structure [is] no higher than 6.1 m (20 feet) above ground level at its site or no higher than 6.1 m above any natural object or existing manmade structure, other than an antenna structure . . ." Thus, if you are planning a structure no higher than 20 feet above surrounding trees, and you are not near an airport (more than 20,000 feet away, which is 6.1 km or 3.8 miles), you have an automatic exemption for FAA and FCC limits.

Nonetheless, please consult the FCC web page to see if the rule applies to you. See **http://www.fcc.gov/wtb/antenna/infoCenter/gettingStarted_1.html** or see the CD-ROM, filename: **FCC Registering Antennas.PDF**.

Painting and Lighting

Furthermore, and again assuming that painting and lighting is not required by the FAA regulations in your situation, if the Board wishes to make it a condition of the permit that the structure will be *neither* painted for marking *nor* lighted, that's fine with you too! After all, the condition is totally harmless.

For greater detail, see FAA Advisory Circular 70/7460-21 "PROPOSED CONSTRUCTION OR ALTERATION OF OBJECTS THAT MAY AFFECT THE NAVIGABLE AIRSPACE." For tremendous detail, see FAA Advisory Circular AC 70/7460-1H "Obstruction Marking and Lighting." See **http://www.faa.gov/ATS/ATA/ai/index.html**.

The actual regulation, upon which the FCC public information page is based, is found at 14 CFR Part 77. The 200-foot height rule is covered, along with rules concerning nearby airports and exemptions.

If the question comes up, it may be a good idea to hand out the printout of "1. Do You Need To Register," found at **http://www.fcc.gov/wtb/antenna/infoCenter/ gettingStarted_1.html** to the Chairman at the public meeting, although doing so at the meeting may slow down the process while the Board studies the new material. (This document is on the CD-ROM, filename: **FCC Registering Antennas.PDF**.) Handing over a printout of this Federal government document is another way to assure the Board that you've done your homework and you are really prepared. It is a confidence-building measure.

FAA Permission

Now, let's look more closely at the "FAA permission" question. Since most applicants are not located within 20,000 feet, or even 1.52 km (5,000 feet) of an airport, FAA permission is very seldom necessary. However, a common delaying tactic by opponents is to ask the Board if FAA permission must be obtained. Most Boards will accept your assurance that you've checked and FAA permission is not required. Some Boards will want to see the rule for themselves. A few Boards will want a lawyer's letter opining that no FAA permission is required.

Yet all Boards will be impressed with your preparation if you show up with an FAA "No Hazard" letter. In general, this is a question of lead-time. If you are planning now for a hearing in six months to a year, you may apply to the FAA for what is not really "permission," but rather a Certificate or Determination of No Hazard, sometimes also called a No Hazard letter. An example of such a letter, issued to Jeff Briggs, K1ZM, is on the CD-ROM, filename: **FAA No Hazard K1ZM.PDF**.

Incidentally, a "No Hazard to Aviation" decision is fairly bulletproof. See *Aircraft Owners and Pilots Association v. Federal Aviation Administration*, 600 F. 2d 965 (D.C. Cir. 1979), which affirmed a no-hazard decision and held that, though informal, "the adjudicatory procedures employed by the FAA created a record which contains substantial evidence supporting the no-hazard decision."

The process begins by obtaining and filing FAA Form 7460-1 "Notice of Proposed Construction or Alteration." (See CD-ROM, filename: **FCC FAA AntennaForm.PDF**.). Fill out the form and file it with the appropriate regional FAA office listed on the cover page.

If you absolutely must know in advance, and in a hurry, about whether or not you are likely to receive an FAA No Hazard determination, there are private consultants. One such company is Airspace Safety Analysis Corporation, Atlanta, GA. See David Hunter, "Airspace Safety: An Integral Part of Your Tower Management Program," *Cellular Business*, October 1991, p 28ff.

If you do require a Notice to Airmen (called a NOTAM), you must also file FCC Form 854, and eventually you will receive an FCC Structure Registration.

ATTRACTIVE NUISANCE AND CHILD SAFETY

If you live in a suburban neighborhood, someone may jump up at the Public Hearing and suggest that an antenna-support structure is inherently an *Attractive Nuisance*. This is some-

thing dangerous that attracts children to climb it, who may then suffer an accident by falling off the structure. This objection is usually raised by someone whose real objection relates to something else, but you should ignore that fact.

You can probably predict who this person will be. It will be someone in law, insurance or real estate (who else knows about the doctrine of "attractive nuisance"?). This person probably has a child, usually a curious male child. If you respond by saying that there are no children in the neighborhood, even if it is true, you are effectively conceding that the claim is true and that you wish to ignore the potential danger and hope for the best. Bad strategy. Remember, as you respond, that you are trying to be a good guy (wearing your white hat).

Anti-Climbing Devices

The best answer is: "Well, I certainly agree with (person's name, beginning with Mr, Ms or Mrs, as a sign of public respect) that my proposed structure is attractive. (Pause and smile!) But I cannot agree that this structure is an *attractive nuisance*, as the legal term implies. Nonetheless, I'd like to call the attention of the Board to page nnn of the application, where I have shown the type of anti-climbing device I propose to construct."

See the photos in **Fig 6-1**, which are also included on the CD-ROM, filenames: **K1ZM Anti-climb.PDF** and **K1HT Anti-climb.PDF**.

Bushes, Guy Guards

As guy wires near the ground, it becomes possible to consider them a hazard, in the sense that a child could run into a set near the anchor. One attractive solution is to plant evergreen bushes near the anchor rod.

Here's another solution. Utility companies use slit plastic tubes, called "guy guards," on their guy wires to provide visibility. One manufacturer is Preform Line Products, who also make the so-called "big grips" for guy wires. Check: **http://www.ctcjoslyn.com/catalog/plasticguy_guards_ order.html**.

AESTHETIC IMPACT

For most opponents, *aesthetic impact* is really the heart of the matter. As always, you've got to figure out: "What is the *real* question?" It is very important for you to frame their question in a way that is favorable to the outcome you desire.

Let's face it: You and I think that Amateur Radio antenna systems are majestic. We show pictures of antenna systems to friends just like car buffs swap photos of cars and just like grandmothers swap photos of grandchildren. However, the truth is that some people might not agree with us, and they may be well-respected citizens in their communities. The fact that they disagree on aesthetic issues doesn't mean that they should come out on top in the discussion. The usual test found in an ordinance is *not* whether something is *pretty*.

At this point in the discussion, you should remind all concerned that if you were to do at 35 feet what you want to

(A)   **(B)**

Fig 6-1—At A, an anti-climbing shield at K1ZM, made using hardware cloth on Rohn 25G tower. At B, a plywood anti-climbing shield at K1HT, mounted with U-bolts, also on Rohn 25G tower.

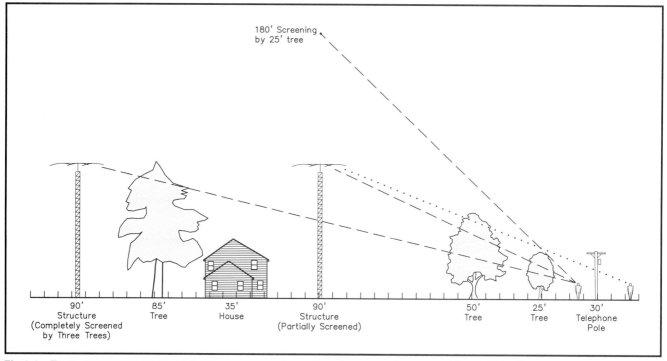

180' Screening
by 25' tree

90'	85'	35'	90'	50'	25'	30'
Structure	Tree	House	Structure	Tree	Tree	Telephone
(Completely Screened			(Partially Screened)			Pole
by Three Trees)						

Fig 6-2—Trees can screen even a tall antenna support structure from view from street level. This illustrates perspective.

6.4   Possible Objections

do at 130 feet, there would be no discussion at all. (This is in the absence of the cross-covenants and restraints (CC&Rs) sometimes found in developments or condominiums.) Below a certain height dictated by town ordinance or bylaw, in almost every municipality in America, you are permitted to put up an antenna. (The exceptions are where the whole town is one big development subject to CC&Rs and in historic districts.)

So the use for Amateur Radio is not in question. Amateur Radio is inherently a non-commercial use, most often carried out from home. It is very important for you and your town's officials to understand that Amateur Radio is a *permitted use* from virtually every home in America. What we're really talking about is *height*, because that same tribander, quad or vertical would be permissible below 35 feet, or whatever height your local ordinance dictates. You must be adamant about this.

So, now that the real question is height, the next question is: "How high?" One of your best answers is: "High enough to get above the trees, because you don't want to make a big hole in the forest." You may find that this is the time to find common ground with the local conservationists, who don't much like to see trees cut down.

See if you can find a spot where only one tree needs to be removed, or perhaps none, and you may make a potential opponent into an ally. Wouldn't it be nice for someone to stand up and argue that going above the tops of the trees has less impact on the neighborhood than an alternative where many trees are felled?

Another thing you must remember is that trees want to grow. So if you live in what was formerly a farmed field, and it was converted into housing 30 years ago, the neighborhood trees have not yet reached maturity. Allow plenty of room for further growth before setting the height you propose.

Nonetheless, the discussion above relates just to the proposition that you want to get above the trees. In fact, your communications needs may not be dictated by tree height, but rather by the propagation angles required. This may require a more sophisticated discussion, along the lines of the ARRL article by R. Dean Straw, N6BV, and Jerry Hall, K1TD, *Antenna Height and Communications Effectiveness*. (A copy is on the CD-ROM, filename: **Antenna Height and Communications Effectiveness.PDF**.) But in the meantime, if you are planning only a relatively modest height (say, 95 feet or less), remember that you'll just barely be clearing the trees, especially when seen from the perspective of a neighboring street.

What is meant by *perspective*? Here's an example of how a 100-foot structure can be blocked by a six-foot tree. See **Fig 6-2**, which is also located on the CD-ROM, filename: **Tree Screening.PDF**. You should also use your own photographs in the neighborhood to your advantage.

Photos

As engineers like to say, "A kiloword is worth a picture." Remember, film and film developing is cheap, especially if you take advantage of inexpensive mail-away developers. It is especially cheap compared to lawyer time. As I suggested in Chapter 4, go take some pictures!

- From the proposed site and aim toward:
  1. the street
  2. neighboring streets
  3. every neighbor's house
  4. your house.
- Aim toward the proposed site from:
  1. the street
  2. neighboring streets
  3. every neighbor's house
  4. your house.

Don't try to be cute and take your photos in the middle of the summer when the leaves are fully leafed out. Do that and someone at the public hearing is going to pretend he is Perry Mason, shouting: "But how will it look in winter?" Actually, this is a pretty silly question, because your neighbor will be outdoors working on his lawn and garden much more in the summer, not the winter. Even during the cold months, your neighbor is not too likely to be tilted over on his side, looking up through a window to see the top of your structure.

Furthermore, watch carefully to see if the opponent makes conflicting statements, which you can then point out to the Board. Here is a common example of conflicting statements: "The photos were taken in the summer when leaves block the view of this monstrosity." Later, he says: "It will stick out like a sore thumb above the trees."

The opponent's problem is that he can't have it both ways. Either your antenna may be visible through the trees in winter, or it is above the trees (more probably), in which case the trees (leaves or no leaves) are irrelevant because the view will be unobstructed. Of course, there are times when your antenna is only visible through the trees in winter, which means that his expression that it will "stick out like a sore thumb above the trees" was wrong. You might ask the Board if it wouldn't be a good idea for the opponent to make up his mind.

For pictures in the directions toward adjacent houses, it is probably adequate to mount up to four 3 × 5-inch prints per page for color photocopying. For other pictures, two 4 × 6-inch prints per page will do nicely. Be sure to label each photo with some helpful remarks, such as "Taken in mid-winter to show lack of visibility without foliage." Using a digital camera and printing the photos yourself, with labeling, will make you look like a real pro.

The best possible photo shows the exact same installation taken at your last home. This shows several things:

- That some other town gave you permission.
- That it wasn't very obtrusive there either.
- What it will look like when erected here.

A second-best is a photo of similar installations, whether in your town or not. If photos can be taken of existing installations in your town, so much the better. It should then be obvious to the Board that civilization didn't come to an end because of these other antennas. Nonetheless, a comparable installation in another town will do also.

Whatever you do, however, it is important to get some photos in front of the Board, because (1) you want to confront the fear of the unknown, and (2) you want to make it obvious that what you propose is not unique, but in fact is rather common.

A last warning on taking photos. They must fairly represent the situation. While you and I might think that if you take a photo at exactly the right moment when the antenna was sparkling in the sky that you have a masterpiece, such a photo does not fairly represent the situation. Instead, take a photo on a cloudy day. This represents the most realistic situation, in which there are no distracting, shiny reflections off brand-new aluminum. After only a few months in the sky, all of the shiny metal (aluminum or galvanized steel) will have oxidized and will remain dull for the rest of its erected life.

Balloon Testing

You may run into a situation where you will be accused of erecting a support structure that will be ugly from a certain vantage point. If you know, or suspect, that it can't even be seen from a particular place, you may wish to consider doing your own *balloon test*. What you do is float a balloon up to the height you propose, from the location you propose, while communicating with another ham by handy-talkie (HT) on a simplex frequency. Doing this with two people is a good idea because you might not know that the balloon has drifted one way or another due to wind by the time you get to the spot from which you want to take the photo.

It is very powerful to show the Board that some intervening obstruction prevents a view of the balloon, or perhaps that the balloon can be seen, but only just barely, through intervening trees.

Here's an inexpensive way to perform a balloon test. A client of mine used this technique to prove to one neighbor that an 80-foot tall structure, deep in a woods, would not be visible on the neighbor's property—even though it was 20 feet higher than neighboring trees. He used a cluster of six or seven balloons, tied together with some kite string. He got them at a party store, along with a non-refillable helium tank. The whole kit cost him about $20. There was more than enough helium for the two tests he made. Fair Radio and Nebraska Surplus both carry larger weather balloons, and they are often on eBay, but my client found those prices prohibitive for a one-time use.

Crank-Up Towers as a Solution

Should a Board, or staff member representing a Board, suggest that you accept a crank-up structure as an accommodation, think really hard before saying no. In the past, some courts have used an amateur's failure to accept this accommodation offer against him or her.

A condition in the permit limiting the raising of the structure to full height only during nighttime hours is probably illegal. Chris Imlay, W3KD, ARRL General Counsel, points out that "Only the FCC can impose or regulate hours of operation, pursuant to the general enabling clause of the

Communications Act of 1934. There is no municipal jurisdiction over hours of operation of radio stations. The usual situation involves hours when crankup towers can be extended to full height, but to the extent that regulation determines communications ability, the infringement on Federal jurisdiction is the same."

ARRL Volunteer Counsel Jim O'Connell, W9WU, likes to point out that such conditions are silly, because for DXing or emergency communications reasons, many Amateur Radio stations are in almost permanent connection to a local or regional packet radio network. Hams may keep a VHF or UHF repeater on the air at their own locations, available for 24-hour access, as a public service. Therefore, in extreme circumstances you may wish to accept a condition where you are forced to erect a crank-up, and then just leave it up all the time (because it is in use all the time). You might lower it when you leave on vacation (and even then it might not be necessary if your repeater has a control operator who can control the repeater remotely).

Paint

You may be asked if you can paint your structure to reduce visibility. The answer to that requirement is that, in general, towers come in galvanized gray steel. After weathering, this will be the least-visible color already and no painting is necessary. Gray is the preferable color, which is why warships are gray and why military airplanes have gray underbellies and wings.

THE ENVIRONMENT

We live in an age of environmental litigation. Fortunately, you will not be bitten by a snail darter. In fact, you will probably not even be worried about the existence or non-existence of a snail darter at your place. Except for wetlands, buffers to wetlands, or some other special circumstance, you will not be required to do anything with respect to the environment.

No filing is required to comply with the National Environmental Policy Act of 1969. See **http://www.fcc.gov/wtb/siting/npaguid.html**. An environmental assessment (EA) is required only in eight environmentally sensitive situations (47 CFR §1.1307(a)), or for radiation in excess of OET 65 guidelines (47 CFR §1.1307(b)).

ZONING VIOLATIONS— SETBACKS AND YARDS

However, don't try to put anything past the Board. Either someone on the Board will catch it, or you can be assured an opponent will be looking to catch it. So if you need to invade a standard town setback (ie, 20 feet from a rear-lot line) or obtain a variance (such as a variance from a 1:1 setback for structure height), be sure to spell it out and ask for it.

For example, the right place to put your structure for least aesthetic impact—the place that a neutral observer would consider to be in the best interest of your neighborhood—may be five feet closer to a side-lot line than permitted by the town bylaw or ordinance. The way to handle this is to propose *in the alternative*. Propose Alternative A, which is permitted by the bylaw or ordinance and then explain why this is a less-attractive choice from the perspective of the neighbors than Alternative B, which requires a variance. An example of a good reason is:

Alternative A would require a self-supporting tower. This involves much more concrete, a wider tower face all the way up, a much wider face at the base—in other words, self-supporting Alternative A is something *really* substantial.

On the other hand, Alternative B might require only a guyed tower with an 18-inch face, 18 inches all the way up. But due to the shape of the lot, it may have to be a few feet into the side-lot area, where it would not normally be permitted. (I had that exact case once.) After we pointed out that the town was much better off with a less imposing structure if a variance were to be granted, the variance was indeed granted.

Fortunately, if the facts support it, you may find yourself in a situation where you are arguing for a variance, which the Board will see is in the best interest of the neighborhood, while your opponents are arguing against the variance. They are hoping that by denying you the variance they may succeed in denying you the permit altogether. In this case you must say that you are perfectly willing to spend the money to meet the setback conditions.

Express your willingness, but carefully and plainly point out that the opponents cannot possibly have the best interests of the neighborhood in mind. After all, the consequence of their position is to force you to build a structure that is 10 feet wide at the base and more plainly visible because the setback forces it into the open area of the yard, where it becomes highly visible.

Bottom line though: No funny business. Present the alternative (with separate plot plans) and tell the Board why the alternative you are promoting is best for the neighborhood. That is always your best argument.

Trust me, the Board does not care if the reason you urge Proposal B is because it is less expensive to you or because your wife thinks it will look better there. If more than one site is possible, you must always cast your choice for a location on your lot that is in the best interest of the neighborhood.

Here are some other good reasons for moving an antenna-support structure to a place on the lot where it would normally not be permitted under the ordinance:

- If you move it over *there* and it fell—although the odds are so long as to be unthinkable—it would only fall in wild underbrush. In the permitted location, on the other hand, the structure could fall on a neighbor's house.

- If you move it over *there*, views of the structure can be obscured by trees, whereas forcing it into the middle of the lot (because it must be 20 feet from a back-lot line and 50 feet from a side-lot line) would make it much more visible to the whole neighborhood.

- If you put the guy anchor over *there*, guy wires can be snaked through the trees all the way to the ground. However, if the set back must be obeyed, you would have to erect a heavy I-beam to "short stop" the guy wires before they invade the

setback. The guy wires in the woods will never be noticed, but that 14-inch I-beam, sticking 12 feet into the air, will certainly be less attractive to the casual observer.

The Flying Setback

In selecting a site, be sure to account for the possibility that the triangle formed by your boom and longest element (normally the reflector on the lowest frequency band the antenna covers) will not go over the property line as it rotates. By informal inquiry, you may also wish to ask the Building Inspector if temporary intrusions into a setback, only when the antenna is pointed in a certain direction, would be acceptable. After all, this would not be *construction* in the setback area, and it would be a *de minimus* intrusion, just as lamp poles and mailboxes are always permitted within the setback. Your antenna would be no more of an intrusion than a flag that stretches out in the breeze and invades a setback. See **Fig 6-3**.

If you want to put your support structure in the setback, you may have a problem. Perhaps you can claim it is a temporary structure, exempt for some reason under the bylaw or ordinance. Sometimes accessory structures like sheds are exempt from the setback or yard requirements. If it is only the rotary antenna that invades the setback, argue that only location of the base matters, and the antenna is just a protrusion, similar to the way a roof overhang "doesn't count" (usually).

Now let's get technical. A *setback* usually means the distance from a *way*, such as a driveway, a highway or a street. Normally you'll be dealing with the distance from your house to the street in front of your house. You've got to check the definitions section of your town's bylaw or ordinance. Similarly, you've got to check the definitions section of the bylaw to find out what a *yard* is. Normally it means the distance between a lot line and something. Here's one town's definition:

"*YARD*—An area open to the sky, located between a structure or other property line and any principal structure or element thereof other than projections allowed to encroach on building lines and yards under the State Building Code. Depth is to be measured perpendicular to the street or property line."

Here's an example of how you can make a very strong legal argument. An antenna-support structure is an *accessory structure*, not a *principal structure*. While the antenna may be an element of the antenna-support structure, the antenna is *not* an element of the principal structure. Therefore the yard requirement under this bylaw applies to *neither* the antenna *nor* the antenna-support structure.

Here's another argument. You may discover that the yard requirement applies to a principal structure. However, you may be able to argue that the yard requirement does not apply to an *appurtenance* to a principal structure. Here, the support is the principal structure and the antenna is the appurtenance.

Average Height

Since we're talking about guy wires going to guy anchors

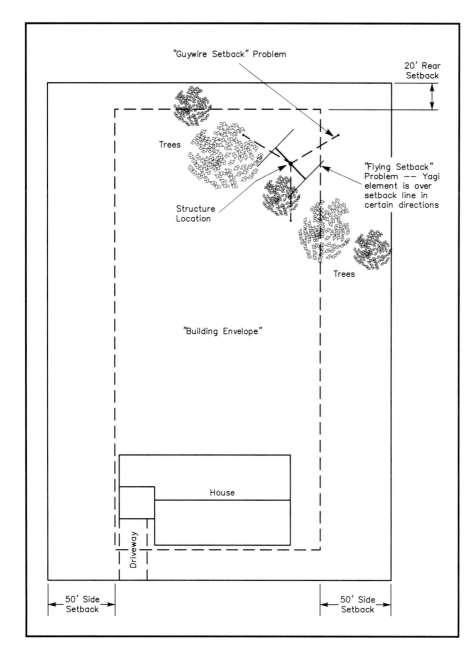

Fig 6-3—An illustration of two problems: a "flying setback" situation where the antenna can invade the setback as it is rotated in certain directions, and a situation where one of the guy wires invades the setback. In either case, the proposed structure site is best for the neighborhood due to partial screening from sight by the trees.

antenna proposals. Legally, it is also the most untenable. Frankly, the Board shouldn't even hear such arguments. If this were a court your lawyer would jump up and shout, "Objection" and the Judge would reply, "Sustained." However, this is not a courtroom and the Board will be very reluctant to prevent people from speaking out at a Public Hearing.

People who stand and object to your proposal on the grounds that it may interfere with TV reception, stereos, garage-door openers and alarm systems come in several flavors. As you would expect, many of them are just reaching for yet another argument to make, in what I call the *spaghetti defense*. These people throw every argument possible against the wall to see what sticks.

Whatever the reason for putting forth the argument, remember you are not trying to satisfy the person making the objection. You are trying to satisfy the Board. This is a very big distinction. Here's an example of why it is a big distinction.

Assume that someone who lives four blocks away rises to make the objection that he fears that you will interfere with his pager. If you respond that the inverse-square distance law (by which the electromagnetic field of your transmitted signal decreases as the inverse of the square of the distance) will prevent this, you may have satisfied the guy who lives four blocks away. Unfortunately, you've just told the Board that the guy who lives next door may have a problem. Bad idea.

There are several ways to deal with this complaint. Not wishing to waste the Board's time by making the application any fatter than necessary, I prefer not to include a legal brief in the application stating all the reasons why the Board cannot rule in this area. However, I certainly bring with me copies of the *Broyde, Southwestern Bell* and *Freeman* cases.

in the ground, you may run into a zoning bylaw that limits the height of a structure within the setback. Sometimes it is a 1:1 setback, sometimes it is a simple maximum height—something like 12 feet, a number chosen because that is the height of a basketball net with backboard. Don't be shocked, it's an American sport!

Just because your top guy wire may be 21 feet above the ground as it enters the setback area, do not hesitate to propose it. Just explain that (1) a $^3/_{16}$- or $^1/_4$-inch galvanized steel guy wire against the backdrop of trees disappears from view. So it is *de minimis* (a trifle) and the law should not concern itself with trifles. Furthermore, argue that the *average* height within the setback of the guy wire, or perhaps even the guy set, still meets the 1:1 setback test.

INTERFERENCE: RFI OR TVI

This is one of the most common arguments made against

The Broyde Case

Broyde v. Gotham Tower, 13 F. 3d 994 (6th Circuit, 1994), **http://pacer.ca6.uscourts.gov/cgi-bin/getopn. pl?OPINION=94a0007p.06**, was a case where the neighbors sued the operator of an 800-foot tall commercial tower and the FM radio station tenants, claiming common-law nuisance by interference to all manner of radio, TV, telephone, garage door opener and other home electronic devices. The Court found implied preemption of the field and ruled that even if everything the plaintiff (Broyde) said was true, the complaint had not stated a claim upon which relief could be granted. This document is also available on the CD-ROM, filename: **Broyde v. Gotham Tower.PDF**.

The Southwestern Bell Case

Southwestern Bell Wireless, Inc. v. Johnson County Board of County Commissioners, No. 98-3264 (10th Cir. Dec. 27, 1999) **http://www.kscourts.org/ca10/cases/1999/12/98-3264.htm**, enjoined the Board of County Commissioners from enforcing an ordinance against interference. The court found that there was complete Federal preemption of the field. This document is on the CD-ROM, filename: **SW Bell Wireless.PDF**.

The Freeman Case

Freeman v. Burlington Broadcasters, No. 97- 9141 (2d Cir. February 23, 2000) **http://www.tourolaw.edu/2ndCircuit/February00/97-9141.html**, 2000 U.S. App. LEXIS 2672 involved a 199-foot commercial tower on Pease Mountain, in Charlotte, Vermont. A condition in the grant of the permit for the tower required the permittees to remedy any radio frequency interference ("RF interference" or "RFI") from tower signals with appliances and devices in local homes. The Second Circuit court held that any attempt by the Zoning Board of Appeals to enforce the condition was preempted by Federal law, which preempts the field, giving the FCC exclusive authority over RFI. In a little-noted last sentence of the opinion, the Court wrote: "The Appellees may recover their costs." So WIZN, Charlotte Fire & Rescue Services and Bell Atlantic NYNEX Mobile were entitled to collect their legal costs. This document is on the CD-ROM, filename:
Freeman vs Burlington Broadcasters.PDF.

I also like to bring along several printed copies of my own short memorandum of law (found in Chapter 7 and on the CD-ROM included with this book, filename:
Memorandum of Law.PDF).

If your town has a Town Planner, you should meet with this person in advance of the public meeting and lay out the cases and memorandum. There is a good chance that the Town Planner will brief the Board in advance of the meeting that this area is off-limits legally.

The Applicant's Assurance

No matter how secure your legal position, be sure to practice your *assurance* in advance. As with other responses, this appears on an answer card that you may print straight from the CD-ROM, filename: **Answer Cards.PDF**. The idea here is that you must not promise to cure the problem, because some people own equipment you cannot cure. Second, you don't really want to personally cure any neighbor's gear. Once you touch it, the neighbor is going to blame you

for any subsequent breakdown.

Let's say you install a 0.01 µF bypass capacitor inside his VCR. Years later, when some mechanical part of the VCR drive fails, the neighbor will assume that you caused the breakdown. Never mind that you never touched that portion of the machine—You were the only person who ever put his hands inside. Your neighbor will never be convinced otherwise. So, unless you are willing to take on free repairs of home-entertainment equipment, don't offer to fix anything and don't put your hands inside.

On the other hand, the cost of capacitors, filters and toroids is not great. You might choose to offer to pay for the components necessary to fix the problem. Just don't mention at the hearing who will have to install them. So where does this leave you? Think about a response something like this:

"Members of the Board, this subject area is off-limits to the town. I've brought with me citations to legal cases that make it abundantly clear that municipalities have no power to act in this area. The Federal Communications Commission is the sole authority in cases of radio-frequency interference."

"However, I understand the concern you've heard here. First, let me say that I'm already on the air with the same transmitter, using an antenna at a lower height, closer to the set in question and you didn't hear any complaint. This present antenna does not provide effective communications, which is why I'm here tonight. But the new antenna, by virtue of its additional height, will be further away and therefore less likely to interfere."

"The truth is that such interference issues are so uncommon that some manufacturers choose not to include the few extra parts necessary to calm down interference in millions of sets, when they can help with the occasional problem and save a lot of money cumulatively. As a result, the Consumer Electronics Manufacturers Association maintains a Web page on whom to contact about such problems, generally using an 800 number. The repairs are simple. In any event, I pledge to cooperate fully with my neighbors to help them to resolve any complaint that may arise."

Note that "cooperate fully" doesn't require you to fix anything. Again, you don't want to touch anything your hostile neighbor owns, or you may find yourself replacing all of his gear at your expense.

The Local TVI Committee

It is useful if you can add that your community has an existing *RFI/TVI Committee* to help straighten out potential interference. If such a committee does not yet exist, there's still no problem. Ask three local hams if they would be willing to be an RFI Committee for the purposes of your hearing. The likelihood that they will eventually be called upon to do something is low. However, by naming such a committee in the public hearing, you are really offering a comforting assurance to the Board.

Installing Filters

You can always offer to purchase and "help" to install

filters and toroids. The cost of purchase is low and they are usually easy to install. Just remember that what you are offering to do is to buy the filters or toroids and instruct the neighbor on how to install them. Just be aware of the old warning: "Touch it and you own it."

PROPERTY VALUE

The claim that installing your antenna will lower property values is patently untrue. It is another element of the "spaghetti defense," and is usually put forward by someone who wants to put up every possible objection. There are several possible strategies available to the ham. They are:

- Borrow someone else's study that shows no impact on home values.

The CD-ROM included with this book has some property-value studies that have been submitted in other cases, both amateur and cellular telephone cases, since the issue is common to both. One strategy is to simply submit those studies and point out that they have been accepted in previous cases for even bigger structures than you propose.

See filenames: **K1IR Assessments.PDF**, **W1UK Assessments.PDF**, **K1NU Assessments.PDF** and **K1ZM Dartantra Dr Study.PDF** for three amateur property-value studies. The Excel files that created the studies are also located on the CD-ROM. The ARRL Regulatory Information desk also has copies of real-estate property studies done for commercial cellular businesses: the "Communications Tower Site Specific Impact Study," done for Farrington Memorial site in Lincoln, MA. This is available on the CD-ROM, under the filename: **Farrington Study-Summary.PDF**. The extremely large and detailed "Impact Study of Two Communication Towers/Three Subdivisions Cordova, Shelby County, Tennessee 38018" is available from ARRL, for photocopying and handling charges. An abbreviated summary is on the CD-ROM, filename: **BellSouth Mobility-Summary.PDF**.

- You could create your own study.

There are at least two fairly easy studies you can do yourself. One is to locate other towers in town and check out neighborhood assessed values before and after the erection of an antenna system, noting that the assessor makes no adjustments for ham-radio antenna systems. The other, requiring far more effort, might involve looking into sales data. The details for creating your own studies are outlined below.

- Bring along your own "expert."

You can hire your own appraiser or you can just bring along your own licensed real estate agent, experienced in your community, to the public hearing. If you can't get an agent who lives in town, try for one who works in town. If you can't find that, find a real estate agent who works nearby. You may even ask around among radio hams. Radio hams are real estate agents too!

- Argue "accommodation."

Don't forget that you have something really good working for you. Under Federal Regulation (47 CFR § 97.15(b),

which states the ruling of PRB-1), the town must accommodate you. This is especially significant where an opponent has argued that the reason that property values will go down is that your proposed system is visible. Your counter argument is that it must rise above the roof and the tree line to be effective. As a result, no decision can be made on the grounds of mere visibility.

What you are really trying to point out to the Board is that your opponents are unwilling to agree to any height where the antenna system is visible. But visibility is a function of effectiveness and the town must accommodate effective communications.

Creating Your Own Property Values Study—Using Real Estate Professionals

The traditional way to present evidence on the subject of property values, used by NQ0I in his litigation and in several cellular-telephone site applications (all on file with the Regulatory Information Branch of the ARRL and also located on the CD-ROM, as filename: **NQ0I Boulder CO Assessment.PDF**), is to hire someone with certification as a real estate appraiser. The appraiser picks *comparables* (neighborhoods of homes that are comparable to yours) where antenna installations are present or absent, and demonstrates that the presence of an antenna has no effect on property values. This approach is expensive. Whether it is persuasive or not depends on the presentation made by your appraiser at the hearing.

Such evidence is always subject to attack on the grounds that the expert has been hired by the amateur applicant and has selected his comparables specifically to prove his/her point. It will also be attacked on the grounds that the appraiser is just one real estate person. Your opponent will say, "I've spoken to several others who have a different opinion." Well, of course, the opponent has spoken to other agents, since the world is full of all sorts of "real-estate persons." Someone who hasn't done the hard work of analyzing the data can usually be found to support almost any position you like!

The reason for this variety of expertise is that real-estate persons come in many flavors. In many states, one may become a real-estate agent by passing a relatively simple examination, or even without passing any examination at all.

For this reason, the world is full of "kitchen brokers." This semi-derisive phrase generally refers to agents, not licensed brokers, and suggests that they are not very serious about the work, that they are not well trained and that they often work from the family kitchen, using the family phone and they have the lowest level of authority in the industry.

The next level up is *broker*. This usually requires a more serious license examination, sometimes accompanied by some amount of experience working with a licensed broker before the designation can be achieved.

Finally, there is the broker who has established his or her own agency and employs agents or brokers-in-training, as well as providing office space, office machines, a secretary and so forth. Obviously this person is running a real-estate business and is more likely than the part-timer to understand the subtleties. However, none of these real-estate persons is necessarily an appraiser, certified by an appraising institute or perhaps having a state license as an appraiser.

Creating Your Own Property Values Study— The Hopengarten Technique

My position is that instead of relying on an appraiser, the best way for a radio amateur to prepare for a Public Hearing is to prepare his/her own exhibit using public data. This can be a lot less painful than you might think. This approach to the question of property values rests on several assumptions:

- Public records, such as those of the Town Assessor, are entitled to the *presumption of regularity*. That is, a Board may presume that assessments are not prejudiced and were prepared by a neutral party. Since the data was produced long before your controversy came along, no one can say that it was produced with a view toward how it would impact the present case.

- An assessor's data may be introduced without bringing the assessor to the hearing, simplifying the applicant's life.

- In a typical town it is possible to avoid the charge of "specially selected data," by simply obtaining the data for every ham-radio antenna system in town. It is hard to charge that you were *selective* when you have been *exhaustive*. If your city or town is so large that this is impossible, simply reduce the area of search and be exhaustive within that area (presumably the village or section of town around the applicant's house). If there is one especially well-known ham-radio antenna installation in town, be sure to gather the data for that one (or two, if there are two prominent installations), since such installations may come up in the course of the evening's discussion.

ZIP Code Data

Go to the Web URL:
http://www.arrl.org/fcc/fcclook.php3 or **http://ifsclinux.ifsc.ualr.edu/callsign.html**. Once you're there, enter your ZIP code. Print out a list of all radio hams in your ZIP code. Using a street map, drive around and see who has antenna support structures and who does not.

Drive By and Photograph

If you see an antenna system, take a photo. Be sure that the photo fairly represents what you see when you are driving around the neighborhood. Don't try to make the photo so that the antenna is too prominent, since this will be used against you (as in, "Oh my Gawd, it's going to look like *that*?"). Don't try to make the photo so that the antenna is minimized, since this will also be used against you (as in, "No wonder that antenna didn't impact value. You can hardly see it!").

For those radio hams who do have antennas, make a note of the addresses of the neighbors and the names on their mailboxes. This is not completely necessary, since the information should all be available back at the assessor's office but it will

make you feel a lot more comfortable when you are trying to look up the records. If you want to go that extra step, make a note (and perhaps a photo) of whether the antenna can be seen from a particular address. This is in preparation for the "But you can't see the antenna from there" argument. However, I've never seen this discussion go to that level of detail in a Public Hearing.

Visit the Assessor

Start with the assessor's *Index Map*. This will tell you which sectional map you'll need. Let's assume you want map B 12. Go to map B 12 and find the ham's house. Now note the names and addresses of the abutters, as well as the name and address of the house (or houses) across the street. Now go to the cards for those houses, or in a more modern office, go to the computer in the public area. You will normally be looking things up by address. Fill out your spreadsheet. If the house has changed hands during the period (more likely if you look back 10 years than five), use the name of the present owner on your spreadsheet. By the way, you are keeping the name of the owner for your own convenience. Don't use it on the spreadsheet you eventually submit, as names just result in unnecessary and wasted time discussing the special circumstances of that house.

Don't be concerned or intimidated about asking the assistant in the assessor's office for this information or for help in gathering it. That's what he or she is paid to do. And trust me, she doesn't care why you are there. You won't be asked what you are trying to prove. However, if you are worried about this, just reply: "Oh, it's nothing much. I'm just trying to get the feel for the neighborhood."

There is no need to tip off anyone about what you are trying to do. Most people doing this type of research are trying to get their assessments lowered—and they are usually angry. Be pleasant and you'll be ahead of the crowd in the estimation of the people behind the counter.

Examples of such a collection of data appear in **Figs 6-4** and **6-5** (the work of W1UK, Coventry, CT) and of K1NU, Andover, MA, available on the CD-ROM, filenames: **K1NU Assessments.PDF, W1UK Assessments.PDF** and **K1IR Assessments.PDF,** and in the Excel spreadsheets with the same base names). Note the differences between them. K1NU did not compare neighboring homes to the town as a whole. Instead, he determined the change in value for homes in the neighborhood and compared those with a view of an Amateur Radio antenna system and those without such a view.

Town-wide data may be surprisingly easy to find. In Massachusetts it can be found at: **http://www.state.ma.us/dls/mdm.htm**. If you are inclined to believe that the presence of an Amateur Radio antenna system has an impact on home values, then these two documents show that the presence of an Amateur Radio antenna system tends to *increase* the value of neighboring homes.

Possible Attacks on Your Property Valuation Data

The Applicant, or his attorney, may benefit from the

Appreciation Worksheet - Single Family Residential Assessments - Coventry, Connecticut in the Vicinity of various Amateur Radio Antenna Structures									
Address	Antenna/ Neighbor	View of Antenna?	Most Recent (a)		Previous (a)		Appreciation		Avg.
			Year	Amount	Year	Amount	Total	Annualized	Apprec.
15 Epsilon Drive	Antenna	YES	1991	103,740	1981	52,270	98%	7.1%	
27 Epsilon Drive	Neighbor	YES	1997	100,520	1985	51,600	95%	5.7%	
50 Epsilon Drive	Neighbor	YES	1991	101,850	1981	52,740	93%	6.8%	6.1%
49 Epsilon Drive	Neighbor	YES	1991	93,520	1981	49,930	87%	6.5%	
561 Golf Lane	Neighbor	YES	1996	149,940	1981	78,740	90%	4.4%	
67 Epsilon Drive	Neighbor	NO	1991	111,330	1981	61,050	82%	6.2%	
85 Epsilon Drive	Neighbor	NO	1991	102,270	1981	55,600	84%	6.3%	6.2%
328 Mexico Drive	Antenna	YES	1993	101,570	1988	51,600	97%	14.5%	
355 Mexico Drive	Neighbor	YES	1991	91,350	1981	45,310	102%	7.3%	10.9%
354 Mexico Drive	Neighbor	NO	1991	97,720	1981	48,270	102%	7.3%	
379 Mexico Drive	Neighbor	NO	1991	88,760	1981	37,970	134%	8.9%	
397 Mexico Drive	Neighbor	NO	1991	89,180	1981	40,800	119%	8.1%	
314 Mexico Drive	Neighbor	NO	1991	84,350	1981	40,960	106%	7.5%	
319 Mexico Drive	Neighbor	NO	1991	84,070	1981	41,080	105%	7.4%	7.8%
684 Charlie Rd.	Antenna	YES	1991	136,920	1984	58,360	135%	13.0%	
662 Charlie Rd.	Neighbor	YES	1998	102,310	1984	53,260	92%	4.8%	8.9%
650 Charlie Rd.	Neighbor	NO	1999	88,900	1981	37,640	136%	4.9%	
692 Charlie Rd.	Neighbor	NO	1991	111,020	1981	59,260	87%	6.5%	5.7%
1976 Bravo	Antenna	YES	1995	127,610	1981	73,240	74%	4.0%	
1960 Bravo	Neighbor	YES	1991	75,530	1981	36,750	106%	7.5%	7.4%
2000 Bravo	Neighbor	YES	1991	75,390	1981	36,030	109%	7.7%	
26 Lima	Neighbor	YES	1995	74,060	1981	31,350	136%	6.3%	
27 Lima	Neighbor	YES	1991	75,740	1981	31,650	139%	9.1%	
34 Lima	Neighbor	YES	1991	81,550	1981	31,880	156%	9.8%	
1946 Bravo	Neighbor	NO	1991	81,270	1981	43,400	87%	6.5%	7.6%
35 Lima	Neighbor	NO	1991	80,780	1981	34,840	132%	8.8%	

Notes:
(a) Individual Coventry assessments were provided by the Coventry Assessor's Office June 6, 2000

James P. Parise
June, 2000

Fig 6-4—W1UK's assessment spreadsheet for his town in Coventry, CT. Addresses have been changed to protect his neighbors' privacy.

experiences of those who have made such presentations. Even if you are good on your feet, it is always useful to know in advance the kinds of questions to expect. Here are some typical attacks on the data you present.

- "You are not a real estate professional." This is a classic *ad hominem* (literally, *against the person*) argument.

Response: "It is true that I am not a real-estate professional. [Say this next line if appropriate.] However, no one else presenting here tonight is a qualified appraiser either."

"Nonetheless, I have gathered public records assembled by the Town Assessor. So, if you attack my presentation, you are asking the Board to believe that the Assessor is right with respect to all other homes in town and wrong with respect to those located near ham-radio antennas. I'm sure you'll agree that this is an unlikely prospect."

"You are asking us to believe that the Assessor, in his professional capacity, routinely *must be increasing* the values of homes near radio hams—a remarkable thought—because if, as you say, ham-radio antenna systems

negatively impact home values, then the assessments for ham neighbors should be lower."

- "It's just not true." This is another veiled ad-hominem argument.

Reply: "Assessments by the Town Assessor are entitled to the *presumption of regularity*. The numbers were created by a neutral party, before this controversy arose. Please note that the assessments presented here have survived the process of appeal, if there was any appeal, indicating at least a passive acceptance of the valuation by even the neighbors of the radio ham. No amount of opinion by townspeople here tonight or by real estate agents should give this Board cause to reject actual assessments."

- "These are not matched pairs."

Reply: "They don't have to be. The reason for selecting matched pairs is to evaluate absolute dollar values for the selling price of a house. The question here is not 'how much should this house sell for?' The argument that opponents have put forward is that the mere presence of a ham-radio

Appreciation Worksheet - Single Family Residential Assessments - Anywhere Massachusetts in the Vicinity of various Amateur Radio Antenna Structures

Address	Antenna/ Neighbor	View of Antenna?	Most Recent (a)		Previous (a)		Appreciation		Avg. Apprec.
			Year	Amount	Year	Amount	Total	Annualized	
362 High Pi Rd.	Antenna	YES	1999	282,000	1993	232,900	21%	3.2%	
1 Pi Ct.	Neighbor	YES	1999	453,900	1993	414,600	9%	1.5%	
2 Pi Ct.	Neighbor	YES	1999	453,900	1993	365,400	24%	3.7%	2.8%
4 Pi Ct.	Neighbor	YES	1999	460,100	1993	391,200	18%	2.7%	
366 High Rho Rd.	Neighbor	NO	1999	306,200	1993	282,200	9%	1.4%	
361 High Rho Rd.	Neighbor	NO	1999	278,000	1993	238,400	17%	2.6%	2.5%
6 Phi Ct.	Neighbor	NO	1999	489,300	1993	409,100	20%	3.0%	
3 Phi Ct.	Neighbor	NO	1999	464,500	1993	391,200	19%	2.9%	
421 High Pi Rd.	Antenna	YES	1999	358,800	1993	329,900	9%	1.4%	
411 High Pi Rd. (c)	Neighbor	YES	1999	252,000	1996	226,600	11%	3.6%	
416 High Pi Rd.	Neighbor	YES	1999	229,900	1993	166,500	38%	5.5%	3.2%
1 Kappa Dr.	Neighbor	YES	1999	410,400	1993	334,600	23%	3.5%	
3 Kappa Dr.	Neighbor	YES	1999	440,900	1993	387,400	14%	2.2%	
407 High Pi Rd. (c)	Neighbor	NO	1999	257,200	1996	214,800	20%	6.2%	
412 High Pi Rd.	Neighbor	NO	1999	309,000	1993	268,000	15%	2.4%	4.3%
15 Omega St.	Antenna	YES	1999	231,400	1993	163,900	41%	5.9%	
13 Omega St.	Neighbor	YES	1999	196,500	1993	155,500	26%	4.0%	
11 Omega St.	Neighbor	YES	1999	196,600	1993	141,700	39%	5.6%	5.9%
5 Omega St.	Neighbor	YES	1999	201,300	1993	125,500	60%	8.2%	
17 Omega St.	Neighbor	NO	1999	184,100	1993	150,700	22%	3.4%	
18 Omega St.	Neighbor	NO	1999	151,500	1993	130,600	16%	2.5%	2.9%
20 Gamma Rd. (b)	Antenna	YES	1997	254,600	1993	230,500	10%	2.5%	
3 Epsilon Lane (b)	Neighbor	YES	1997	219,700	1993	180,900	21%	5.0%	3.6%
4 Epsilon Lane (b)	Neighbor	YES	1997	258,700	1993	227,700	14%	3.2%	
2 Epsilon Lane (b)	Neighbor	NO	1997	218,500	1993	185,300	18%	4.2%	
3 Alpha Lane (b)	Neighbor	NO	1997	237,600	1993	210,100	13%	3.1%	3.7%
5 Omicron Dr.	Antenna	YES	1999	277,200	1993	218,200	27%	4.1%	
6 Omicron Dr.	Neighbor	YES	1999	251,500	1993	212,100	19%	2.9%	2.9%
7 Omicron Dr.	Neighbor	YES	1999	262,800	1993	236,000	11%	1.8%	
2 Omicron Dr.	Neighbor	NO	1999	271,500	1993	243,600	11%	1.8%	
3 Omicron Dr.	Neighbor	NO	1999	269,600	1993	278,100	-3%	-0.5%	1.7%
8 Omicron Dr.	Neighbor	NO	1999	287,600	1993	230,300	25%	3.8%	

Notes:

(a) Individual Anywhere, MA, assessments were provided by the Assessor's Office August 30, 1998

(b) Gamma Rd. analysis uses 1997 as Most Current data; antenna was removed when owner moved in 1998

(c) 1996 used as prior year; 1993-5 not available on computer

Leonard E. Kay, PhD, PE
August, 1999

Fig 6-5—K1NU's assessment spreadsheet for Andover, MA. Again, addresses have been changed to protect his neighbors' privacy.

antenna causes a decline in the value of neighboring homes. As measured by a neutral party, the Town Assessor, this is simply not true."

- "The other antennas are lower than what you propose."

Reply: "It is true that those antennas are lower. That's why they are more visible and why they should impact home values *more* if the charge that antennas impact home values were true. Due to what artists call "perspective," the higher the antenna, the smaller it looks. If you wish, I can show the Board some photographs that illustrate this matter of perspective."

- "The value of some neighboring houses, as seen in the assessment, probably reflect homeowner improvements."

Reply: "You are absolutely correct. This is even better proof about this topic than mere speculation about value. Spending on a scale large enough to increase the assessment is undertaken rationally. The homeowner has demonstrated a belief in the rising value of the neighborhood by investing even more dollars in that neighborhood. To suggest otherwise is to suggest that the neighbor who improved the house was throwing good money after bad."

Think of the *Hopengarten maxim* of public hearings, "Some evidence always trumps no evidence." It is not really true, of course, because the Board could legally decide to give your own testimony or studies no credibility whatsoever. Nonetheless, I encourage you to prepare thoroughly for the property-values question with some evidence. You can never predict how much effort your opponents are willing to put in, or how much money they are willing to spend. If you anticipate a pack of wolves howling at you, you should create your own study based on actual assessments in your town.

RADIATION AND EMISSIONS SAFETY

The individual who is afraid that his children may suffer headaches or some other health effect may know that there is really no good science to back up his position. As a result, it has probably taken considerable nerve for him or her to speak up. This person deserves respect and a thoughtful answer. Moreover, the Board will appreciate a thoughtful reply.

The Difficulty of Proving a Negative

You might say: "Mr. Chairman, the concern expressed puts me in an awkward position. Logically, I will never be able to prove the absence of harm, because even after I point to 100 years of experience with radio communications, the questioner can always reply that we just haven't pinpointed the harm yet. This is the inherent problem with what is known as 'proving the null hypothesis.' Nonetheless, there are several things I can say that may aid the Board in its decision making."

Is it Safe?

"I have already done what Federal law requires with respect to investigating this question of safety. Using the equations provided by the Federal Communications Commission, developed after an extensive public process that included all of the relevant agencies and professional organizations, including the EPA, I have calculated the power density at my property line [or at the property line of my nearest neighbor]. The system I propose is well within Federal requirements and presents a lower exposure than an antenna system mounted lower to the ground."

"In fact, should you have continuing doubts about the safety of this installation, the correct engineering response is to suggest a *higher* antenna support structure. Increasing the height above ground would surely reduce exposure. Nonetheless, let me round out my response by saying that at the maximum legal output for an Amateur Radio transmitter—which I do not exceed—my average transmitter power is equivalent to about half of that used by a kitchen toaster."

Make sure you do your own calculations of the estimated RF Power Density as a percentage of the Maximum Permissible Exposure (MPE) for an uncontrolled environment. This is the relevant test for a homeowner situation. To calculate your own situation, go to **http://n5xu.ae.utexas.edu/rfsafety/** or use the K1TR program **Pwr_dens.EXE** located on the CD-ROM.

As you do your calculations, be sure to remember that you should reduce average transmitter power delivered to the antenna by:

- Feed-line loss (see Ed Hare's ARRL book *RF Exposure and You*, Figure 5.6 then Figure 5.2)
- Connector loss (at VHF or UHF)
- Duty factor (see Ed Hare's Figure 5.4—generally, use a value of 40%)
- Time (generally, you multiply power by 0.67 for 10

minutes on, 10 minutes off, and 10 minutes on—a 50% duty-cycle during a 30-minute test period).

- Calculate distance to the area of interest by doing the trigonometry (Hare, Figure 5.9) Save yourself some time if you're proposing a tribander and a small 40-meter beam. Go right to 28 MHz, where the test is strictest.
- Include ground reflections.
- Consider whether you should submit the page labeled "Calculation Results" with your permit application or whether you should hold it in reserve to see if the issue is raised during the public meeting. [There are many communities where the issue never arises, and perhaps you should give no reason to scare people in advance.]

Local Health and Safety Regulations

Is Amateur Radio exempt from local health and safety regulation of RF exposure? No. In the Amateur Radio section of the FCC's Report and Order, FCC 96-326, August 1, 1996, paragraphs 164-168, the FCC decided:

164. . . . To date the Commission has declined to preempt on health and safety matters. However, the Commission has noted that should non-Federal RF radiation standards be adopted that adversely affect a licensee's ability to engage in Commission-authorized activities, the Commission would consider reconsidering whether Federal action is necessary.
. . .
167. . . . At this point, it does not appear that the number of instances of state and local regulation of RF emissions in non-personal wireless services situations is large enough to justify considering whether or not they should be preempted.
. . .
168. . . . Once states and localities have had an opportunity to review and analyze the guidelines we are adopting, we expect they will agree that no further state or local regulation is warranted.

The complete text of the Report and Order is available in the ARRL book, *RF Exposure and You*, by Ed Hare W1RFI, or from the FCC web site **http://www.fcc.gov/oet/rfsafety**, also located on the CD-ROM, filenames: **FCC OET-65.PDF** and **FCC OET-65 Supplement B.PDF**. Also very useful for local governmental authorities considering RF Safety is the FCC document on the CD-ROM, filename: **FCC Local Government Guide to RF Safety.PDF**.

Thus, while amateurs are not exempt from state or local regulation in matters of RF safety, if you run into a situation where a municipality attempts to regulate your operations on the basis of power output, please make it known to your ARRL Volunteer Counsel and to the ARRL Regulatory Affairs Department.

If you are pressured to show conformance with a state law, try a letter similar to the one shown below, available on the CD-ROM as filename: **State RF Safety Letter.DOC**.

January 10, 2000

Mr. Health Agent
Health Agent, Town of Orleans
Town Office Building
Yourtown, MA 02xxx   FAX: 508/111-2222

Dear Mr. Agent:

You have asked if 105 CMR §122: NONIONIZING RADIATION LIMITS FOR THE GENERAL PUBLIC FROM NON-OCCUPATIONAL EXPOSURE TO ELECTROMAGNETIC FIELDS, EMPLOYEES FROM OCCUPATIONAL EXPOSURE TO ELECTROMAGNETIC FIELDS, AND EXPOSURE FROM MICROWAVE OVENS is applicable to a proposed Amateur Radio tower owned and operated by Joe T. Ham, of 6 Hostile Lane, Yourtown, MA 02xxx.

The short answer is that, since "amateur intermittent single-source emitters of less than 1 kW average output" may be installed "without the approval of the Director," no filing or approval is necessary. See 105 CMR §122.021.

Mr. Ham does not propose, nor does he use at present, an emitter that exceeds that threshold. He is thus exempt.

In the interest of putting any concern to rest, I am pleased to explain why amateurs in Massachusetts do not make filings seeking approval of the Director of the Department of Public Health.

The maximum permissible power of an Amateur Radio station is 1500 watts output. The Massachusetts regulation (consistent with the FCC regulation) measures "average values over any 0.5 hour period" (see footnote to 105 CMR §122.015: Table 1). So if we calculate power on the basis of 50% transmitting, and 50% listening, and assume the worst case over that half hour, that would be 10 minutes on, 10 minutes off, and 10 minutes on. That would represent 67% of the time period. This is, by the way, exactly how the FCC makes such a calculation. See "Evaluating Compliance with FCC Guidelines for Human Exposure to Radiofrequency Electromagnetic Fields, Additional Information for Amateur Radio Stations", Supplement B (Edition 97-01) to OET Bulletin 65 (Edition 97-01), page 13. See: **www.fcc.gov/oet/info/documents/bulletins/#65**.

In addition, it is appropriate (and the FCC also uses this technique), to calculate average power by using a duty cycle of 40-50% for single-sideband voice or Morse Code CW (more properly: interrupted continuous wave) transmissions. See "Evaluating Compliance . . . ", supra, Table 2, page 14.

The calculation is: $1500 \times 0.6666 \times 0.50 = 500$ watts.

Thus, under the Massachusetts regulation, an amateur emitter with an average of 500 watts is clearly not required to seek approval of the Director of the Department of Public Health.

The precise answer you seek is that, like all citizens, Mr. Ham is subject to the requirements of 105 CMR §122, but the regulation does not require him to make any filings, nor seek any permissions, from either the Director of the Department of Public Health or a town health agent.

Sincerely,

Fred Hopengarten

Counsel for Mr. Ham

c: Co-counsel, Esq.
   Joe T. Ham

If you are seriously concerned about this issue and do not wish to rely on the Federal regulation (though you would be perfectly correct to rely on the Federal regulation), you may obtain a letter from a Professional Engineer, such as the one prepared by K1NU and available on the CD-ROM, filename: **K1NU Professional Engineer-RF Safety.PDF**.

ALTERNATIVE TECHNOLOGIES—INTERNET, SATELLITES, SMALLER ANTENNAS

There's always someone in the crowd at the hearing who is thinking, and sometimes says: "Why do we have to grant a permit for a big antenna system when we have more modern methods of communications available, such as the Internet, cellular telephone, satellites and technologies that shrink the size of antennas?"

This person doesn't really believe that this is a serious argument. He or she just wants to see you dance. It is another piece of spaghetti to throw against the wall to see if it sticks. Don't get rattled. The strategy is always the same. Politely acknowledge the objection and then bury it.

"Mr. Chairman, I share Mr. Smith's interest in new technologies. I am fascinated by them too. I hope to use this antenna-support structure to do some experiments using different Amateur Radio technologies, such as packet radio, PSK31, satellite communications and so forth. Yet it is the burden of this Board to accommodate effective Amateur Radio communications, without limiting those communications to new or experimental methods. In times of emergency, the oldest methods, sometimes including Morse code, are still the most effective under less-than-ideal conditions. The law does not require me to use methods that satisfy opponents. Instead, the law requires the Board to accommodate my need to use existing, perhaps old-fashioned but still reliable, systems. What I propose here is an ordinary accessory use of my land, with a lot of case law to back me up."

"In addition, Mr. Chairman, there is a basic truth here. In an emergency situation, you can't track an OSCAR (Orbiting Satellite Carrying Amateur Radio), waiting for it to come over the horizon, using it for a few minutes and then waiting for the next pass. Emergencies still require the same technology used by our police and fire departments because of their reliability—and that's *repeater technology*. Furthermore, for long-distance communication, antennas at the right heights are still required."

THE HEIGHT PROPOSED IS NOT REQUIRED

This objector is really saying that she/he doesn't want to see something tall. The argument is, however, put in terms of making the radio amateur show his need. There are two ways to show the need: For VHF or UHF coverage and for HF coverage.

VHF or UHF Needs

A method that every panel should understand is to show a need for reliable communications by voice or packet radio for emergency situations. Thus, you may use US Geological Survey (USGS) topographic information to portray intervening landmasses that are higher than your location. You could also print out a wide topographic view from the **http://www.topozone.com/** Web site.

A topographic map presentation can show the need for height to improve a path that requires line-of-sight communications. It is easy to discuss a parallel with your local police and fire communications needs. These public services use similar frequencies, and you should remind the Board that police and fire communications require a tall structure for their antennas—for exactly the same reasons.

Fig 6-6B shows a path profile created using DeLorme *Topo 2000* software for W1UK's terrain towards a VHF repeater located to the west-northwest. Accessing a repeater in this direction shown would be difficult, because of the intervening hill about 6.7 miles away. Assuming that the repeater tower was 100 feet high, W1UK could, however, access the repeater if he had a 200-foot high tower!

The experimental software program *Radio Mobile Deluxe* created as freeware by VE2DBE can also be used to analyze terrain obtained from the USGS DEM (digital elevation map) database for VHF/UHF line-of-sight capability. The program has a fairly steep learning curve, particularly when it comes to how to access the necessary terrain databases. However, it is also very powerful, especially when you're trying to make a compelling, full-color presentation to a Planning Board showing that your path to a particular repeater or Packet Node is blocked by the intervening terrain. See **http://www.cplus.org/rmw/english1.html**.

HF Propagation Needs

I showed an example for the crucial direction of Europe from my QTH in Chapter 2, **The Process in a Nutshell**. This illustrated a detailed terrain analysis created using the *YT* program, which is bundled with *The ARRL Antenna Book*. This program uses terrain profile data manually picked off the USGS paper 7.5-minute Topographic quadrant map. Effective operation on the lower HF frequencies, such as 40 or 80 meters, requires high horizontal antennas for DX work. The *YT* program is particularly useful to illustrate this reality.

HAM RADIO IS "JUST A HOBBY"

The person who rises to object that Amateur Radio is "just a hobby" is really saying that the neighborhood should not be disturbed by what he/she considers an aesthetic blight. This remark is more of a passing comment than an argument. Nonetheless, you should be prepared. In my experience, the two most effective arguments to counter this complaint are:

• Amateur Radio is different from other ordinary accessory uses

Amateur radio is *not* "just a hobby." It is not the same as gardening, playing the flute or horseback riding. Unlike those activities, each worthy in its own right, Amateur Radio has a special place among potential ordinary accessory uses of a home. It is a *public service*. The position of a radio amateur in the permitting process is uniquely enhanced by a Congressional finding that "reasonable accommodation should be made for the effective operation of Amateur Radio from residences, private vehicles and public areas, and that regulation at all levels of government should facilitate and encourage Amateur Radio operation as a public benefit." See Section 1(3). Public Law 103-408, October 22, 1994. See the CD-ROM, filename: **Public Law and Amateur Radio.PDF**.

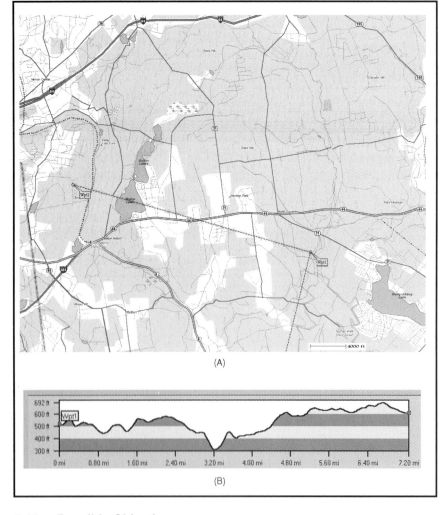

(A)

(B)

Fig 6-6—At A, a map showing the propagation path from W1UK's location in Coventry, CT, to a repeater in Bolton, CT. At B, a topographic profile of that path, showing that the hill about 6.7 miles away would obscure a direct line-of-sight path. This hill could be overcome if the repeater were mounted on a 100-foot high tower and if W1UK were allowed to put up a 200-foot tower!

- Times of Emergency Are Too Late.

Nobody knows when a radio amateur may be called upon to provide critical emergency communications, whether as a part of Civil Defense or an overseas effort to coordinate health and welfare traffic. When the time comes, it is too late. An antenna system must be up and working before the emergency comes.

Don't forget: The amateur must have *practiced* his/her skills by being on the air regularly in order to prepare for possible emergencies. How can you practice if you can't talk to anyone because you don't have antennas?

To support these points, I have collected letters from some individuals who are very grateful to amateur communicators. Sample of such letters are found on the accompanying CD-ROM, ready for printout and submission, as filenames: **Gartenberg.DOC** and **KC4AAA Letter of Thanks.DOC**. If you ever get such a letter yourself, please send along a copy to ARRL (Att: Regulatory Information).

ANTENNAS ARE NOT SPECIFIED IN APPLICATION

You may note that the generic permit application included in Chapter 7, **Preparing the Permit Application**, does not specify the exact type of antenna that will be mounted atop the support structure. This is because (1) most towns do not require specificity with respect to the antenna (and with good reason), and (2) Amateur Radio is by its very nature an experimental service. It is terrible public policy for a town to require a hearing process for each new experiment.

Typically the person who gets up and complains that the application does not include specifics on the antenna is not making a safety argument. The argument is most likely another form of aesthetic argument. The tip off is that the objection is usually phrased: "Mr. Chairman, we don't even know what this antenna is going to look like." So, once again, it is *the looks* of the antenna that are in question. There are several ways to deal with this objection, and there is no reason whatsoever for the applicant to limit himself to one response.

Specify Maximum, and Remember Wires

Start with the manufacturer's maximum number of square feet of antenna that your structure can hold. This number is ordinarily inserted in the section of the application describing the support structure. You must then match up that number with the size (in square feet) of the antenna(s) you are thinking about.

There are two schools of thought regarding inclusion of any wire antennas you have been contemplating. One school holds that wire antennas are *de minimus* and believes strongly in the old expression, "The law should not concern itself with trifles." Remember, an antenna made of hard-drawn copper wire, whether solid or stranded, is going to break long before it could do damage to a structure supported by $3/16$-inch Extra High Strength (EHS) steel guy wire.

The second school of thought holds that, in an attempt to be all-inclusive and to insulate yourself from criticism, all potential antennas should be included in your proposal. This is a judgment call. However, it is likely that you won't be

erecting any wire antennas until after you've put up a Yagi or quad (to allow more freedom of movement during the erection process). By that time, even the most ardent opponent will have realized that the additional wire is trivial.

Nonetheless, if you are concerned, bring a one-foot length of wire that you may be using to the hearing. I've never seen a situation where it was necessary to talk about wire antennas, except to say that in a structural sense they are irrelevant. However, you'll have it there just in case the Board wants to know what the opponent is talking about. Remember, the Board may not be familiar with Amateur Radio, and you need to be prepared with answers. You do not want to see the hearing held over to another occasion.

Like Sails on a Sailboat

When responding to questions about the antennas, experience has shown it is important to offer a parallel to the concepts of flags on a flag pole and sails on a sailboat. So long as the flag or sail is not too big (in the number of square feet of wind load), then the size, configuration or color doesn't matter. You can say: "The manufacturer's specification for maximum wind load is included in the application. I'd be happy to accept a condition in the permit to the effect that I will not exceed the manufacturer's specification."

Consequences of Yielding on Specifying Antennas Directly

There are times when, despite the fact that it is bad public policy, you are simply forced to specify the antenna(s) you intend to erect. The Building Inspector may just insist (despite the fact that he wouldn't mind if you changed windows in your house plan without notifying him). The Planning Board or Board of Appeals may just insist, given the opposition they are hearing that night. If you yield, the following bad things may happen (which is just what the opposition wants):

- Your present permit could expire when you go to change antennas. This could mean that, depending on your bylaws, you might have to apply under any new bylaw that has been passed since the original grant of a permit.
- You might be forced to advertise and go through the Public-Hearing process all over again.
- You might face an additional building permit fee, even when the Building Inspector has no intention of climbing up to have a look anyway.

Be sure to point out that any structure in town is *always* subject to inspection by the Building Inspector under his police power, and to removal—at the cost of the landowner and enforced by a lien on the property—if the structure or its appurtenances is unsafe. This should obviate the need for an additional proceeding.

Strategies for Yielding

However, if none of the above succeeds with the Board during the Public Hearing, here are some strategies for yielding and disclosing what antennas you intend to erect. Just disclose what you intend to erect and argue to the Board in your closing that the Board's decision and order should permit minor changes without additional hearing if the total wind loading specified in the manufacturer's specifications is not exceeded.

If the Board simply cannot stand to see any change without some sort of application to the Building Inspector, then seek to have minor changes (defined as changes that do not increase the present maximum permissible windload on the structure) subject to permission of the Building Inspector.

If the Board seems ready to buy this concept, then seek to have such permission to change granted upon filing, unless the Building Inspector objects, in writing to the applicant, stating the reasons for his objection, within 10 days.

The advantage of this "Building Inspector strategy" is that decisions delegated to the Building Inspector do not require a Public Hearing (with fees, advertising, notice, hearing, decision and order). In addition, Building Inspectors make decisions all the time in the practical world. Sadly, too many Boards of Appeals are populated by people who have no real idea about construction issues and who value process over result. At one time, my hometown five-member Board of Appeals included four lawyers, none of whom was in the construction industry.

Insurance Agency Letter

I haven't seen it done yet, but I suppose that the insurance agency letter included in the exhibits could include a favorable sentence concerning any change of antennas. For example, "Assuming that the construction is within the Building Code, this coverage is effective without respect to the type or style of antenna installed."

NOT LICENSED FOR THIS LOCATION

This objection has appeared only once in over 20 years of practice and for good reason. It is totally without merit. It was raised by a town's attorney, after a thorough reading of the documents. He realized that the address on the license and in the FCC database did not match the address for the building permit.

Argue the Law

Essentially, we live in a land where something that is not prohibited is permitted. Put another way, something is only illegal if there is a law declaring it illegal. Radio amateurs may operate anywhere. Challenge opposing counsel to find a statutory or regulatory citation where it declares that the radio amateur must be licensed for the location at which the building permit is sought. In Amateur Radio, which is in this respect completely different from commercial situations, the *operator* is licensed—not the location.

Amateurs are also not licensed for a particular location or frequency and, by accepting the license, amateurs accept the potential for interference. By contrast, commercial situations (such as repeaters and broadcast stations) are designed to avoid interference to nearby frequencies and are required to remain on a fixed frequency, at a fixed location.

File for a Change of Location

Under the modern Universal Licensing System (ULS), an amateur may file for his new location over the Internet and see his location changed in the FCC database almost immediately. For further instructions on filing under the ULS, go to the ARRL site: **http://www.arrl.org/fcc/uls101.html**.

To register for the ULS, visit **http://www.fcc.gov/wtb/uls** and click on "TIN/Call Sign Registration." For more information, call toll-free 888-CALL FCC (225-5322).

LIGHTNING

The thought that an antenna-support structure might present a danger by attracting lightning is usually presented to a Board of Appeals in the form of a question: "Won't this attract lightning?" Or "Will this attract lightning?"

In the midst of an otherwise vicious and mean-spirited attack on your proposal to erect an antenna-support structure, it is easy to think that almost any remark is also vicious and mean-spirited. Nonetheless, in my experience, this question is most often posed by someone who did not grow up on a farm and who knows nothing about lightning. Should this question arise, do not snap at the questioner. It could well be a totally innocent question. Fortunately, it is easily answered.

"The Cone of Protection"

The most effective way to answer the question is to bring along a graphic, available on the CD-ROM, under filename: **Cone of Protection.PDF**. It is also reproduced here in **Fig 6-7**. Basically, the "cone of protection" principle states that objects within a cone defined by a 45° down angle from the highest grounded thing in the area are protected because lighting will tend to seek the easiest path to ground.

For further information, see **http://www.lightningrod.com/manual5_how.html** for a neat illustration of this principle. Don't think this works? At America's explosives processing plants, lightning protection is accomplished by a series of tall masts, usually four, placed at each corner of the building. The cones of protection overlap, protecting the building. Sometimes a wire is strung between masts. Thanks to Mark Lowell, N1LO, for this example.

NOISE

The claim that an antenna rotator will make noise at all hours of the day and night has been made at Public Hearings. It is totally bogus. Certainly it can be expressed with any legitimacy only by an immediate neighbor. Neighbors one house away should not be able to make this claim with a straight face.

Most Board members are old enough to remember pre-Cable-TV days, when antenna rotators were common. Those members can ask themselves if such a rotator really made noise. Most Board members will understand that antennas are rotated infrequently. Even then, the odds are high that the noise will never be heard indoors. The Amateur Radio Applicant would be wise to note whether or not the neighbor has air conditioning, for two reasons:

1. You should point out that the complainer's air conditioner makes more noise than the rotator, by a wide margin.
2. Air conditioning means that windows and doors are

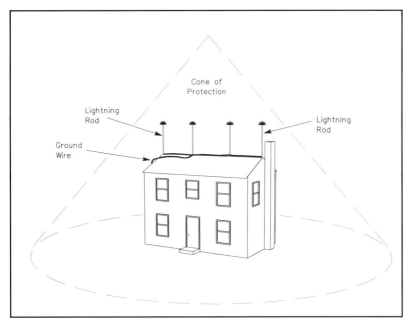

Fig 6-7—A depiction of the "cone of protection" concept in lighting protection.

closed. It is impossible for even those with exceptional hearing ability to detect an antenna rotator through closed doors and windows.

Then there is the actual question of noise level. For that purpose, the author has obtained the following letter (and also located on the CD-ROM, under filename: **Dinman No Noise Letter.PDF**) from Saul Dinman, PE, W1SBD.

April 22, 1999

Attorney Fred Hopengarten
Volunteer Counsel,
American Radio Relay League
Six Willarch Road
Lincoln, MA 01773-5105

Dear Mr. Hopengarten:

You have asked if Amateur Radio antenna-support structures, at any height below 200 feet, create noise problems for neighbors. I am pleased to respond that the short answer is: No.

There are several potential sources of noise in an Amateur Radio antenna system—but none that are bothersome, or perhaps even within the ability of the human ear to detect a few feet away. These sources are an antenna rotator, the antennas, guy wires and the support structure.

The Antenna Rotator. This is normally in the shape of an inverted bulb, about ten inches across and one foot high. When activated, it typically turns the antenna at a pace of one revolution per minute. The typical rotator uses a highly geared, small fractional horsepower motor (similar to an oversized electric clock motor) and emits a small hum, which is the sound of the motor and gears turning. I have never heard the hum of a rotator motor more than five feet away.

The Antennas. Typically made of 6061-T6 aluminum tubing, Amateur Radio antennas are rarely made of

tubing greater than one inch, with booms (cross-piece supports) rarely greater than two inches in diameter. In my experience, when the wind is blowing hard enough so that sound is created in the vortex behind the elements, the sound of the wind itself is much louder than that of the wind shed by the antenna. This is why I have never heard an antenna make such a sound and doubt that anyone has. They do not flap like a flag on a flagpole, since they do not present enough wind loading and are firmly attached to the boom supports. The ends of the properly maintained antenna are sealed with caps to prevent them from whistling in high winds. Even if the caps were no longer in place, any whistle produced by the wind would not be audible more than a few feet away from the structure.

Guy Wires. Guy wires are typically $^1/_4$ or $^3/_{16}$-inch steel cable, similar or identical to the guy wires that support telephone poles everywhere. No matter the wind, they never produce detectable sounds, even when long.

The Structure. Amateur Radio antenna support structures, whether lattice or monopole, also shed the wind effectively. I know of no case where any steps had to be taken to reduce sound. Besides, the support structure is firmly fastened to a base at ground level, usually embedded in concrete below ground level, and presents no resonance possibilities from any vibrations that may be induced in the structure from very high winds.

Given the above analysis, I know of no reason that any Town board, or the neighbors of any radio amateur, should be concerned about acoustic noise from an Amateur Radio antenna system. There will be no objectionable noise.

I received a BS degree in Electrical Engineering from the Pennsylvania State University in 1959, and have practiced as a professional engineer for over 35 years. I am licensed in the state of Massachusetts, having also been registered in four other states at various times. I have been involved with the erection of over 50 Amateur Radio antenna systems and hold the FCC Amateur Advanced Class license. I have been a licensed Amateur for 45 years.

A list of publications and further curriculum vitae information is available on request.

Sincerely,
Saul B. Dinman, PE
MA PE License #19566

DANGER TO BIRDS

The claim here is that the proposed structure is a danger to birds. As you might expect, inquiries on this topic are really grasping at straws by someone who is looking for a reason, any reason, to complain about your proposed antenna-support structure. To the best of my knowledge, and after making good-faith inquiries, the claim that an antenna-support structure for Amateur Radio presents a danger to birds (even migrating birds) has never succeeded.

The CD-ROM includes two letters for you to print out and introduce at the hearing if someone should come up with a complaint like this. You can find them under filenames:

Fairfax Bird Letter.DOC and **Fraasch Bird Letter.DOC**. The CD-ROM also contains a very comprehensive study done for Minnesota Public Radio by Svoboda Ecological Resources, filename: **Svoboda MPR Radio Tower Study.PDF**.

Steve Fairfax, President, MTechnology
Date: Wed, 09 Dec 1998
Subject: Birds

Hi Fred;

I looked into this several years ago during my stint at Failure Analysis Associates. The basic answer is this:

Birds have lightning-fast reflexes and very keen eyesight. They can fly through a thick woods they have never seen, in almost any kind of light or weather, and never touch a branch until they are ready to land. When they are ready to land, they will land precisely on the branch they want. If they are gregarious birds, like crows, that spot is often a matter of inches away from another bird. They can spot an insect or seed from scores of yards away, fly through a maze of branches, vines, and twigs, and land within inches of their target, every time.

Why are they so good at this? It's what they do. They are birds. Their flight control systems have evolved for thousands of centuries and are far more sophisticated and complex than the best mankind has to offer. Birds will almost certainly continue to outperform human aircraft controls for a long time to come.

Ham-radio antennae, cell towers, telephone poles, tall trees, cliffs, wires and other obstacles present no hazard to birds. Extremely fine wires that are hard to see can potentially trick them, but remember that their eyesight is several times keener than ours, and their idea of "extremely fine" is correspondingly smaller than ours. Tower guys may make attractive roosting spots, but they pose no hazards. It requires specially constructed "mist nets" to catch birds in flight. Modern "mist nets" are so fine that even the birds can't see them in dim light, but it took the development of things like Kevlar to make threads that were fine enough and strong enough for a practical net.

The one hazard that does confuse birds is reflection of skylight from glass windows and building facades. Birds use their eyes to determine their flight path, and sometimes will head for daylight reflected from a window, flying into it at full speed. Some tall buildings hurt dozens of birds annually that way, and anyone who keeps a backyard birdfeeder has probably seen or heard a bird smack into their windows. This is due entirely to the false cue given by reflected skylight, not to the bird's clumsiness. One can completely eliminate birds flying into windows by putting a silhouette of a hawk on the window, which the birds will see and avoid.

As to more authoritative sources, there are tens of thousands of articles in the literature on bird flight, published over the last 300 years or more. Chet Raymo answered a question along the lines of "How can a bird fly through the trees without hitting anything?" in the Boston Globe about a year ago. His answer was very close to mine, though more succinct. Anyone (and I do mean anyone) who has closely watched birds fly, land, feed, quarrel, and mate knows that birds are masters of their aerial environment. Mankind must resort to things like guns, rapidly spinning wind turbine blades, or high-speed aircraft to make a serious threat to a flying bird.

The Audubon Society possesses the necessary information and credentials, but they have agendas that may discourage them from supporting your case. The fundamental point is this: Birds fly using their eyes, and they can easily see and avoid virtually any obstacle we choose to put up.

A few birds, like homing pigeons, use the earth's magnetic field for navigation. Navigation is not the same as flight control. Big chunks of steel may distort the local magnetic field enough to cause a pigeon to veer "off course" but so do many other things, including air currents, natural deposits of iron ore, and the sight of tasty seeds or fresh water on the ground below. Once they have flown out of the immediate vicinity of the steel, they will find their way home.

Last but not least: if towers were hazardous to birds, we would have found out about it 50 years ago, if not earlier. There have been towers and avid bird watchers around for a long time.

Here are a few citations: I like the first—the big predator birds LIKE the densest towers for building nests!

AUTHOR: Steenhof, Karen.; Kochert, Michael N.; Roppe, Jerry A.
TITLE: Nesting by raptors and common ravens on electrical transmission line towers.
SOURCE: *The Journal of Wildlife Management*, v 57 (Apr 1993) p 271-81 bibl il map.
ABSTRACTS: A study of the attraction to artificial structures in nesting populations of raptors and common ravens (*Corvus corax*). A 596-km segment of a 500-kV transmission line in southern Idaho and Oregon was the chosen site. The breeding success of raptor and raven pairs, their fidelity to a nest site, and the condition of the nest on successive years were assessed by helicopter survey. Those towers with a dense steel latticework, which afforded the nest greater protection from wind, were preferred. Provision of stable nesting substrates improved raptor nesting opportunities. Guidelines on how utility companies could increase nest site availability are provided.

AUTHOR: Osborn, Robert G.; Dieter, Charles D.; Higgins, Kenneth F.
TITLE: Bird flight characteristics near wind turbines in Minnesota.
SOURCE: *The American Midland Naturalist*, v 139 (Jan 1998) p 29-38 bibl il.
ABSTRACTS: During 1994-1995, we saw 70 species of birds on the Buffalo Ridge Wind Resource Area. In both years bird abundance peaked in spring. Red-winged blackbirds (*Agelaius phoeniceus*), mallards (*Anas platyrhynchos*), common grackles (*Quiscalus quiscula*), and barn swallows (*Hirundo rustica*) were the species most commonly seen. Most birds (82-84%) flew above or below the height range of wind turbine blades (22-55 m). The Buffalo Ridge Wind Resource Area poses little threat to resident or migrating birds at its current operating level.

AUTHOR: Cuthill, Innes.; Guilford, Tim.
TITLE: Perceived risk and obstacle avoidance in flying birds.
SOURCE: *Animal Behaviour*, v 40 (July 1990) p 188-90 bibl il.

From: Steve Fraasch, KØSF

Fred:

First off, as of 9:45 CDT, 31 Aug, the Corcoran, MN city council voted NO ENVIRONMENTAL ASSESSMENT WORKSHEET REQUIRED !!!

Summary:

At the last minute, I managed to persuade a prominent birder, Mr. Robert Janssen, editor of 32 years of the MN Ornithologist Union's journal, "The Loon," and writer of numerous ornithology books, to appear and testify. He was able to counter the opponents' other expert's testimony quite effectively. [The opponent] claimed the swans lived in my wetlands (I have no confirmed spottings), and were especially vulnerable to power lines, towers, and other structures.

The atmosphere was not as contentious as the previous 7 hearings; the Speakers were limited to 3-5 minutes, with discussion limited to only the impacts alleged in the environmental quality board petition.

Of possible use to the fraternity (and now you'll understand his value): Mr. Janssen conducted a 1-year study on short tower bird strikes on behalf of Minnesota Public Radio (MPR), who is applying to a metro suburb for 3 each 395' AM towers.

Mr. Janssen's study group found no strikes whatsoever, after studying 4 other tower sites (3 ea 260' AM, 127' and 195' AM, 295' Cellular, and NSP power lines in nearby wetlands).

Conclusion: Towers of these heights cause insignificant kills, if at all.

I read some of your e-mail testimonials last night to the council, but had all of them available for record. They're all in my continuity file, and I will condense them into a text file to make available on request.

My mayor (who voted against the EAW) said that the ham's testimony was relevant and crucial, since no other ham tower-bird strike data were available.

Also, heroes of the evenings are: Jay Bellows, KØQB, ARRL volunteer counsel. What else can I say about Jay? He's simply the best. Dave Wester, KØIEA, for his appearance and testimony and Bob Garwood, NØBG, for his extremely relevant testimony of a 130' tower he owned near a wildlife area, and endorsement letter from a DNR official citing no affect of the tower on the trumpeter swans and other rare birds in the area. He had appeared without asking; only by reading about it in our local paper. I had forgotten all about that, but he showed on his own initiative.

Again, any and all of my experience and documentation are available upon request. Pardon the pun: Us "birds of a feather" need to stick together on tower actions. Legal action may be pursued in court, but we're ready.

Very 73 and again thanks for the wonderful testimony, Steve Fraasch, KØSF

Attachment:
"Final Report: Study to Assess the Potential Effect of Three AM Radio Towers on Bird Migration and Local Bird Movements." Prepared in 1994-1995 by:
Franklin J. Svoboda & Associates
25580 Nelsine Dr.
Shorewood, MN 55331
Specializing in Wetland Services and Wildlife/Vegetation Studies

REMOTE CONTROL

The question here is: "Couldn't you operate your station by remote control? It isn't really necessary for you to have an antenna system here, is it?" The question of remote control is really not an objection, but rather a suggestion that you don't need to do what you've applied to do. It is really a cover for other fears.

It is fair to ask in return: "Why would I want to do that?" Then you'll learn the real objection, since the suggestion of remote controlling an Amateur Radio station is really masking more central issues, such as: "I'm not going to allow you to put that ugly, dangerous thing in my neighborhood." The answer to this has several parts:

- "Some equipment is available today that permits some types of operation by remote control. This is an area of developing technology. However, Amateur Radio is well established by law as an *ordinary accessory use* in a residential zone and is protected by a federal preemption that is absolute in the case where a municipality seeks to prohibit antennas entirely. The idea that an amateur may be prohibited from erecting the antennas he needs is absolutely forbidden by Federal regulation, and the municipality must accommodate the amateur's needs for effective communications."

- "What I've proposed is the minimum to meet my need for effective communications. Asking me to move the antennas off site could never be construed to be an accommodation at this location."

TWO SUPPORT STRUCTURES

Those who object to two structures are absolutely limited to aesthetic objections, because the question may legitimately be asked: "What other difference can there be between an application for one structure and two?" The best strategy is to stick with your needs as a radio amateur and then discuss the alternatives. The need is for effective communications on a number of frequency bands. The alternatives are:

- A much bigger structure—bigger in width to hold a lot larger wind load, and taller to permit spacing between the antennas to avoid electrical interactions
- Or multiple structures.

In addition, "The fact that [the amateur] makes good use of the existing antenna should not prevent him from attempting to maximize his ability to connect with other Amateur Radio operators throughout the world with whom he is presently unable to communicate with because of the inadequacy of his present antennas and the topography of the property." *Kleinhaus et al v. Zoning Board of Appeals*, Cortlandt (NY), Supreme Court of NY, Index No. 19396/95, slip opinion at 8, by Judge Lefkowitz.

7

Preparing the Permit Application

This is an annotated discussion of the issues arising in the course of drafting an application. The accompanying CD-ROM has the text ready for you to open as Microsoft Word files to modify using your word processor. There are also numerous files in Adobe PDF format you can incorporate into your own permit application.

PURPOSES OF THE PERMIT APPLICATION

- To concentrate the discussion on technology, not aesthetics
- To force the ham to think through all elements of his/her application
- To impress the Town with your thoroughness
- To shift the burden to those who would deny the permit, using a thoughtful presentation
- To give the permit-granting authority a peg or two to hang their hats on.

You will no doubt edit the sample documents on the CD-ROM, since it is unlikely that all issues brought up here are relevant to all applicants. Import the document into a word processor, such as *Microsoft Word*, *AMI Pro* or *WordPerfect*, to make editing easier. Remove sections that are not relevant to your application.

Be sure that the wording is appropriate to your situation. If you are applying for a Building Permit, talk about a Building Permit. If you are applying for a Special-Use Permit, talk about a Special-Use Permit and so forth.

K1VR would appreciate a copy (preferably as an e-mail attachment) of any actual applications based on this "universal application," and later, when available, the results. Users' experiences will be helpful to improve the document, so please let us (K1VR and friends) know.

Please send all correspondence to:
Fred Hopengarten K1VR
Six Willarch Road
Lincoln, MA 01773-5105
Telephone: 781-259-0088 (days or evenings)
FAX 419-858-2421
e-mail:**hopengarten@post.harvard.edu**

FILING THE PERMIT APPLICATION

Should you submit your application by registered mail? It won't really help you much. Even if you can prove that you filed by a certain date, if your application is somehow lost, notices won't go out to your neighbors and you still won't be on the agenda. If the neighbors haven't been notified, your application won't be considered, even if you filed it in a timely fashion.

However, you will be doing yourself a favor if you call in advance and make an appointment with the Code Enforcement Officer or Building Inspector and ask him/her to go through your application with you. The purpose of this "walk through" is not to get a feel for the reaction of the Building Inspector. Rather, it is to make sure that you have included everything that the inspector needs. Later, the Planning Board (or Zoning Board of Appeals, or Planning Commission—various names for this Board are used across the country) will make a decision using this information.

For example, it is far better to learn early-on that you must get clearance from the Health Department for the placement of a guy anchor near your septic system, that you've left off a measurement or failed to include an exhibit, or that you haven't met the side-yard requirement, than it is to learn about it the night of the Public Hearing. Boards like thorough applications.

When you are ready to hand over the application, ask them to time-stamp both your document and the duplicate cover you should bring for this purpose. This is a routine aspect of public office life and no one will think the less of you for requesting a time stamp. Experienced hands will tell you that it is very important to start the clock running, because many states have building code rules that town officials must grant or deny within so many days. There may be rules that Boards must meet within so many days. Delay plays into the hands of your opponents, who hope that you will get frustrated and move away. So start the clock with a good date/time stamp.

FORMAT OF THIS SAMPLE PERMIT APPLICATION

For purposes of illustration, any specific numerical data, such as antenna height or manufacturer for example, will be highlighted in the text by underlining. You will fill in your own specific data. Any author's comments, recommendations or optional approaches will be highlighted by italic text within square brackets, as demonstrated in the paragraph fragment below.

[Alternatives: This could also be a Special Permit, or an appeal from the Building Inspector's (Building Commissioner's) denial of an application for a building permit, etc. For the latter, you would include as an exhibit the actual Building Inspector's denial.]

A copy of the complete application, without imbedded comments so that you can easily see the whole document structure, is on the CD-ROM in the back of this book. See filename: **Antenna Application Sample.PDF**.]

INFORMATION SHEET

[This sheet will be useful to a lawyer filling out your application or appeal. You would not submit this sheet with the permit application itself.]

Name of Applicant: <u>George S. Ham</u>
Call Sign: <u>WE1XXX</u>
Class of FCC License: <u>Amateur Extra</u>
FCC License Held Since (Year): <u>1981</u>
Address of Applicant: <u>1234 Anywhere Street</u>
City or Town: <u>Belmont</u>
State: <u>MA</u>
Zip Code: 02178
e-mail: <u>we1xxx@arrl.net</u>
Home Telephone: Area Code + Number: <u>617-555-1213</u>
Home FAX: <u>617-555-1213</u>
Work Telephone: Area Code + Number: <u>617-555-1214</u>
Work FAX: <u>617-555-1214</u>
Can you be called at work? <u>Yes</u>
Can you receive a FAX at work? <u>No</u>
Name of Property Owner, if Different from Applicant:
Type of Application (For example, Variance, Special-Use Permit, etc.): <u>Building Permit</u>
Distance to Nearest Property Line: <u>80 feet</u>
Distance to Nearest Neighbor's Home: <u>120 feet</u>
Manufacturer of Antenna Support Structure: <u>Rohn Manufacturing Company</u>
Model Number: <u>45G</u>
Proposed Total Height: <u>100 feet</u>
Will Antenna Support Structure be Guyed? (Y/N) <u>Yes</u>
If Guyed, How Many Sets of Guy Wires? <u>Three</u>
Height of First Set of Guy Wires: <u>98 feet</u>
Height of Second Set of Guy Wires: <u>68 feet</u>
Height of Third Set of Guy Wires: <u>38 feet</u>
Height of Fourth Set of Guy Wires:
Height of Fifth Set of Guy Wires:
Description of Antenna #1: <u>Hy-Gain TH7DX</u>
Weight of Antenna #1 (in lbs.): <u>75 pounds</u>
Windload of Antenna #1 (in square feet): <u>12 sf</u>
Maximum Transmitter Power Output into Feed Line for Antenna #1: <u>1500 W</u>
Type of Feed Line (place an X): RG-58__, RG-8X__, RG-213 <u>x</u>, Other__
If Other, Specify dB Loss per 100 feet: <u>2.1</u> dB at <u>29.7 MHz</u>.
Maximum Forward Gain of Antenna #1 (in free-space dBi): <u>8</u> dBi.
[And so forth for subsequent antennas.]

[The cover page follows. Cover pages are a nice touch.]

Massachusetts   *[Name of State or Commonwealth]*

Town of Belmont   *[Town/City of Name]*

Board of Appeals   *[or Zoning Board of Appeals, Planning Board, etc.]*

APPLICATION FOR A BUILDING PERMIT

[or SUPPLEMENT TO APPLICATION FOR A BUILDING PERMIT, APPEAL OF THE DENIAL OF A BUILD-ING PERMIT, APPLICATION FOR A SPECIAL PERMIT, APPLICATION FOR A VARIANCE, or APPEAL OF A CEASE AND DESIST/STOP WORK ORDER—whatever it is that you are applying for.]

Name of Applicant*:* George S. Ham
Address of Applicant: 1234 Anywhere Street
City, State, ZIP: Belmont, MA 02178
Home telephone: 617-555-1213
Home FAX: 617-555-1213
e-mail: we1xxx@arrl.net
Work telephone: 617-555-1214 *[or omit]*
By his attorney:
Fred Hopengarten
Six Willarch Road, Lincoln, MA 01773-5105
781-259-0088; e-mail: hopengarten@post.harvard.edu
Date: March 1, 2001

TABLE OF CONTENTS

INTRODUCTION
DESCRIPTION OF THE PROPOSED SYSTEM
        The Support
        The Antenna(s)
        Site Selection
WHY THIS HEIGHT?
GOOD ENGINEERING PRACTICE
INSURANCE
PROPERTY VALUES
PREEMPTION
BYLAW CRITERIA ARE ALL SATISFIED
CONCLUSION
EXHIBITS and APPENDICES
- Exhibit A: Building Inspector's Letter Denying Building Permit *[Obviously, only if this applies]*
- Exhibit B: Information About Amateur Radio
- Exhibit C: Photocopy of FCC amateur radio license *[Preferably a color photocopy.]*
- Exhibit D: Public Service Resume for Applicant
- Exhibit E: Permission of Owner *[If needed]*
- Exhibit F: Manufacturer's Specification Sheet for Proposed Antenna-Support Structure
- Exhibit G: Manufacturer's Instructions for Guying
- Exhibit H: Photographs of Antenna-Support Visibility
- Exhibit I: Manufacturer's Specification Sheet for Proposed Antenna *[Optional and not recommended]*
- Exhibit J: Plot Plan
- Exhibit K: Neighborhood Map, indicating lots and owners *[Optional drawing showing distances to neighboring houses]*
- Exhibit L: MSN TerraServer satellite photo image, with terrain and showing surrounding forest **[http://terra-server.microsoft.com/default.asp]**
- Exhibit M: Photograph of Proposed Anti-climbing Device
- Exhibit N: Insurance Letter
- Exhibit O: Public Law
- Exhibit P: Letter from the Attorney General, Confirming that Massachusetts Municipalities May Not

Regulate Interference. *[This applies only in Massachusetts, of course.]*
- Exhibit Q: Pentel v. Mendota Heights
- Exhibit R: Letter to Neighbors Who Were Not at Home
- Exhibit S: Letter(s) Of Support
  Sample letter from a Neighbor
  Sample letter from Civil Defense
  Sample letter from Amateur Radio Emergency Service
  Sample letter from Chief of Police
  Sample letter from Emergency Management Agency
- Appendix A1: "Antenna Height and Communications Effectiveness," by R. Dean Straw and Gerald L. Hall, ARRL.
- Appendix A2: Importance of Antenna Height at George S. Ham's Location, Anywhere, MA
- Appendix B: POTENTIAL OF RADIO-FREQUENCY INTERFERENCE
- Appendix C: ENVIRONMENTAL EFFECTS
- Appendix D: NOISE, by Saul B. Dinman, PE *[Optional, since the subject of noise rarely comes up.]*
- Appendix E: SETBACK

[Note to Applicants: Remember to remove sections from the Table of Contents, Exhibits and Appendices that you remove from the submitted text!]

Application of <u>George S. Ham</u>, page ___

INTRODUCTION

This is an application under Section <u>123.456</u> for a building permit *[Alternatives: This could also be a Special Permit, or an appeal from the Building Inspector's (Building Commissioner's) denial of an application for a building permit, etc. For the latter, you would include The Building Inspector's denial as <u>Exhibit A</u>.]* to erect and maintain a private, non-commercial antenna system for personal use by the Applicant, an individual licensed by the Federal Communications Commission (FCC). An excerpt of the FCC fact sheet, "Information About Amateur Radio" appears as <u>Exhibit B</u>. *[Alternative: Should the Board (Commission) desire more information about the amateur radio service, applicant will be pleased to provide such information. Additionally, more information is available from FCC at:* **http://www.fcc.gov/wtb/amateur/aminfo.html**.*]*

The Applicant is the holder of a (an) <u>General</u> *[Extra / Advanced / Technician / Novice]* Class amateur radio license, call sign <u>WE1XXX</u> (see <u>Exhibit C</u>) *[Include a color photocopy of both sides of your FCC license to make it look official.]*, and has been licensed by the FCC since <u>1981</u>. The applicant participates in municipal and regional Civil Defense / Radio Amateur Civil Emergency Service (RACES) / Amateur Radio Emergency Service (ARES) activities, and this antenna system will further the purposes of those organizations. *[Applicants claiming exemption from height limitations based on a "municipal use" should amplify this last sentence.]* See Applicant's Public Service Resume, <u>Exhibit D</u>.

*[General Comment: Do not apply for a Variance just because the Building Inspector tells you to apply for a Variance. If your town's bylaw or ordinance does not meet the accommodation requirements of PRB-1, as shown in the Izzo and Pentel cases, you should speak with a knowledgeable attorney before proceeding. You may be better off going to the Board of Appeals on a straight appeal from the denial of a building-permit application, on the grounds that the bylaw is illegal because it does not permit accommodation. [**Izzo v. River Edge,** 843 F2d 765 (3d Cir. 1988)— Upholds preemptive effect of PRB-1 to 35-foot height limitation. **Pentel v. Mendota Heights, MN**, 13 F3d 1261 (8th Cir. 1994)—Absolute 25-foot height limit in ordinance preempted.]*

[Comment: It is also a good idea to get in the concept of emergency communications early. Even if you haven't been active in emergency communications in the past, join now. It is the right thing to do, and it will be helpful on an emotional level, despite the fact that PRB-1and 47 CFR §97.15(b) do not require participation in emergency communications.]

The Applicant and his wife own the property. The Applicant's wife enthusiastically supports and encourages this application. *[Alternatives: The Applicant is the owner of the property. The Applicant has the permission of the property owner to erect this antenna system, which is attached as <u>Exhibit E</u>. The Applicant is married to the owner, who joins enthusiastically to support and encourage this application. This concept above, which is that you have the permission of the landowner, is critical. You could be bounced out of the hearing and told to come back when you have permission.]*

An Amateur-Radio antenna system is normally carried above the roofline. Amateur radio, inherently non-commercial in nature [see 47 CFR §97.1 (a)], is an ordinary accessory use of a residence (see below). Neither the FCC nor the FAA requires notice, lighting or marking of this structure. See 47 CFR §17.7. *[You want to put to rest any concern that you will be erecting something large, painted orange-and-white and lighted.]*

This structure will be used for *amateur radio*, not cellular telephone or any other commercial purpose. The applicant will accept a permit condition to the following effect: "The structure shall not be used to support common-carrier cellular telephone or any other commercial purpose."

[Comment: Given the brouhaha about cellular telephone, it is important to establish early in the game that you are not in this for the money. Be careful however in how you allow the condition to be written, since someday you may end up using a cellular-telephone phone patch into a repeater, or something like that, and create a technical violation of a sloppily drafted condition.]

The position of a radio amateur in the permitting process is uniquely enhanced by a Congressional finding that "reasonable accommodation should be made for the effective operation of Amateur Radio from residences, private vehicles and public areas, and that regulation at all levels of government should facilitate and encourage Amateur Radio operation as a public benefit." Public Law 103-408, §1(3), October 22, 1994. See <u>Exhibit O.</u>

*[Comment: This paragraph is part of the effort to show that the Board must also pay attention to "the supreme law of the land." The filename on the CD-ROM is: **PL103-408.PDF**.]*

DESCRIPTION OF THE PROPOSED SYSTEM

[Comment: If this is an appeal involving a structure that has already been erected, remove "proposed" from the line above. It is no longer a proposed system!]

The Support

The Applicant proposes to erect a support manufactured by <u>Rohn Manufacturing Company, Model number 45G,</u> *[25G, 45G, SSV, etc.]* to a height of <u>100 feet</u>. A copy of the manufacturer's specification sheet is attached as <u>Exhibit F</u>. The support will be guyed at <u>98, 68,</u> and <u>38</u> feet, in accordance with the manufacturer's instructions for the proposed height, see <u>Exhibit G</u>. *[Alternative: The structure is unguyed at this height, as it is designed to hold the proposed weight and windload without guying under such circumstances. Another alternative: In addition, the support will be bracketed to the house at a height of <u>30 feet</u>.]*

The system has been designed for wind loading of <u>30</u> lbs per square foot, equivalent to a windspeed of <u>86.6</u> miles per hour. In Massachusetts, the State Building Code, Sixth Edition, requirements for such a structure are found at 780 CMR §1611.4. As the site is in Zone 3, Exposure B (suburban), and at a height of 100 feet, the state building code specifies a design requirement of 21 psf. The structure will therefore have an abundance of safety margin, as the building code itself has safety margins within it.

[An alternative, if relevant and useful, is shown below.]

[The system has been designed for wind loading equivalent to a windspeed of 110 miles per hour. The TIA/EIA (Telecommunications Industry Association/Electronic Industries Association) Standard TIA/EIA-222-F for <u>Middlesex County</u> is <u>80</u> miles per hour. The EIA/TIA Standard has been adopted by the Uniform Building Code (UBC) and has been incorporated by reference in many state and local building codes. The EIA/TIA -222 Standard includes a table with a minimum windspeed rating for every county in the United States. The Standard also includes the formulas to be used in calculating the wind-exposure surface area for a variety of antenna support structures and antennas.

See <u>Exhibit F</u>. Ability to withstand a windload equal to <u>30</u> psf. is equal to a windspeed of <u>86.6</u> MPH. The structures will therefore have an abundance of safety margin, since the TIA/EIA code itself has safety margins within it. For example, while the standard for <u>Middlesex County</u> is <u>80</u> miles per hour, this assumes open, level country and grass-lands, whereas the Applicant's site is heavily wooded, providing extra protection against wind.

When installed as designed, the support, according to the manufacturer's specifications, is capable of holding antennas with a total of <u>20</u> square feet of windload at the top.]

Effective Visual Impact

A <u>Rohn 45G</u> tower, with an <u>18</u>-inch triangular lattice-style face, has an effective visual impact equivalent to that of a <u>5-inch</u> diameter round flagpole. The galvanized steel weathers quickly to a non-reflective, dull-gray finish, further diminishing its visibility. The rest is open air.

To keep things in perspective, you should note that an ordinary telephone pole is about 12 inches in diameter. It is tar-black in color, and may be more noticeable against blue or gray skies than a dull-gray galvanized steel lattice tower—yet few people pay much attention to telephone poles.

[For a 100-foot Rohn SSV structure, assuming 60-foot trees and 40 feet of structure above the tree line, the visible steel "see-through" lattice face averages just 22 inches in width. Above the tree line, this has the effective visual impact of a 5^1/$_2$-inch round flagpole. Similarly, Rohn 25, which has a 12-inch triangular face, has the effective visual

impact of a 4¹/₂-inch diameter flagpole. WB1S computes that a 55-foot high US Tower model HDX-555 has the effective visual impact of a 4-inch diameter flagpole.]

See Exhibit H for photographs comparing the visibility of the proposed structure to that of a typical utility pole. *[Take both photos so that the support structure and the utility pole are set against woods. One is "see through," the other blocks the view.]* A structure of the same make and manufacture may be seen at the police/fire station. *[Or somewhere else?]*

The Antenna(s)

*[Comment: I do **not** like to include a description of antennas, as it is the practice of radio amateurs to experiment and change them. I would prefer to state merely that the weight and windload of the antenna system shall not exceed XX lbs. and YY square feet, within the manufacturer's specifications for this antenna support structure. If, however, the code enforcement officer absolutely insists, be sure to use the word "initial" below.]*

Total windload of the proposed system will not exceed 12 square feet, with a resulting safety factor of: 2.5. Amateur Radio is, by design promoted in Federal law, an experimental service. It is natural and expected that amateurs will change their antenna systems as interests change, and as propagation changes with the sunspot cycle. Nonetheless, the antenna system shall not exceed the building code requirements of 30 psf. of windload, well within the manufacturer's specifications for this antenna support structure. *[Note: There are certain inland locations where the wind-load number could be 28 or 26, etc.]*

Windload is the equivalent horizontal force that will act on the structure. It is directly related to the surface area of the antenna. Safety factor describes the ratio between the maximum resistance load and the normal load. For example, if the windload is 10 square feet, and the structure can hold a windload equivalent to 20 square feet, the safety factor is 2. Specification sheets on the proposed antennas are attached as Exhibit I.

[Comment: I recommend against including antenna specification sheets, emphasizing instead that Amateur Radio is inherently an experimental service. Stick with the position that anything less than the maximum that structure will hold is safe. Of course, if you must specify antennas to show what they'll look like, then you must, but try not to get stuck with the need to go back for a change if you decide to take down your TH6DXX and install an X-9.

Any wire antennas that may be hung from the structure are inconsequential, and need not be included in these calculations.]

Site Selection

The proposed site, see plot plan attached as Exhibit J, was chosen because the site minimizes visual impact on neighbors *[mounting against the house provided a rigid mounting a significant way up the support / the site is approximately on the mid-line of the property / and permits all guy supports to be located more than 25 feet from all lot lines / the Town setback requirement virtually dictates the choice / in addition, the height of the structure does not exceed the distance to any property boundary]*. To put the Applicant's home in context, a neighborhood map, showing distances, is included. See Exhibit K.

[Comment: Most Boards want a really clear understanding of your answer to their question: "Why do you want to put it there?" Give it to them. If there is more than one spot, which would be acceptable, give the Board some options. Better to have them spend time and effort on "where" than "if."]

[To give the board some ideas about your neighborhood, a photographic image taken from space could be useful. Try **http://terraserver.microsoft.com/default.asp***, and set up an Exhibit L to show your neighborhood. Using the present Web site navigation scheme this may be difficult, but it is possible. Another tip: Don't forget to create your own plot plan to show the location and distances from your proposed site to property lines, the house, neighbors and so forth.]*

[Optional paragraph: No filing is required to comply with the National Environmental Policy Act of 1969. See **http://www.fcc.gov/wtb/siting/npaguid.html***. An environmental assessment (EA) is required only in eight environmentally sensitive situations (47 CFR §1.1307(a)), or for radiation in excess of OET 65 guidelines (47 CFR §1.1307(b)). Caution: Don't use this unless you have good reason to believe the question might arise. Opponents and Commission/ Board members "opposed on principle" will jump on this like a lion on red meat. Keep this in your "back pocket" just in case it is thrown in your face during a public hearing.]*

WHY THIS HEIGHT?

For communications at frequencies above 30 MHz, trees and buildings can cause significant signal loss. Thus, antennas that are above, free and clear of such obstructions permit the amateur to use significantly lower power levels to communicate. These are the frequencies at which most local emergency communications are conducted. In addition, doubling the height of the antenna is considered to be approximately equivalent to doubling the power output (permitting lower power, consistent with emergency batteries as power sources). Considered together, these two factors are strong arguments for higher antennas.

For communications at frequencies below 30 MHz, the height of an antenna has a controlling impact on the angle at which signals are transmitted into the ionosphere. Unless the antenna is high enough, some paths are simply not accessible. In other words, communications to certain parts of the world will be strictly limited, or nonexistent, with lower antennas—especially lower-frequency antennas that are not very directional.

The height of 100 feet is a compromise involving all manner of complex factors. It will provide Mr. Ham adequate communication capabilities, while still being sensitive to neighborhood considerations.

Appendix A1 is a white paper "Antenna Height and Communications Effectiveness" by R. Dean Straw and Gerald L. Hall, of the American Radio Relay League (ARRL). This gives the theoretical background behind the choice of heights for the proposed antenna structure. **Appendix A2** gives customized details for the worst-case terrain profile for the Applicant.

*[The filename for the white paper on the CD-ROM is: **Antenna Height and Communications Effectiveness.PDF**.]*

*[If you like, you might want to cite a paper by Utlaut, W.F., "Effect of Antenna Radiation Angles Upon HF Radio Signals Propagated Over Long Distances," J. of Research of the National Bureau of Standards—D. Radio Propagation, Vol. 65D, No. 2, March-April 1961, pp. 167-174, or the paper by Epstein, M.R., et al., "A Comparison of Long-Distance HF Radio Signal Reception at High and Low Receiving Sites," Radio Science, Vol. 1 (new series), No. 7, July 1966, pp. 751, 762. A copy of the Utlaut article is also reproduced on the accompanying CD-ROM, as filename: **Utlaut Article.PDF**.]*

*[There is another approach to the height question. Find a VHF/UHF repeater or a regional civil-defense installation whose line-of-sight is blocked by a hill or a ridge. To prove the blockage, use USGS topographic maps, available from the Government Printing Office or local camping stores. Photocopy the relevant path in color and include it as an exhibit. Topo maps and 3-D versions of topo maps may be ordered on CD-ROM from the DeLorme Map Store, Two DeLorme Drive, Yarmouth, ME 04096 (800/569-8313, FAX 800/575-2244, or **www.delorme.com/quads** (for an interactive online demo), or **http://www.delorme.com/topousa/** for path profile software, costing ~$39 for a section of the USA on CD-ROM). It is hard to cross-examine a map, or question its integrity. The DeLorme CD-ROM of USGS 7.5-minute quadrangle maps, assembled into one seamless database (it comes with its own software engine), solves the problem of creating an exhibit that crosses quad map boundaries. Another source of topographic maps is **http://www.topozone.com/**.*

GOOD ENGINEERING PRACTICE

The antenna system will be erected in accordance with good engineering practice, following the manufacturer's specifications, and in full accordance with the state building code. It will be permanently and effectively grounded *[Massachusetts applicants should insert this citation: ", see 780 CMR 3108.5,"]* in accordance with the National Electrical Code (NEC) Section 810-21.

The NEC requires two ground rods, eight feet long, with solid copper wire, 4 AWG or greater, installed without sharp bends in the grounding wires.

*[Optional (but a good idea if you live in a suburban neighborhood) is to specify that you will employ a tower shield to prevent climbing. The filenames showing such tower shields on the CD-ROM are: **K1ZM Anti-Climb.PDF** and **K1HT Anti-Climb.PDF**.]*

While not required by the building code, the structure will be surrounded at the base by the type of anti-climbing device pictured in <u>Exhibit M</u>.

The Applicant does not anticipate that this installation will cause television interference, a subject that is not within the jurisdiction of this Board. On the contrary, higher antennas are more likely to reduce the potential for interference. Nonetheless, the Applicant is prepared to offer aid beyond the requirements of law. Should it be necessary, the Applicant pledges to cooperate with any individual, whether or not an abutter, who owns equipment that might be affected.

INSURANCE

The Applicant's standard Massachusetts "HO Form 3" homeowner's policy *[or renter's policy]*, <u>Section 2</u> *[Section whatever]*, provides coverage for personal liability and medical payments due to failure of an amateur radio antenna structure, without additional premium. See <u>Exhibit N</u>. Speaking from an actuarial point of view, this means that these structures are safer than allowing a teenage boy to drive.

[Comment: Every Board wants to know the answer to the question: "What happens if it falls over?" You want to say that it doesn't happen. One way of proving to the Board that these are rare events is to show that there is no surcharge when a ham erects antennas. Note that this insurance form is commonly used in other states besides

Appreciation Worksheet - Single Family Residential Assessments - Anywhere Massachusetts in the Vicinity of various Amateur Radio Antenna Structures

Address	Antenna/ Neighbor	View of Antenna?	Most Recent (a)		Previous (a)		Appreciation		Avg. Apprec.
			Year	Amount	Year	Amount	Total	Annualized	
362 High Pi Rd.	Antenna	YES	1999	282,000	1993	232,900	21%	3.2%	
1 Pi Ct.	Neighbor	YES	1999	453,900	1993	414,600	9%	1.5%	
2 Pi Ct.	Neighbor	YES	1999	453,900	1993	365,400	24%	3.7%	2.8%
4 Pi Ct.	Neighbor	YES	1999	460,100	1993	391,200	18%	2.7%	
366 High Rho Rd.	Neighbor	NO	1999	306,200	1993	282,200	9%	1.4%	
361 High Rho Rd.	Neighbor	NO	1999	278,000	1993	238,400	17%	2.6%	2.5%
6 Phi Ct.	Neighbor	NO	1999	489,300	1993	409,100	20%	3.0%	
3 Phi Ct.	Neighbor	NO	1999	464,500	1993	391,200	19%	2.9%	
421 High Pi Rd.	Antenna	YES	1999	358,800	1993	329,900	9%	1.4%	
411 High Pi Rd. (c)	Neighbor	YES	1999	252,000	1996	226,600	11%	3.6%	
416 High Pi Rd.	Neighbor	YES	1999	229,900	1993	166,500	38%	5.5%	3.2%
1 Kappa Dr.	Neighbor	YES	1999	410,400	1993	334,600	23%	3.5%	
3 Kappa Dr.	Neighbor	YES	1999	440,900	1993	387,400	14%	2.2%	
407 High Pi Rd. (c)	Neighbor	NO	1999	257,200	1996	214,800	20%	6.2%	
412 High Pi Rd.	Neighbor	NO	1999	309,000	1993	268,000	15%	2.4%	4.3%
15 Omega St.	Antenna	YES	1999	231,400	1993	163,900	41%	5.9%	
13 Omega St.	Neighbor	YES	1999	196,500	1993	155,500	26%	4.0%	
11 Omega St.	Neighbor	YES	1999	196,600	1993	141,700	39%	5.6%	5.9%
5 Omega St.	Neighbor	YES	1999	201,300	1993	125,500	60%	8.2%	
17 Omega St.	Neighbor	NO	1999	184,100	1993	150,700	22%	3.4%	
18 Omega St.	Neighbor	NO	1999	151,500	1993	130,600	16%	2.5%	2.9%
20 Gamma Rd. (b)	Antenna	YES	1997	254,600	1993	230,500	10%	2.5%	
3 Epsilon Lane (b)	Neighbor	YES	1997	219,700	1993	180,900	21%	5.0%	3.6%
4 Epsilon Lane (b)	Neighbor	YES	1997	258,700	1993	227,700	14%	3.2%	
2 Epsilon Lane (b)	Neighbor	NO	1997	218,500	1993	185,300	18%	4.2%	
3 Alpha Lane (b)	Neighbor	NO	1997	237,600	1993	210,100	13%	3.1%	3.7%
5 Omicron Dr.	Antenna	YES	1999	277,200	1993	218,200	27%	4.1%	
6 Omicron Dr.	Neighbor	YES	1999	251,500	1993	212,100	19%	2.9%	2.9%
7 Omicron Dr.	Neighbor	YES	1999	262,800	1993	236,000	11%	1.8%	
2 Omicron Dr.	Neighbor	NO	1999	271,500	1993	243,600	11%	1.8%	
3 Omicron Dr.	Neighbor	NO	1999	269,600	1993	278,100	-3%	-0.5%	1.7%
8 Omicron Dr.	Neighbor	NO	1999	287,600	1993	230,300	25%	3.8%	

Notes:

(a) Individual Anywhere, MA, assessments were provided by the Assessor's Office August 30, 1998

(b) Gamma Rd. analysis uses 1997 as Most Current data; antenna was removed when owner moved in 1998

(c) 1996 used as prior year; 1993-5 not available on computer

Leonard E. Kay, PhD, PE
August, 1999

Fig 7-1—A detailed worksheet created by Len Kay, K1NU, for his neighborhood. (He has changed the addresses to protect the privacy of his neighbors.)

*Massachusetts. The filename for the sample letter on the CD-ROM is: **Insurance Company Coverage Letter.DOC.**]*

PROPERTY VALUES

Research by the ARRL (American Radio Relay League) has failed to find any evidence in the appraisal literature, or anywhere else, that home values are harmed by the presence of Amateur Radio antenna systems. The only study found concluded:

"In the course of this study, I have looked at seven different locations. I have considered thirty-three matched pairs. As I indicated in the introduction, this has covered a variety of types, styles locations, time periods, and lot sizes. In no instance have I been able to discover any measurable, uniform decline in value that can be attributed to the presence of a radio antenna. This is verified by my general real estate experience in over 35 years of selling various kinds of residential properties throughout the Denver Metropolitan Area. The presence of a radio antenna has not only failed to make a measurable difference in value, it has not affected the sales time for the properties involved. Therefore, I have concluded that it is not a measurable factor in value." Russ Wehner, Jr., MAI, SRPA (Appraiser), evidence in *Evans v. Boulder*, 994 F2d 755 (10th Cir., 1993) (decided on other grounds).

*[**I do not** recommend including the next exhibit in your application, but it should be kept "in your back pocket" for the public hearing, if one is necessary. See **Fig 7-1**. The filenames on the CD-ROM are: **K1NU Assessments.PDF** and **K1NU Assessments.XLS**. Make extra copies to hand out at the hearing. Dr Leonard E. Kay, PhD, K1NU, prepared*

this exhibit. It details the single-family assessments in his town of Andover, MA, over the period from 1993 to 1998. The locations were chosen to be near existing amateur antenna-support structures, and they include neighbors located close enough to actually have a view of the antenna. (The addresses have been disguised to protect the privacy of K1NU's neighbors.)

The average annual appreciation in the five-year period varied from 1.7% to 5.9% for the five locations analyzed. Interestingly enough, in three of the five cases the average appreciation was actually greater for those homes that had a view of the antenna than ones that didn't see the antenna. This assessments clearly illustrate that the nearby presence of an Amateur-Radio antenna-support structure doesn't subtract from the assessed value of either the amateur's or a neighbor's property.

Another approach is illustrated in the files: **K1IR Assessments.PDF** and **K1IR Assessments.XLS**. These are provided courtesy of Jim Idelson, K1IR. Jim Parise, W1UK, has kindly provided the files: **W1UK Assessments.PDF** and **W1UK Assessments.XLS**.

An increasing number of counties have information available via Internet. For example, several Minnesota counties have Real Estate Assessor's records accessible on-line. A good example is Dakota County, Minnesota (**http://www.co.dakota.mn.us/**) . The information for each parcel in the county may be accessed merely by address or from the on-line map. The records include the estimated market value and assessed value for the past five or more years. You may even be able to secure a letter from the local Tax Assessor stating that the presence of an Amateur Radio support structure is not a consideration in valuing real estate.]

*[As a matter of strategy, I do **not** favor including such a detailed study in the initial application, as to do so implies legitimacy to the argument that antenna structures affect home prices, which is not true. However, the mere fact that I do not believe an argument is valid does not mean that an opponent will not make it and that you will not be forced to counter it during a public hearing. Here's another possible approach.*

The case involving property at 98765 Hamsway Ave, which drew some attention in 1986, is instructive. That antenna system has been in use for 15 years now. [Another alternative: The Applicant wishes to call attention to the many other amateur antenna systems in Belmont, of varying heights, which have existed for some years now.] Abutting and nearby homes have not suffered a decline in value, nor have they risen at a slower rate than comparable properties when sold in the open market. Rather, they have increased in value in proportion to property value increases elsewhere in Belmont.

Furthermore, Belmont's Assessor has never noted any effect of ham radio antenna systems on property values by degrading assessed value on properties where there are antenna systems. Nor does the Applicant believe that the Assessor will reduce the value of his property, or of any neighbor's property, after installation of the proposed antenna system.]

[Comment: The thought that a ham radio antenna degrades property values is nonsense. Your job is to deny at every opportunity that these systems are ugly (because they are not ugly), and, if it works for you, to piggyback on any studies that may have been submitted by the cellular-telephone carriers to show that property values are not affected. Your argument is simple: If a commercial antenna system doesn't affect property values, my amateur antenna system won't either. This is especially so since your support structure is going to be smaller, with no building, gravel, fencing and so forth at the base.]

Finally, the Applicant assures the Board that should he no longer reside at the property, assuming no other person residing there wishes to continue using the structure, he will remove the antenna-support structure and the antennas. He has every intention of bringing the structure and antennas to his next home.

*[Comment: If necessary, make an offer to the Board that, with the exception of the case in which a subsequent owner is a ham, you are prepared to accept a condition in your permit that the system must be removed when you no longer reside there. Do not accept a condition based on your **domicile**, as this might mean that you'd be forced to take down the system should you become a "snowbird," becoming domiciled in Florida, a state with low or nonexistent estate taxes, living there for six months and one day each year for tax reasons.]*

PREEMPTION

The Applicant wishes to call attention to Federal law, which preempts certain elements of regulation by a municipality. Federal Communications Commission Order PRB-1, 101 FCC 2d 952, 50 Fed. Reg. 38813 (September 25, 1985), declares in pertinent part:

[L]ocal regulations which involve placement, screening, or height of antennas based on health, safety or aesthetic considerations must be crafted to accommodate reasonably amateur communications, and to represent the minimum practicable regulation to accomplish the local authority's legitimate purpose.

The 1985 order subsequently became a federal regulation, as 47 C.F.R. §97.15(b). A copy of the FCC's Order is attached as <u>Exhibit O</u>.

*[Comment: I do **not** like to include this last sentence and attach the entire text of PRB-1. It is unnecessary; however, you may feel it's necessary to bulk-up your application to give it additional heft. The filenames on the CD-ROM are: **FCC PRB-1 (1985).PDF** and **FCC PRB-1 (1999).PDF**. However, I do recommend that you include the statement from the US Congress, entitled Public Law 103-408. This is on the CD-ROM as: **PL103-408.PDF**.]*

Except as otherwise provided herein *[Applicant's note: This refers to antenna systems near an airport.]*, a station antenna structure may be erected at heights and dimensions sufficient to accommodate amateur service communications. State and local regulation of a station antenna structure must not preclude amateur service communications. Rather, it must reasonably accommodate such communications and must constitute the minimum practicable regulation to accomplish the state or local authority's legitimate purpose.

Since 1985, some courts and communities have mistakenly taken the position that the FCC rule in this matter permits a balancing of the amateur's interests with those of the community. In this regard, it is important to note the FCC's 1999 comments on this question:

[T]he PRB-1 decision precisely stated the principle of "reasonable accommodation." In PRB-1, the Commission stated: "Nevertheless, local regulations which involve placement, screening, or height of antennas based on health, safety, or aesthetic considerations must be crafted to accommodate reasonably amateur communications, and to represent the minimum practicable regulation to accomplish the local authority's legitimate purpose."

Given this express Commission language, it is clear that a "balancing of interests" approach is not appropriate in this context. The Commission continued:

[T]he very least regulation necessary for the welfare of the community must be the aim of its regulations so that such regulations will not impinge on the needs of amateur operators to engage in amateur communications.

ORDER In the Matter of RM-8763, cite as DA 99-2569, adopted November 18, 1999, released November 19, 1999.

A substantial question is presented as to whether or not the present town bylaw meets the requirements of 47 C.F.R. §97.15 (b). Bylaw *[xx-yy (z) (1)—fill this local reference in yourself]* appears on its face to violate the rule of law found in 47 C.F.R. §97.15 (b). See <u>Exhibit Q</u>, <u>Pentel v. Mendota Heights, MN</u>, 13 F.3d 1261 (8th Cir., 1994) (in which the Federal Circuit Court held that the city's absolute height limit was preempted, and that a balancing of interests was not permitted).

The FCC's preemption in these matters has resulted in several cases where municipal height restrictions have been found to fail the requirements of Federal law and attorney's fees for the radio amateur applicant were paid by the municipality. See, for example, the Consent Decree, Order and Final Judgment subsequent to *Thernes v. Lakeside Park, KY*, 779 F. 2d 1187 (6th Cir. 1986); Final Judgment 62 Pike and Fischer Radio Regulation 2d, 284 (E.D. KY, 1987) (in which the City of Lakeside Park was ordered to pay $13,800 to the radio amateur applicant); and *Bodony v. Sands Point, NY*, 681 F. Supp. 1009 (E.D. NY, 1987) (in which the community of Sands Point was ordered to pay more than $60,000 in attorney's fees to the radio amateur applicant).

In addition to the above matters of Federal law, <u>Massachusetts</u> law limits municipal action. <u>M.G.L. Chapter 40A, §3</u> requires of municipalities that:

No zoning ordinance or by-law shall prohibit the construction of or use of an antenna structure by a federally licensed amateur radio operator. Zoning ordinances and bylaws may reasonably regulate the location and height of such antenna structures for the purposes of health, safety, or aesthetics; provided, however, that such ordinances and bylaws reasonably allow for sufficient height of such antenna structures so as to effectively accommodate amateur radio communications by federally licensed amateur radio operators and constitute the minimum practicable regulation necessary to accomplish the legitimate purposes of the city or town enacting such ordinance or by-law.

[In addition to the above matters of Federal law, <u>Maine law limits municipal action. 30-A M.R.S. §3012</u> has been enacted to read:

§3012. Radio antenna towers; construction in conformance with federal requirements
A municipality may not adopt or enforce any ordinance or regulation that is preempted by a Federal Communications Commission regulation that states that local regulations that involve placement, screening or height of radio antennas based on health, safety or aesthetic considerations must be crafted to reasonably accommodate amateur radio communications and to represent the minimum practicable regulation to accomplish the municipality's legitimate purpose.

Excerpt from www.state.me.us/legis, including new Chapter 269, signed by the Governor on May 20, 1999, creating 30-A MRS §3012]

[Comment: Note the difference between the Massachusetts and the Maine statutes. The Massachusetts statute is limited to a zoning ordinance or bylaw (and wetlands ordinances are not zoning ordinances). The Maine statute refers to any ordinance or regulation.]

[In addition to the above matters of Federal law, the <u>State of Washington</u> law limits municipal action. <u>RCW 36.32.600</u> has been enacted to read:

RCW 36.32.600 Amateur radio antennas—Local regulation to conform with federal law. No county shall enact or enforce an ordinance or regulation that fails to conform to the limited preemption entitled "Amateur Radio Preemption, 101 FCC 2nd 952 (1985)" issued by the Federal Communications Commission. An ordinance or regulation adopted by a county with respect to amateur radio antennas shall conform to the limited federal preemption, that states local regulations that involve placement, screening, or height of antennas based on health, safety, or aesthetic considerations must be crafted to reasonably accommodate amateur communications, and to represent the minimal practicable regulation to accomplish the local authority's legitimate purpose. [1994 c 50 s 3.]

NOTES:

Effective date—1994 c 50: See note following RCW 35.21.315.]

*[Comment: If you are ever involved in drafting a state statute, do not reference the 1985 PRB-1 preemption, as that could be seen by a court to **limit** the usefulness of the statute to a radio ham. The Massachusetts statute is therefore more useful.] [To find another state's "PRB-1" style law, see **http://www.arrl.org/field/regulations/statutes.html**]*

[Comment: The above discussion of the law follows the lawyer's classic dictate — "If the law is on your side, pound on the law."]

BYLAW SECTION <u>NNNN</u> CRITERIA ARE ALL SATISFIED

[Note: This portion of the application may refer to the criteria of a specialized antenna ordinance, or to criteria of the general requirements to obtain a special permit (or "special exception").]

Bylaw Section <u>NNNN</u> requires that

a) " . . . the proposed use will not be detrimental to the neighborhood and zoning district"

This project meets that test. To demonstrate that the project is advantageous to the neighborhood and zoning district, the Applicant has provided a letter from the Federal Emergency Management Agency, and demonstrated in the discussion of property values that it is benign.

b) " . . . the proposed use will not significantly alter the character of the zoning district"

This project meets that test. An amateur radio antenna system is an ordinary accessory use of a single-family residential lot. This use is common throughout the Commonwealth *[or state]* and, when the project is completed, the zoning district will still be clearly residential, indistinguishable from what it was before the use commenced.

c) " . . . the proposed use will not be injurious, noxious, or offensive to the neighborhood by reason of the emission of odors, fumes, dust, smoke, noise or other cause, nor hazardous to the community on account of fire, explosion or other cause."

This project meets that test. The amateur radio antenna system emits nothing except invisible, odorless, fumeless, dustless, smokeless, noiseless radio signals. The structure is steel and aluminum, not subject to fire or explosion, and not hazardous to the community.

[Comment: It is very important that you satisfy yourself first, and then the Board, that you are entitled to the permit you seek because you meet all the criteria of the bylaw or ordinance. In towns that have a special amateur-radio antenna bylaw section, it is rare for the "tests" to be included in that section. For this reason, you must have a copy of the whole bylaw, to refer to the standard tests for a special permit.]

CONCLUSION

In proposing this project, I have attempted to consult with all of my abutters. Those who were not at home when I called on them received the letter shown in <u>Exhibit R</u>. This project is supported by the neighbor whose house is closest to the project, as well as additional neighbors and townspeople.

[Comment: Yes, it can be difficult to go to your neighbors and beg for a letter. However, you absolutely, positively will be better off if you can respond affirmatively to a question from the Board such as: "Have you spoken to your neighbors about this?" The law does not require you to speak to your neighbors, but most Boards are hoping for the

*"Can't we all get along?" solution. A sample letter is included on the CD-ROM as filename: **Neighbors Who Were Not Home.DOC**.]*

For the reasons set forth above, the Applicant requests that this application be granted for the antenna system as submitted. Should any questions arise, please feel free to contact me.

Respectfully submitted,

George S. Ham

cc: All abutters

Doc: AntAppl

*[P. S. If any reader has **any** suggestions on draftsmanship, they will be welcomed.]*

EXHIBITS AND APPENDICES

EXHIBIT A: THE BUILDING PERMIT DENIAL

[A copy of this document would be included here as Exhibit A if this application addresses an appeal of a denial for a building permit.]

EXHIBIT B: EXCERPTED FCC INFORMATION ABOUT AMATEUR RADIO

*[See **FCC Amateur Radio Information.PDF** on CD-ROM.]*

Amateur Radio Information

The amateur and amateur-satellite services are for qualified persons of any age who are interested in radio technique solely with a personal aim and without pecuniary interest. These services present an opportunity for self-training, intercommunication, and technical investigations.

Millions of amateur operators in all areas of the world communicate with each other directly or through *ad hoc* relay systems and amateur-satellites. They exchange messages by voice, teleprinting, telegraphy, facsimile, and television. In areas where the services are regulated by the FCC, an amateur operator must have an FCC or Canadian license.

All frequencies are shared. No frequency is assigned for the exclusive use of any amateur station. Station control operators cooperate in selecting transmitting channels to make the most effective use of the frequencies. They design, construct, modify, and repair their stations.

Six classes of operator licenses, each authorizing varying levels of privileges, have been issued by the FCC. The class for which each examinee is qualified is determined by the degree of skill and knowledge in operating a station that the examinee demonstrates to volunteer examiners (VEs) in his or her community.

Most new amateur operators start at the Technician Class and then advance to the General Class or Amateur Extra Class operator license. The VEs give examination credit for the license class currently held so that examinations required for that license need not be repeated. The VEs construct the written examinations from question pools that have been made public. Helpful study guides and training courses are widely available.

Source: **http://www.fcc.gov/wtb/amateur/aminfo.html**

EXHIBIT C: FCC AMATEUR RADIO LICENSE

[Show here a color photocopy of your FCC Amateur Radio license, front and back. Note (if applicable): FCC Application Form 605 for Change of Address filed on (date)]

EXHIBIT D: APPLICANT'S PUBLIC-SERVICE RESUME

- Past Member, Town of Hamlet, NY, Civil Defense
- Provided communications support for New York Yacht Club America's Cup Trials
- Volunteer installer of two-way radios in police cruisers
- Volunteer installer of CB radios at local Fire Department and Catholic churches
- Handled emergency health and welfare traffic during international emergencies; eg, hurricanes, tornados, earthquakes
- Provided overseas phone patches for US service personnel serving in Desert Storm
- Helped draft Town of Hamlet, NY, Disaster Emergency Plan. Author of Communications amateur-radio coordination section.

- Advisor to Hamlet, NY, Zoning Board of Appeals (ZBA) on all tower matters (amateur and commercial), including work on drafting cellular-tower bylaw.
- Host Boy Scouts for annual Boy Scout Jamboree on the Air
- Host Cub Scouts for demonstrations of radio communications

EXHIBIT E: PERMISSION FROM OWNER *[IF NEEDED]*

[SEE OWNER PERMISSION LETTER.DOC ON CD-ROM.]

Mrs. George S. Ham
1234 Anywhere Street
Belmont, MA 02178
Telephone: 617-555-1213* Home
FAX: 617-555-1213
e-mail: mrsgsham@arrl.net

July 1, 2000

The Board of Appeals
Town of Belmont
Town Hall
Belmont, MA 02178
Ladies and Gentlemen:

I am the owner of the property at 1234 Anywhere Street, and the wife of George S. Ham, an applicant for a special permit to erect and maintain an amateur radio antenna support structure at this location. This letter provides to you, should it be necessary, the permission of the owner, for Mr. Ham's proposed project.

This letter also represents my unqualified support for the application and is a request that you grant the permit application.

Sincerely,

Sally (Mrs. George S.) Ham

EXHIBIT F: MANUFACTURER'S SPECIFICATIONS SHEET FOR PROPOSED ANTENNA-SUPPORT STRUCTURE, WITH BASE

[See Rohn 25G Specs.PDF, Rohn 45G Specs.PDF, and Rohn Bases.PDF on CD-ROM.]

EXHIBIT G: MANUFACTURER'S INSTRUCTIONS FOR GUYING

[See Rohn 25G Guying.PDF and Rohn 45G Guying.PDF on CD-ROM.]

EXHIBIT H: PHOTOGRAPHS OF ANTENNA-SUPPORT VISIBILITY

[Insert your own photographs around the neighborhood showing what the view will be from various locations.]

EXHIBIT I: MANUFACTURER'S SPECIFICATION SHEETS FOR PROPOSED ANTENNA

[I really don't recommend including detailed information about your antennas in the permit application, but if you are forced to do this, insert the specification sheets here.]

EXHIBIT J: PLOT PLAN

[Insert your plot plans here.]

EXHIBIT K: NEIGHBORHOOD MAP, SHOWING LOTS WITH THEIR OWNERS

[Insert neighborhood map here.]

EXHIBIT L: MSN TERRASERVER SATELLITE PHOTO IMAGE

[If it helps make your case, insert satellite photos from MSN Terraserver Web site here.]

EXHIBIT M: PHOTOGRAPH OF PROPOSED ANTI-CLIMBING DEVICE

*[See **K1ZM Anti-climb.PDF** or **K1HT Anti-climb.PDF** on CD-ROM.]*

EXHIBIT N: INSURANCE LETTER

*[To help your insurance agent help you, when you ask him or her for a letter saying that your amateur support structure(s) is (are) (will be) covered by your existing policy, you may provide the following letter for typing on agency letterhead and the signature of the agent. The letters below are based on the text of real letters, lest your agent tell you that he cannot provide such a letter. The sample letter is on the CD-ROM under filename: **Insurance Company Coverage Letter.DOC**.]*

Date

George S. Ham
1234 Anywhere Street
Belmont, MA 02178
Re: Peerless Homeowner Policy #HP 0987654321
          07/01/01 to 07/01/02

Mr. Ham:

On behalf of Peerless Insurance Company, for your information and as a matter of record, your Amateur Radio towers located at your residence in Hamlet, State, are insured under your Homeowner's Policy under Coverage "B" (Other Structures), without additional premium, provided they are not used in any way for business, nor rented to anyone. These latter two situations would simply require a separate policy underwritten by commercial underwriters.

The towers are insured against the same types of losses (with the same exclusions) as the Coverage "A" (Dwelling). The Direct Bill Department at Peerless has confirmed that the policy is in force and the annual premium has been paid in full for the 2001 - 2002 policy term.

I trust this addresses your questions and concerns. In any case, should you need additional information, you are welcome to call us.

Kind Regards,
Friendly Insurance Agency, Inc.
Agent Friendly, President

[An alternative letter:]

This is to confirm that your homeowners liability insurance will not increase in premium as the result of the installation of a 100-foot tall Amateur Radio antenna system on your property at (address).

Property coverage for the antenna system is also afforded under the homeowners policy under the "additional structures" benefit of your policy. An aggregate limit of 10% of the building limit is extended to any additional "structures" on the residence premises.

Please feel free to call with any additional questions.

EXHIBIT O:

*[This is on the CD-ROM under filename: **Public Law and Amateur Radio.PDF**.]*

LETTER FROM THE ATTORNEY GENERAL

*[This is on the CD-ROM under filename: **Mass Attorney General Letter.PDF**. This letter confirms that Massachusetts Municipalities may not regulate interference.]*

The Commonwealth of Massachusetts
Department of the Attorney General
John W. McCormack State Office Building
One Ashburton Place
Boston 02108

Francis X. Belotti
Attorney General

September 8, 1981

Elden R. Salter
Town Clerk
Office of Town Clerk
Andover, Massachusetts 01810

Dear Mr. Salter:

I enclose the amendments to zoning bylaws adopted under Articles 15a and 16 of the warrant for the Andover Annual Town Meeting that convened May 26, 1981, with the approval of the Attorney General endorsed thereon with the exception that in Article 16 the proposed insertion of paragraph 3(a) in Section VI(o) (Towers) of the Andover Zoning By-law is stricken and deleted therefrom.

Paragraph 3(a) seeks to regulate amateur radio equipment and any interference resulting therefrom. The Federal Government has adopted a comprehensive scheme for the assignment of frequencies and the prevention of interference phenomena. (47 U.S.C. ss 151 *et seq.*) (47 CFR 97.73, 97.131, 97.133). See *Schroeder v. The Municipal Court of the Los Cerritos Judicial District*, 73 Cal. App. 3d 841, 141 Cal. Rptr. 85, 87 (1977), appeal denied 435 U.S. 990 (1978). A local community may not legislate in this area.

Very truly yours,
/s/
Henry F. O'Connell
enclosure
HFO/ehm
Assistant Attorney General

EXHIBIT Q: PENTEL V. MENDOTA HEIGHTS

*[This shows the requirements of PRB-1 for an amateur operator. This is on the CD-ROM under filename: **Sylvia Pentel v City of Mendota Heights.PDF**.]*

United States Court of Appeals

FOR THE EIGHTH CIRCUIT
No. 93-1026

o

Sylvia Pentel, Appellant,	*	Appeal from the United
v	*	States District Court
	*	for the District of Minnesota.
City of Mendota Heights,	*	
Appellee.	*	

Submitted: October 13, 1993

Filed: January 18, 1994

_____

Before McMillian, Bowman, and Magill, Circuit Judges.

_____

Bowman, Circuit Judge.

Pursuant to its zoning ordinance, the City of Mendota Heights, Minnesota, denied Sylvia Pentel, an amateur radio operator, permission to erect a 68-foot radio antenna tower in her yard. Pentel then sued the city, claiming that the zoning ordinance was preempted by a Federal Communications Commission ruling known as PRB-1, which requires the city reasonably to accommodate her amateur communications. The District Court granted summary judgment to the city, and Pentel appeals. Because we conclude that the city did not reasonably accommodate Pentel when it limited her to the continuing use of her ineffective 56.5-foot antenna, we reverse and grant summary judgment to Pentel.

I.

Pentel is an Amateur Radio operator who uses radio communications to serve the public interest. After she was licensed by the FCC in December 1988 to operate an Amateur Radio and a station from her home, she installed on her roof a vertical radio antenna that reaches a height from the ground of 56.5 feet. Over the next two years, Pentel was unable to establish reliable radio communications with other amateurs across the United States, and she was able to establish only one international contact. Pentel concluded that her existing antenna thus was not adequate for domestic, much less international, communications.

Accordingly, Pentel began preparing to install a more sophisticated antenna. The replacement was to be a retractable steel tower that measured 30 feet when lowered and 68 feet when fully extended. This tower, which Pentel planned to have installed professionally in accordance with its manufacturer's specifications, was to have mounted on its top two directional aluminum antennas.1/

Pentel was unaware when she installed her original antenna that she was violating the city's zoning ordinance, which limits all structures, including radio antennas, to a height of twenty-five feet.2/ While preparing to install her new antenna, Pentel became aware of the city's restrictions, and in January 1991 she filed for a variance pursuant to Mendota Heights, Minn., Zoning Ordinance § 5.5 (1981).

The city evaluated Pentel's application through a planning report prepared by a city staff member, and at a planning commission meeting and two city council meetings. The city then sent Pentel a letter in February 1991 telling her that her application had been denied. The letter did not state any factual findings, reasons for the denial, or what Pentel could do to gain the city's approval. In an attempt to offer Pentel a reasonable accommodation, as required by In re Federal Preemption of State and Local Regulations Pertaining to Amateur Radio Facilities, 101 F.C.C. 2d 952, 50 Fed. Reg. 38, 813 (1985) (codified at 47 C.F.R. § 97.15 (e) (1992)) [hereinafter PRB-1], the city council granted Pentel a special-use permit that allowed her to continue using her existing antenna, which she had erected in contravention of the city's zoning ordinance.

Pentel then filed suit against the city in the District Court, claiming that the city's ordinance was preempted by PRB-1 in that the city had not reasonably accommodated her. Agreeing that there were no disputed issues of material fact, Pentel and the city both moved for summary judgment. The District Court granted summary judgment in favor of the city on all claims.3/ Pentel appeals.

II.

We review _de novo_ the district court's grant of summary judgment. United States ex rel. Glass v. Medtronic, Inc., 957 F. 2d 605, 607 (8th Cir. 1992). Because the parties agree that no material facts are in dispute, summary judgment is appropriate in favor of the party that is entitled as a matter of law to a judgment in its favor. See Fed. R. Civ. P. 56(c); Celotex Corp. v. Catrett, 477 U.S. 317, 322-23, 326 (1986).

Cases centering on zoning regulations governing Amateur Radio antenna towers present a unique tension among the various parties' interests. On the one hand, a local municipality, through the exercise of its traditional police powers, may regulate the height and placement of radio antenna towers erected in residential districts. A municipality's motivations for such regulation include the possibilities that an antenna may block the line of sight of pedestrians or drivers; constitute a prominent eyesore that also may interfere with a scenic view; fall on nearby residences; or decrease property values.

Amateur radio operators, on the other hand, plainly have an interest in maintaining successful amateur communications and in sustaining a strong network of radio amateurs. The federal government's interests are aligned with those of the amateurs, for amateur radio volunteers afford reliable emergency preparedness, national security, and disaster relief communications. Because there is a direct correlation between an amateur's antenna height and her ability successfully to transmit and receive radio signals, federal interests are furthered when local regulations do not unduly restrict the erection of amateur radio antennas.

The FCC was attempting to referee the tension between these interests when it issued PRB-1, in which it attempted "to strike a balance between the federal interest in promoting amateur operations and the legitimate interests of local governments in regulating local zoning matters." PRB-1 para. 22. After weighing local, federal, and amateur interests, the FCC issued a ruling that has a limited preemptive effect on local regulations. See PRB-1 para. 24. The federal courts that have addressed this ruling have upheld its preemptive effect. See, e.g., Evans v. Board of County Comm'rs, 994 F. 2d 755, 760-61 (10th Cir. 1993); Thernes v. City of Lakeside Park, Ky., 779 F. 2d 1187, 1188-89 (6th Cir. 1986) (per curiam).

Courts applying PRB-1 have discerned two means by which PRB-1 may preempt a local ordinance. First, the local regulation may be preempted on its face. The city's zoning ordinance does not conflict on its face with PRB-1 because it neither bans nor imposes an unvarying height restriction on amateur radio antennas. See Evans v. Board of County Comm'rs, 752 F. Supp. 973, 976-77 (D. Colo. 1990); Bulchis v. City of Edmonds, 671 F. Supp. 1270, 1274 (W.D. Wash. 1987).4/

Second, PRB-1 also preempts a zoning ordinance that a city has not applied in a manner that reasonably accommodates amateur communications. See Evans, 994 F. 2d at 761; MacMillan v. City of Rocky River, 748 F. Supp. 1241, 1248 (N.D. Ohio 1990). The FCC refused to specify a height below which local governments could not regulate, and instead declared that "local regulations which involve placement, screening, or height of antennas based on health, safety, or aesthetic considerations must be crafted to accommodate reasonably amateur communications, and to represent the minimum practicable regulation to accomplish the local authority's legitimate purpose." (PRB-1 para. 25)

Initially, we must discuss the extent to which this language requires municipalities to yield to amateur interests. Although some courts have evaluated whether the municipality properly balanced its interests against the federal government's interests in promoting amateur communications, see Williams v. City of Columbia, 906 F. 2d 994, 998 (4th Cir. 1990); MacMillan, 748 F. Supp. at 1248, we read PRB-1 as requiring municipalities to do more—PRB-1 specifically requires the city to accommodate reasonably amateur communications.5/ See Evans, 994 F. 2d at 762-63. This distinction is important, because a standard that requires a city to accommodate amateur communications in a reasonable fashion is certainly more rigorous than one that simply requires a city to balance local and federal interests when deciding whether to permit a radio antenna.

Application of this reasonable accommodation standard, however, does not require the city to allow the amateur to erect any antenna she desires. Instead, it requires only that the city "consider the application, make factual findings, and attempt to negotiate a satisfactory compromise with the applicant." Howard v. City of Burlingame, 937 F. 2d 1376, 1380 (9th Cir. 1991); see, e.g., Evans, 994 F. 2d at 762 (stating that the county was willing to permit a crank-up tower, a shorter tower, or a tower located elsewhere); Williams, 906 F. 2d at 997 (stating that the city suggested a limitation on the hours the antenna could be extended, and noting that the amateur could apply for a shorter antenna). Under this approach, a local regulation that impairs amateur radio communications is preempted as applied if the city has not crafted it "to accommodate reasonably amateur communications" while using "the minimum practicable regulation (necessary) to accomplish the local authority's legitimate purpose." (PRB-1 para.25).

The city informed Pentel that her application had been denied via a bare-bones letter that did not list any bases for the denial. Because the city council failed to make any factual findings,6/ see White Bear Rod & Gun Club v. City of Hugo, 388 N.W. 2d 739, 742 (Minn. 1986) (holding in a case reviewing a city council's denial of a special-use permit that a cryptic listing of reasons for the denial did not constitute factual findings); VanLandschoot v. City of Mendota Heights, 336 N.W. 2s 503, 509 n. 7 (Minn. 1983) (stating that variances and special-use permits are treated identically on judicial review), we need not consider whether, if it had, such findings would be afforded preclusive effect here, see University of Tenn. v. Elliott, 478 U.S. 788, 797-99 (1986).

Although the city failed to make any factual findings, the planning report and hearings suggest four potential justifications for the city's denial of Pentel's variance application. We now turn to those justifications. First, the city had no reason to fear that the antenna would interfere with other residents' television and radio reception; the city's planning report states that Pentel was prohibited by the FCC from causing, and that she could lose her license if she failed to correct, such a problem.

Second, the city expressed concerns about the tower's safety in light of the strong winds that frequent the Mississippi River valley. Pentel presented to the city the manufacturer's specifications, which rate the tower secure in eighty-mile-per-hour winds. Although the city generally relies on such specifications produced by manufacturers, it declined to do so in this case. In addition, the tower was retractable, and the city could require Pentel to retract it whenever bad weather threatened. Moreover, the city in 1987 allowed a nearby amateur radio operator to erect a similar tower, and that one was closer to the operator's property line than Pentel's was to be. The record before us thus does not establish a factual basis for the city's safety concerns.

Third, the city claims that it believed it reasonably accommodated Pentel because she already successfully engages in amateur communications. Pentel submitted with her application a letter of commendation for her public services. The city's planning report concluded that this letter demonstrated the adequacy of Pentel's current antenna. Pentel has pointed out, however, that the public services cited in the letter were not related to the amateur communications in which she engaged from her home. In fact, the letter makes it clear that the amateur communications for which Pentel was to be commended were conducted at the Air National Guard base in Minneapolis.

In addition, the mayor and some members of the city council indicated in their depositions that they concluded from Pentel's statements at the hearings that she already was communicating effectively, albeit not to the extent she desired. The hearings' minutes indicate that Pentel stated that she was able to reach only sporadically various places in the United States, and that her current antenna did not allow reliable long-range transmissions. When prompted, her attorney reluctantly attempted to quantify the communications: he characterized Pentel's current chances for making contact at 40 percent, and estimated those chances at 80 to 90 percent with the improved tower. The context of these remarks and Pentel's other statements indicate that these chances of success referred to domestic communications only.

This quantification of Pentel's ability to communicate was thoroughly mischaracterized by the mayor at his deposition, where he stated that Pentel was able to communicate worldwide 60 to 70 percent of the time, but that she wanted to have reliable worldwide communications 100 percent of the time. One city council member understood Pentel's statements regarding her transmission success, but others demonstrated a fuzzy understanding, at best, of Pentel's situation. Although what constitutes "successful" amateur communications is difficult to quantify, the evidence in the record does not justify a finding by the city that Pentel's old antenna enabled her "successfully" to engage in amateur communications, and the city was unreasonable if it so found. On the record before us, the city's first three concerns lack factual support.

The city's last reason for denying Pentel's application, that the antenna tower would be unsightly, rests on subjective considerations and is difficult for a reviewing court to evaluate. This reason is undercut, however, by the city's willingness to allow Pentel to keep her present roof-mounted antenna, which reaches a height only slightly below that of her proposed antenna tower, and by the city's allowance of a similar antenna tower nearby. We acknowledge the possible aesthetic difference between an antenna tower and a roof-mounted antenna, but there is no indication in the record that the city attempted to find any compromise that would have accommodated Pentel's amateur communications.

The city's decision to grant a variance that allows Pentel to continue using a wholly inadequate antenna does not constitute an accommodation in any practical sense. In addition, because the city did not reasonably accommodate Pentel, it obviously did not use the least restrictive means available to meet its legitimate zoning purposes. We therefore hold that the city's zoning ordinance as applied in this case is preempted by PRB-1.

III.

We exhort the parties to work together to arrive at a satisfactory solution to this controversy. PRB-1 requires the city reasonably to accommodate Pentel's needs as an amateur radio operator; what is allowed is the "minimum practicable regulation (necessary) to accomplish the local authority's legitimate purpose." (PRB-1 para. 25). The District Court's grant of summary judgment to the city is reversed, and the case is remanded to the District Court for the entry of summary judgment in favor of Pentel. Our decision does not mean that the city necessarily must grant Pentel's application as it now stands, but it does mean that the city must make a reasonable accommodation for her interests.

A true copy.

Attest:

CLERK, U. S. COURT OF APPEALS, EIGHTH CIRCUIT.

FOOTNOTES

1. Pentel's proposed antenna would be more effective than her existing set-up for two reasons. First, Pentel's current vertical antenna dissipates signals in all directions, while her proposed directional antenna would concentrate and collect signals, thus increasing her ability to transmit and receive in a specific direction. Second, an antenna's effectiveness increases with its height. Pentel's existing antenna is blocked by trees. Her taller replacement antenna, when extended, would be at or near the tops of nearby trees, thus improving her signal transmission and reception.
2. The parties failed to furnish this Court a copy of Section 8B.4 (1) of the Mendota Heights zoning ordinance, and the city was unable to furnish a copy when contacted by this Court. We do not pursue the issue, however, because the parties agree, and the District Court found, that this section limits Pentel's radio antenna tower to a maximum height of 25 feet.
3. In addition to her preemption challenge, Pentel raised various other constitutional challenges that are not renewed here.
4. Pentel's argument that the city's ordinance is void for vagueness is without merit. See Kolender v. Lawson, 461 U.S. 352, 357-58 (1983); Williams v. City of Columbia, 906 F. 2d 994, 998 (4th Cir. 1990).
5. At various places in PRB-1, the FCC states that, in considering the issue before it, it weighed federal and amateur operator interests against those of local governments. After balancing these interests, the standard that the FCC concluded was appropriate was that a local government must reasonably accommodate amateur radio communications. See PRB-1 paragraph 22, 24.
6. Mendota Heights, Minnesota, Zoning Ordinance Sec. 5.5 (5) (1981) states that the city council's action in denying a variance application "shall constitute a finding and determination by the City Council that the conditions required for approval do not exist." This conclusory language does not provide a court with any documented, enumerated factual findings to review. The city may have made factual findings for its purposes, but it has not for ours.

EXHIBIT R: LETTER TO NEIGHBORS WHO WERE NOT AT HOME

[This is found on the CD-ROM under filename: ***Neighbors Who Were Not Home.DOC.****]*

Mr. George S. Ham
1234 Anywhere Street
Belmont, MA 02178
July 1, 2000

Dear Neighbor,

I live at 50 Neighborly Road. You recently received a letter in the mail saying that I have applied for a permit for an "amateur radio facility" *[use exact language of the hearing notice]*. In plain English, what that means is I've asked for a permit to put a ham-radio antenna in my back yard. I have been a ham all my life and moved to Belmont early this year. Obtaining such a permit is a standard town procedure and the hearing is a standard procedure, too.

You are invited to come to the hearing, but you are not required to come. Over the past several weeks I have gone around the neighborhood trying to speak with every abutter who got that letter, to answer any questions they may have about my project.

Unfortunately, I have not been able to catch you at home. Nevertheless, I wanted to make sure you knew that I had tried, and also to give you my phone number, 555-5555, in case you had any questions for me. You may also reach me by e-mail: WE1XXX@ARRL.NET.

Thanks for your time.

Sincerely,
George Ham

EXHIBIT S: LETTER(S) OF SUPPORT

[This letter is on the CD-ROM, ready to be modified to suit your circumstances, under filename: ***Letters of Support from Neighbors.DOC.****]*

Letter From Neighbors

Hampton H. Smith
1238 Anywhere Street
Belmont, MA 02178
July 1, 2000

The Board of Appeals
Town of Belmont
Town Hall
Belmont, MA 02178

Ladies and Gentlemen:

I live just two houses away *[next door]* from the Mr. Ham's family, who are at 1234 Anywhere Street. Mr. Ham has explained his antenna project to me, and has satisfactorily answered all of my questions about it.

[Alternative 1 (for "friends of the project"):]

I have no objection to the granting of a Special Permit [Special Exception, Variance] to him, and I encourage the Board to do so.

[Alternative 2 (for "neutrals to the project"):]

I do not object to this project.

[Alternative 3 (for "grumpy to the project"):]

Mr. Ham has reviewed the alternatives with us. The woodsy site he proposes is the most favorable to us from an aesthetics perspective. *[OR The woodsy site he proposes to use offers favorable screening to me as an abutter. OR The site he proposes is the least objectionable site.]*

Sincerely,
John Q. Smith

[Note from K1VR: The following are real letters that have been obtained in the past, disguised as to location and edited for grammar.]

Letter from Town Civil Defense

*[This letter can be found on the CD-ROM, under filename: **Civil Defense Letter.DOC**.]*

Town of Belmont
Massachusetts
Department of Civil Defense
[on town letterhead with Town seal if at all possible]

July 1, 2000

The Board of Appeals
Town of Belmont
Town Hall
Belmont, MA 02178

In re: Application of George S. Ham

Ladies and Gentlemen:

I would like to add my support for the antenna project before you for your consideration. The proposed height of the antenna system will significantly enhance communications reliability. The many benefits of an antenna system such as proposed are never noticed until a real disaster takes place.

Since 1990, Mr. Ham has been a Radio Amateur Civil Emergency Service (RACES)/Amateur Radio Emergency Service (ARES) operator for the Town. His commitment is well appreciated by all of us.

I support this project because it would be beneficial to the Town of Belmont to have his station available to provide emergency backup communications in the event of an emergency or natural disaster.

name
Civil Defense Director
[Radio Officer/Police Chief]
[title as appropriate]

Letter from ARES/SEC

*[This letter is on the CD-ROM as filename: **ARES Letter.DOC**.]*

The American Radio Relay League, Inc.
John Q. Official, SEC
Western Massachusetts
Amateur Radio Emergency Service
Section Emergency Coordinator

[on ARRL letterhead with diamonds if at all possible. To obtain the name and address of your SEC, try **http://www.arrl.org/members-only/fsa/** *]*

July 1, 2000

The Board of Appeals
Town of Belmont
Town Hall
Belmont, MA 02178

Ladies and Gentlemen:

I would like to extend my appreciation to Mr. Ham for his role in the past four years as Emergency Coordinator for Belmont in the Amateur Radio Emergency Service.

His participation in the weekly network and monthly drills has supported our served agencies and has been a public service as well.

I understand that he now contemplates the installation of an amateur radio antenna support structure with appropriate antennas for UHF, VHF and HF (High Frequency) operations. Such an installation would benefit emergency communications for your community, Central Middlesex County, and would cover a large radius within Eastern Massachusetts.

Sincerely,
John Q. Official
Section Emergency Coordinator
[title as appropriate]

[Note to applicants: If you are moving and wish to obtain a letter before you depart, make appropriate changes above such as "Dear Joe: I would like to extend my appreciation to you..." and "I understand that you will be leaving our community, and hoping to install a . . ."

It doesn't matter much whether the letter is addressed to you, to the Board in your new Town, or "To Whom It May

Concern." Here's an example of a letter from a former location coordinator.]

Letter from an SEC at Former Location

*[This letter is on the CD-ROM under filename: **ARRL SEC Letter.DOC**.]*

The American Radio Relay League, Inc.
John Q. Official
Western Washington
Amateur Radio Emergency Service
[on ARRL letterhead with diamonds if at all possible]

July 1, 2000

To Whom It May Concern:

As president of the Western Washington Amateur Radio Emergency Service organization, I have had the privilege of working with many fine people in our group. Mr. Ham was one of those people. The Amateur Radio Emergency Service is a dedicated emergency communications group whose purpose is to provide backup communications to Police, Fire, Cities and Counties in times of emergency when called upon.

Mr. Ham joined WWARES in 1984 and was an active member through 1990 when he moved to the East Coast. He contributed his time and expertise freely to further the goals of WWARES. It was a pleasure knowing and working with him during this time. It is obvious to me that the hobby of amateur radio meant more to Mr. Ham than just talking to other hams. His first priority, as is mine, is community service, providing emergency communications when needed.

Amateur Radio is a proven and valuable resource, which requires that appropriate antenna systems be in place before the emergency happens. I know Mr. Ham stands ready to provide this service to his community.

John Q. Official
President, WWARES

Letter from FEMA or State Emergency Management Agency

*[This letter is on the CD-ROM under filename: **FEMA Letter.DOC**.]*

Federal Emergency Management Agency
Region I, J.W. McCormack Post Office and Court House
Boston, Massachusetts 02109

[or other appropriate letterhead with seal, perhaps also from the state emergency management agency with seal, if possible]

July 1, 2000

For: Town of Belmont, Board of Appeals
From: John Q. Manager, FEMA Region I, Information Technology Manager
Subject: Antenna System Application of Mr. George S. Ham

Dear Members of the Board:

I write to offer information in support of Amateur Radio operations by George S. Ham, a resident of Belmont, MA, FCC license: WE1XXX. Mr. Ham has proudly described his volunteer emergency communications during Hurricane Alicianata in 1991. He is genuinely interested in being able to continue to offer valuable emergency communications service, at no cost to the taxpayer.

In times of crisis, FEMA, state emergency management offices and local governments benefit from amateur radio. It happens almost every day and has saved many lives. Amateur Radio improves communications for grief-stricken folks through volunteer, free messaging services. When disasters disrupt the Public Service Telephone Network (PSTN), a robust antenna, tower, energetic and well-trained operator and good station are important.

I respectfully request that you give full and fair consideration to Mr. Ham's application to erect an amateur Radio tower that coincides with reasonable local codes and safety requirements. Amateur Radio towers typically range in height from 40 to 120 feet, with the higher towers more effective for reliable and long-range communications. Amateur Radio towers do not resemble the much higher and wider towers commonly used by cellular carriers or commercial entities. Amateur Radio systems are much lower profile and are not used for financial gain.

The American Radio Relay League in Newington, CT, has additional information on how helpful amateur radio operations can be. Their literature on the Amateur Radio Emergency Service should reinforce Belmont's ability to endorse Amateur Radio antenna support applications.

Sincerely,
John Q. Manager
Information Technology Manager
FEMA Region One
telephone: (617) 123-4567

Letter from a Police Chief

[Note: Naturally enough, a police chief cannot go too far in taking sides, but it can be very useful to have almost any letter that is not negative on the Town's own stationery. This letter is on the CD-ROM as **Letter from a Police Chief. DOC.**]

July 1, 2000

To whom it may concern:

It has been brought to my attention that <u>George S. Ham</u> of <u>1234 Anywhere Street</u> has requested a permit authorizing him to erect an Amateur Radio structure on his property.

<u>George</u> has been an active member of the Belmont Civil Defense organization since he moved to Belmont in <u>1991</u>. He has participated in various Town activities by providing auxiliary communications support for both the Memorial Day and Fourth of July parades and I expect to continue to utilize <u>George</u> for future events.

If the grant of a permit would not create a hardship to someone, then it would be beneficial to both <u>George</u> and the Town of <u>Belmont</u> to be able to provide emergency backup communications in the event of an emergency or natural disaster. I thank you for your consideration.

Respectfully,
<u>John Q. Policeman</u>
Chief of Police

Letter from Another Ham in Town

[This letter is on the CD-ROM under filename: **Letter from Another Ham in Town.DOC.**]

<u>Joe T. Ham</u>
<u>50 Hamly Road</u>
<u>Belmont, MA 02178</u>

[To obtain a list of other hams in your town, and to solicit letters of support from them, see **www.ualr.edu/~hamradio/callsign.html**]

July 1, 2000

<u>The Board of Appeals</u>
<u>Town of Belmont</u>
<u>Town Hall</u>
<u>Belmont, MA 02178</u>

Ladies and Gentlemen:

I live at <u>52 Hamly Road</u>. <u>Mr. Ham</u> has explained his antenna project to me, and has satisfactorily answered all of my questions about it.

I encourage the Board to grant this permit for the following reasons:

• Despite concerns raised when first I erected my system, I now doubt that many people here in town even know that my antenna system even exists.

• <u>Mr. Ham</u> is a member of the <u>Belmont</u> Civil Defense organization, and the antenna system he proposes will be a useful part of our disaster communications system in time of emergency, when it would be too late to build such a system.

• I have had an antenna system of my own here in <u>Belmont</u> for <u>12</u> years, and no problems have ever arisen *[no problem has ever arisen that wasn't addressed in the spirit of neighborly cooperation / no problem has ever arisen which wasn't resolved to the complete satisfaction of the complaining party].*

I urge favorable consideration of his application.

Sincerely,
<u>Joe T. Ham</u>

Antenna Height

and

Communications Effectiveness

Second Edition

A Guide for City Planners and Amateur Radio Operators

By R. Dean Straw, N6BV, and Gerald L. Hall, K1TD
Senior Assistant Technical Editor and Retired Associate Technical Editor

Copyright ©1999
The American Radio Relay League, Inc.
225 Main Street
Newington, CT 06111

Executive Summary

Amateur radio operators, or "hams" as they are called, communicate with stations located all over the world. Some contacts may be local in nature, while others may be literally halfway around the world. Hams use a variety of internationally allocated frequencies to accomplish their communications.

Except for local contacts, which are primarily made on Very High and Ultra High Frequencies (VHF and UHF), communicating between any two points on the earth rely primarily on high-frequency (HF) signals propagating through the ionosphere. The earth's ionosphere acts much like a mirror at heights of about 150 miles. The vertical angle of radiation of a signal launched from an antenna is one of the key factors determining effective communication distances. The ability to communicate over long distances generally requires a low radiation angle, meaning that an antenna must be placed high above the ground in terms of the wavelength of the radio wave being transmitted.

A beam type of antenna at a height of 70 feet or more will provide greatly superior performance over the same antenna at 35 feet, all other factors being equal. A height of 120 feet or even higher will provide even more advantages for long-distance communications. To a distant receiving station, a transmitting antenna at 120 feet will provide the effect of approximately 8 to 10 times more transmitting power than the same antenna at 35 feet. Depending on the level of noise and interference, this performance disparity is often enough to mean the difference between making distant radio contact with fairly reliable signals, and being unable to make distant contact at all.

Radio Amateurs have a well-deserved reputation for providing vital communications in emergency situations, such as in the aftermath of a severe icestorrn, a hurricane or an earthquake. Short-range communications at VHF or UHF frequencies also require sufficient antenna heights above the local terrain to ensure that the antenna has a clear horizon.

In terms of safety and aesthetic considerations, it might seem intuitively reasonable for a planning board to want to restrict antenna installations to low heights. However, such height restrictions often prove very counterproductive and frustrating to all parties involved. If an amateur is restricted to low antenna heights, say 35 feet, he will suffer from poor transmission of his own signals as well as poor reception of distant signals. In an attempt to compensate on the transmitting side (he can't do anything about the poor reception problem), he might boost his transmitted power, say from 150 watts to 1,500 watts, the maximum legal limit. This tenfold increase in power will very significantly increase the potential for interference to telephones, televisions, VCRs and audio equipment in his neighborhood.

Instead, if the antenna can be moved farther away from neighboring electronic devices-putting it higher, in other words-this will greatly reduce the likelihood of interference, which decreases at the inverse square of the distance. For example, doubling the distance reduces the potential for interference by 75%. As a further benefit, a large antenna doesn't look anywhere near as large at 120 feet as it does close-up at 35 feet.

As a not-so-inconsequential side benefit, moving an antenna higher will also greatly reduce the potential of exposure to electromagnetic fields for neighboring human and animals. Interference and rf exposure standards have been thoroughly covered in recently enacted Federal Regulations.

Antenna Height and Communications Effectiveness

By R. Dean Straw, N6BV, and Gerald L. Hall, K1TD
Senior Assistant Technical Editor and Retired Associate Technical Editor

The purpose of this paper is to provide general information about communications effectiveness as related to the physical height of antennas. The intended audience is amateur radio operators and the city and town Planning Boards before which a radio amateur must sometimes appear to obtain building permits for radio towers and antennas.

The performance of horizontally polarized antennas at heights of 35, 70 and 120 feet is examined in detail. Vertically polarized arrays are not considered here because at short-wave frequencies, over average terrain and at low radiation angles, they are usually less effective than horizontal antennas.

Ionospheric Propagation

Frequencies between 3 and 30 megahertz (abbreviated MHz) are often called the "short-wave" bands. In engineering terms this range of frequencies is defined as the *high-frequency* or HF portion of the radio spectrum. HF radio communications between two points that are separated by more than about 15 to 25 miles depend almost solely on propagation of radio signals through the *ionosphere*. The ionosphere is a region of the Earth's upper atmosphere that is ionized primarily by ultraviolet rays from the Sun.

The Earth's ionosphere has the property that it will refract or bend radio waves passing through it. The ionosphere is not a single "blanket" of ionization. Instead, for a number of complex reasons, a few discrete layers are formed at different heights above the earth. From the standpoint of radio propagation, each ionized layer has distinctive characteristics, related primarily to different amounts of ionization in the various layers. The ionized layer that is most useful for HF radio communication is called the F layer.

The F layer exists at heights varying from approximately 130 to 260 miles above the earth's surface. Both the layer height and the amount of ionization depend on the latitude from the equator, the time of day, the season of the year, and on the level of sunspot activity. Sunspot activity varies generally in cycles that are approximately 11 years in duration, although short-term bursts of activity may create changes in propagation conditions that last anywhere from a few minutes to several days. The ionosphere is not homogeneous, and is undergoing continual change. In fact, the exact state of the ionosphere at any one time is so variable that is best described in statistical terms.

The F layer disappears at night in periods of low and medium solar activity, as the ultraviolet energy required to sustain ionization is no longer received from the Sun. The amount that a passing radio wave will bend in an ionospheric layer is directly related to the intensity of ionization in that layer, and to the frequency of the radio wave.

A triangle may be used to portray the cross-sectional path of ionospheric radio-wave travel, as shown in **Fig 1**, a highly simplified picture of what happens in propagation of radio waves. The base of the triangle is the surface of the Earth between two distant points, and the apex of the triangle is the point representing refraction in the ionosphere. If all the necessary conditions are met, the radio wave will travel from the first point on the Earth's surface to the ionosphere, where it will be bent (*refracted*) sufficiently to travel to the second point on the earth, many hundreds of miles away.

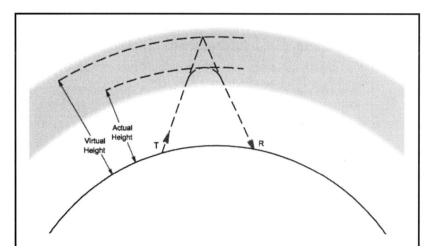

Fig 1—A simplified cross-sectional representation of ionospheric propagation. The simple triangle goes from the transmitter T up to the virtual height and then back down to the receiver R. Typically the F layer exists at a height of 150 miles above the Earth at mid-latitudes. The distance between T and R may range from a few miles to 2500 miles under normal propagation conditions.

Of course the Earth's surface is not a flat plane, but instead is curved. High-frequency radio waves behave in essentially the same manner as light waves—they tend to travel in straight lines, but with a slight amount of downward bending caused by refraction in the air. For this reason it is not possible to communicate by a direct path over distances greater than about 15 to 25 miles in this frequency range, slightly farther than the optical horizon. The curvature of the earth causes the surface to "fall away" from the path of the radio wave with greater distances. Therefore, it is the ionosphere that permits HF radio communications to be made between points separated by hundreds or even thousands of miles. The range of frequencies from 3 to 30 MHz is unique in this respect, as ionospheric propagation is not consistently supported for any frequencies outside this range.

One of the necessary conditions for ionospheric communications is that the radio wave must encounter the ionosphere at the correct angle. This is illustrated in **Fig 2**, another very simplified drawing of the geometry involved. Radio waves leaving the earth at high elevation angles above the horizon may receive only very slight bending due to refraction, and are then lost to outer space. For the same fixed frequency of operation, as the elevation angle is lowered toward the horizon, a point is reached where the bending of the wave is sufficient to return the wave to the Earth. At successively lower angles, the wave returns to the Earth at increasing distances.

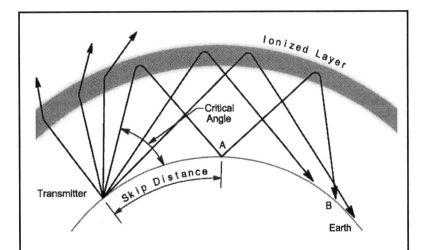

Fig 2—Behavior of radio waves encountering the ionosphere. Rays entering the ionized region at angles above the critical angle are not bent enough to return to Earth and are lost to space. Waves entering at angles below the critical angle reach the Earth at increasingly greater distances as the angle approaches the horizontal. The maximum distance that may normally be covered in a single hop is 2500 miles. Greater distances may be covered with multiple hops.

If the radio wave leaves the earth at an elevation angle of zero degrees, just toward the horizon (or just tangent to the earth's surface), the maximum distance that may be reached under usual ionospheric conditions is approximately 2,500 miles (4,000 kilometers). However, the Earth itself also acts as a reflector of radio waves coming down from the ionosphere. Quite often a radio signal will be reflected from the reception point on the Earth back into the ionosphere again, reaching the Earth a second time at a still more distant point.

As in the case of light waves, the angle of reflection is the same as the angle of incidence, so a wave striking the surface of the Earth at an angle of, say, 15° is reflected upward from the surface at the same angle. Thus, the distance to the second point of reception will be approximately twice the distance of the first. This effect is also illustrated in Fig 2, where the signal travels from the transmitter at the left of the drawing via the ionosphere to Point A, in the center of the drawing. From Point A the signal travels via the ionosphere again to Point B, at the right. A signal traveling from the Earth through the ionosphere and back to the Earth is called a hop. Under some conditions it is possible for as many as four or five signal hops to occur over a radio path, but no more than two or three hops is the norm. In this way, HF communications can be conducted over thousands of miles.

With regard to signal hopping, two important points should be recognized. First, a significant loss of signal occurs with each hop. Lower layers of the ionosphere absorb energy from the signals as they pass through, and the ionosphere tends to scatter the radio energy in various directions, rather than confining it to a tight bundle. The earth also scatters the energy at a reflection point. Thus, only a small fraction of the transmitted energy actually reaches a distant receiving point.

Again refer to Fig 2. Two radio paths are shown from the transmitter to Point B, a one-hop path and a two-hop path. Measurements indicate that although there can be great variation in the ratio of the two signal strengths in a situation such as this, the signal power received at Point B will generally be from five to ten times greater for the one-hop wave than for the two-hop wave. (The terrain at the mid-path reflection point for the two-hop wave, the angle at which the wave is reflected from the earth, and the condition of the ionosphere in the vicinity of all the refraction points are the primary factors in determining the signal-strength ratio.) Signal levels are generally compared in decibels, abbreviated dB. The decibel is a logarithmic unit. Three decibels difference in signal strengths is equivalent to a power ratio of 2:1; a difference of 10 dB equates to a power ratio of 10:1. Thus the signal loss for an additional hop is about 7 to 10 dB.

The additional loss per hop becomes significant at greater distances. For a simplified example, a distance of 4,000 miles can be covered in two hops of 2,000 miles each or in four hops of 1,000 miles each. For illustration, assume the loss for additional hops is 10 dB, or a 1/10 power ratio. Under such conditions, the fourhop signal will be received with only 1/100 the power or 20 dB below that received in two hops. The reason for this is that only 1/10 of the two-hop signal is received for the first additional (3rd) hop, and only 1/10 of that 1/10 for the second additional (4th) hop. It is for this reason that no more than four or five propagation hops are useful; the received signal eventually becomes too weak to be heard.

The second important point to be recognized in multihop propagation is that the geometry of the first hop establishes the geometry for all succeeding hops. And it is the elevation angle at the transmitter that sets up the geometry for the first hop.

It should be obvious from the preceding discussion that one needs a detailed knowledge of the range of elevation angles for effective communication in order to do a scientific evaluation of a possible communications circuit. The range of angles should be statistically valid over the full 11-year solar sunspot cycle, since the behavior of the Sun determines the changes in the nature of the Earth's ionosphere. ARRL did a very detailed computer study in the early 1990s to determine the angles needed for propagation throughout the world. The results of this study will be examined later, after we introduce the relationship between antenna height and the elevation pattern for an antenna.

Horizontal Antennas Over Flat Ground

A simple antenna that is commonly used for HF communications is the horizontal half-wave dipole. The dipole is a straight length of wire (or tubing) into which radio-frequency energy is fed at the center. Because of its simplicity, the dipole may be easily subjected to theoretical performance analyses. Further, the results of proper analyses are well borne out in practice. For these reasons, the half-wave dipole is a convenient performance standard against which other antenna systems can be compared.

Because the earth acts as a reflector for HF radio waves, the directive properties of any antenna are modified considerably by the ground underneath it. If a dipole antenna is placed horizontally above the ground, most of the energy radiated downward from the dipole is reflected upward. The reflected waves combine with the direct waves (those radiated at angles above the horizontal) in various ways, depending on the height of the antenna, the frequency, and the electrical characteristics of the ground under and around the antenna.

At some vertical angles above the horizon, the direct and reflected waves may be exactly in phase—that is, the maximum signal or field strengths of both waves are reached at the same instant at some distant point. In this case the resultant field strength is equal to the sum of the two components. At other vertical angles the two waves may be completely out of phase at some distant point—that is, the fields are maximum at the same instant but the phase directions are opposite. The resultant field strength in this case is the difference between the two. At still other angles the resultant field will have intermediate values. Thus, the effect of the ground is to increase the intensity of radiation at some vertical angles and to decrease it at others. The elevation angles at which the maxima and minima occur depend primarily on the antenna height above ground. (The electrical characteristics of the ground have some slight effect too.)

For simplicity here, we consider the ground to be a perfectly conducting, perfectly flat reflector, so that straightforward trigonometric calculations can be made to determine the relative amount of radiation intensity at any vertical angle for any dipole height. Graphs from such calculations are often plotted on rectangular axes to show best resolution over particularly useful ranges of elevation angles, although they are also shown on polar plots so that both the front and back of the response can be examined easily. **Fig 3** shows an overlay of the polar elevation-pattern responses of two dipoles at different heights over perfectly conducting flat ground. The lower dipole is located a half wavelength above ground, while the higher dipole is located one wavelength above ground. The pattern of the lower antenna peaks at an elevation angle of about 30°, while the higher antenna has two main lobes, one peaking at 15° and the other at about 50° elevation angle.

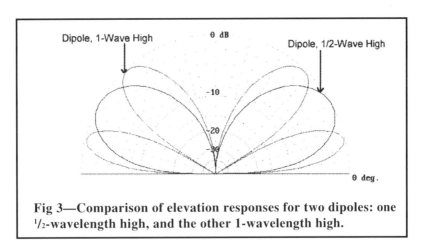

Fig 3—Comparison of elevation responses for two dipoles: one ¹/₂-wavelength high, and the other 1-wavelength high.

In the plots shown in Fig 3, the elevation angle above the horizon is represented in the same fashion that angles are measured on a protractor. The concentric circles are calibrated to represent ratios of field strengths, referenced to the strength represented by the outer circle. The circles are calibrated in decibels. Diminishing strengths are plotted toward the center.

You may have noted that antenna heights are often discussed in terms of *wavelengths*. The reason for this is that the length of a radio wave is inversely proportional to its frequency. Therefore a fixed physical height will represent different electrical heights at different radio frequencies. For example, a height of 70 feet represents one wavelength at a frequency of 14 MHz. But the same 70-foot height represents a half wavelength for a frequency of 7 MHz and only a quarter wavelength at 3.5 MHz. On the other hand, 70 feet is 2 wavelengths high at 28 MHz.

The lobes and nulls of the patterns shown in Fig 3 illustrate what was described earlier, that the effect of the ground beneath an antenna is to increase the intensity of radiation at some vertical elevation angles and to decrease it at others. At a height of a half wavelength, the radiated energy is strongest at a rather high elevation angle of 30°. This would represent the situation for a 14-MHz dipole 35 feet off the ground.

As the horizontal antenna is raised to greater heights, additional lobes are formed, and the lower ones move closer to the horizon. The maximum amplitude of each of the lobes is roughly equal. As may be seen in Fig 3, for an antenna height of one wavelength, the energy in the lowest lobe is strongest at 15°. This would represent the situation for a 14-MHz dipole 70 feet high.

The elevation angle of the lowest lobe for a horizontal antenna above perfectly conducting ground may be determined mathematically:

$$\theta = \sin^{-1}\left(\frac{0.25}{h}\right)$$

Where

θ = the wave or elevation angle
h = the antenna height above ground in wavelengths

In short, the higher the horizontal antenna, the lower is the lowest lobe of the pattern. As a very general rule of thumb, the higher an HF antenna can be placed above ground, the farther it will provide effective communications because of the resulting lower radiation angle. This is true for any horizontal antenna over real as well as theoretically perfect ground.

You should note that the nulls in the elevation pattern can play an important role in communications—or lack of communication. If a signal arrives at an angle where the antenna system exhibits a deep null, communication effectiveness will be greatly reduced. It is thus quite possible that an antenna can be *too high* for good communications efficiency on a particular frequency. Although this rarely arises as a significant problem on the amateur bands below 14 MHz, we'll discuss the subject of optimal height in more detail later.

Actual earth does not reflect all the radio-frequency energy striking it; some absorption takes place. Over real earth, therefore, the patterns will be slightly different than those shown in Fig 3, however the differences between theoretical and perfect earth ground are not significant for the range of elevation angles necessary for good HF communication. Modern computer programs can do accurate evaluations, taking all the significant ground-related factors into account.

Beam Antennas

For point-to-point communications, it is beneficial to concentrate the radiated energy into a beam that can be aimed toward a distant point. An analogy can be made by comparing the light from a bare electric bulb to that from an automobile headlight, which incorporates a built-in focusing lens. For illuminating a distant point, the headlight is far more effective.

Antennas designed to concentrate the radiated energy into a beam are called, naturally enough, *beam antennas*. For a fixed amount of transmitter power fed to the transmitting antenna, beam antennas provide increased signal strength at a distant receiver. In radio communications, the use of a beam antenna is also beneficial during reception, because the antenna pattern for transmission is the same for reception. A beam antenna helps to reject signals from unwanted directions, and in effect boosts the strength of signals received from the desired direction.

The increase in signal or field strength a beam antenna offers is frequently referenced to a dipole antenna in free space (or to another theoretical antenna in free space called an *isotropic antenna*) by a term called *gain*. Gain is commonly expressed in decibels. The isotropic antenna is defined as being one that radiates equally well in all directions, much like the way a bare lightbulb radiates essentially equally in all directions.

One particularly well-known type of beam antenna is called a *Yagi*, named after one of its Japanese inventors. Different varieties of Yagi antennas exist, each having somewhat different characteristics. Many television antenna are forms of multi-element Yagi beam antennas. In the next section of this paper, we will refer to a four-element Yagi, with a gain of 8.5 dBi in free space, exclusive of any influence due to ground.

This antenna has 8.5 dB more gain than an isotropic antenna in free space and it achieves that gain by squeezing the pattern in certain desired directions. Think of a normally round balloon and imagine squeezing that balloon to elongate it in one direction. The increased length in one direction comes at the expense of length in other directions. This is analogous to how an antenna achieves more signal strength in one direction, at the expense of signal strength in other directions.

The elevation pattern for a Yagi over flat ground will vary with the electrical height over ground in exactly the same manner as for a simpler dipole antenna. The Yagi is one of the most common antennas employed by radio amateurs, second in popularity only to the dipole.

Putting The Pieces Together

In **Fig 4**, the elevation angles necessary for communication from a particular transmitting site, in Boston, Massachusetts, to the continent of Europe using the 14-MHz amateur band are shown in the form of a bargraph. For each elevation angle from 1° to 30°, Fig 4 shows the percentage of time when the 14-MHz band is open at each elevation angle. For example, 5° is the elevation angle that occurs 12% of the time when the band is available for communication, while 11° occurs just under 10% of the time when the band is open. The useful range of elevation angles that must accommodated by an amateur station wishing to talk to Europe from Boston is from 1° to 28°.

In addition to the bar-graph elevation-angle statistics shown in Fig 4, the elevation pattern responses for three Yagi antennas, located at three different heights above flat ground, are overlaid on the same graph. You can easily see that the 120-foot antenna is the best antenna to cover all the possible angles for this particular frequency, although it suffers at the higher elevation angles on this particular propagation path, beyond about 12°. If, however, you can accept somewhat lower gain at the lowest angles, the 70-foot antenna would arguably be the best overall choice to cover all the elevation angles.

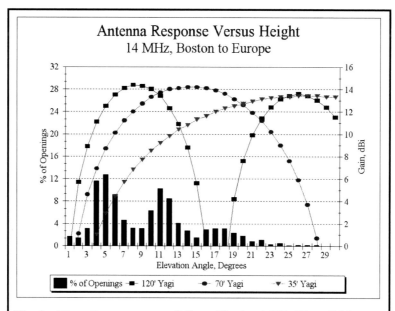

Fig 4—Elevation response of three Yagis at 120, 70 and 35 feet, at 14 MHz over flat ground. The patterns are overlaid with the statistical elevation-angles for the path from Boston to continental Europe over the entire 11-year solar sunspot cycle. Clearly, the 120-foot antenna is the best choice to cover the angles needed, but it suffers some at higher angles.

Other graphs are needed to show other target receiving areas around the world. For comparison, **Fig 5** is also for the 14-MHz band, but this time from Boston to Sydney, Australia. The peak angle for this very long path is about 2°, occurring 19% of the time when the band is actually open for communication. Here, even the 120-foot high antenna is not ideal. Nonetheless, at the 5° elevation angle, the 120-foot antenna is still about 10 dB better than the one at 35 feet.

Fig 4 and Fig 5 have portrayed the situation for the 14-MHz amateur band, the most popular and heavily utilized HF band used by radio amateurs. During medium to high levels of solar sunspot activity, the 21 and 28MHz amateur bands are open during the daytime for long-distance communication. Fig 6 illustrates the 28-MHz elevation-angle statistics, compared to the elevation patterns for the same three antenna heights shown in Fig 5. Clearly, the elevation response for the 120-foot antenna has a severe (and undesirable) null at 8°. The 120-foot antenna is almost 3.4 wavelengths high on 28 MHz (whereas it is 1.7 wavelengths high on 14 MHz.) For certain launch angles, the 120-foot high Yagi on 28 MHz would simply be too high.

The radio amateur who must operate on a variety of frequencies might require two or more towers at different heights to maintain proper elevation coverage on all the authorized bands. Antennas can sometimes be mounted at different heights on a single supporting tower, although it is more difficult to rotate antennas that are "vertically stacked" around the tower to point in all the needed directions. Further, closely spaced antennas tuned to different frequencies usually interact electrically with each other, often causing severe performance degradation.

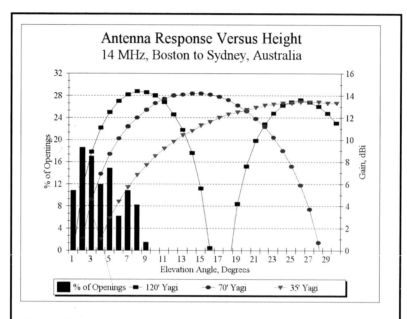

Fig 5—Elevation responses for same antennas as Fig 4, but for a longer-range path from Boston to Sydney, Australia. Note that the prevailing elevation angles are very low.

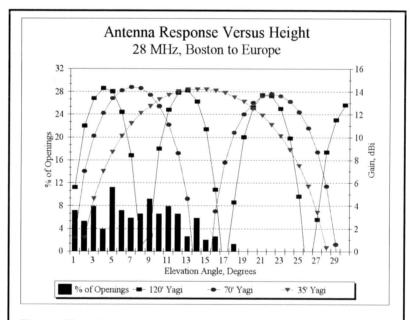

Fig 6—Elevation angles compared to antenna responses for 28-MHz path from Boston to Europe. The 70-foot antenna is the best choice on this path.

During periods of low to moderate sunspot activity (about 50% of the 11-year solar cycle), the 14-MHz band closes down for propagation in the early evening. A radio amateur wishing to continue communication must shift to a lower frequency band. The next most highly used band below the 14-MHz band is the 7-MHz amateur band. **Fig 7** portrays a 7-MHz case for another transmitting site, this time from San Francisco, California, to the European continent. Now, the range of necessary elevation angles is from about 1° to 16°, with a peak statistical likelihood of about 16% occurring at an elevation of 3°. At this low elevation angle, a 7-MHz antenna must be *very* high in the air to be effective. Even the 120-foot antenna is hardly optimal for the peak angle of 3°. The 200-foot antenna shown would be far better than a 120-foot antenna. Further, the 35-foot high antenna is far inferior to the other antennas on this path and would provide far less capabilities, on both receiving and transmitting.

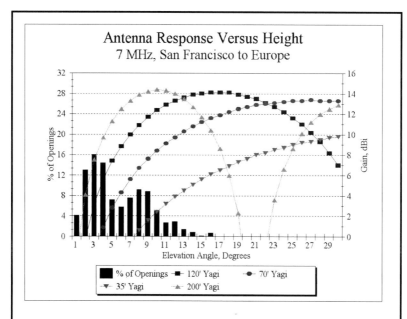

Fig 7—Comparison of antenna responses for another propagation path: from San Frnacisco to Europe on 7 MHz. Here, even a 120-foot high antenna is hardly optimal for the very low elevation angles required on this very long path. In fact, a 200-foot high antenna is far better suited for this path.

What If the Ground Isn't Flat?

In the preceding discussion, antenna radiation patterns were computed for antennas located over *flat ground*. Things get much more complicated when the exact local terrain surrounding a tower and antenna are taken into account. In the last few years, sophisticated ray-tracing computer models have become available that can calculate the effect that local terrain has on the elevation patterns for real-world HF installations-and each real-world situation is indeed different.

For simplicity, first consider an antenna on the top of a hill with a constant slope downward. The general effect is to lower the effective elevation angle by an amount equal to the downslope of the hill. For example, if the downslope is –3° for a long distance away from the tower and the flat-ground peak elevation angle is 10° (due to the height of the antenna), then the net result will be 10° – 3° = 7° peak angle. However, if the local terrain is rough, with many bumps and valleys in the desired direction, the response can be modified considerably. **Fig 8** shows the fairly complicated terrain profile for Jan Carman, K5MA, in the direction of Japan. Jan is located on one of the tallest hills in West Falmouth, Massachusetts. Within 500 feet of his tower is a small hill with a water tower on the top, and then the ground gradually falls away, so that at a distance of about 3000 feet from the tower base, the elevation has fallen to sea level, at 0 feet.

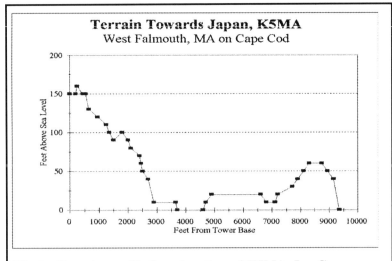

Fig 8—Terrain profile from location of K5MA, Jan Carman, in West Falmouth, MA, towards Japan. This is a moderately complicated real-world terrain on one of the highest hills on Cape Cod.

The computed responses toward Japan from this location, using a 120-foot and a 70-foot high Yagi, are shown in **Fig 9**, overlaid for comparison with the response for a 120-foot Yagi over flat ground. Over this particular terrain, the elevation pattern for the 70-foot antenna is actually better than that of the 120-foot antenna for angles below about 3°, but not for medium angles!

The responses for each height oscillate around the pattern for flat ground-all due to the complex reflections and diffractions occurring off the terrain.

At an elevation angle of 5°, the situation reverses itself and the gain is now higher for the 120-foot-high antenna than for the 70-foot antenna. A pair of antennas on one tower would be required to cover all the angles properly. To avoid any electrical interactions between similar antennas on one tower, two towers would be much better. Compared to the flat-ground situation, the responses of real-world antennas can be very complicated due to the interactions with the local terrain.

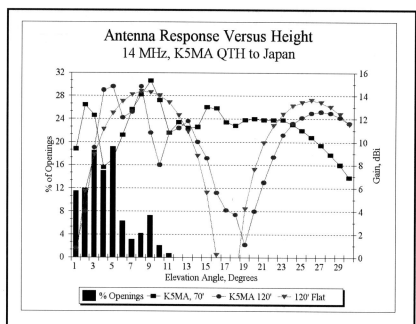

Fig 9—Computed elevation responses of 120- and 70-foot high Yagis, at the K5MA location on Cape Cod, in the direction of Japan and over flat ground, for comparison. The elevation response of the real-world antenna has been significantly modified by the local terrain.

Fig 10 shows the situation for the same Cape Cod location, but now for 7 MHz. Again, it is clear that the 120-foot high Yagi is superior by at least 3 dB (equivalent to twice the power) to the 70-foot high antenna at the statistical elevation angle of 6°. However, the response of the real-world 120-foot high antenna is still up some 2 dB from the response for an identical antenna over flat ground at this angle. On this frequency, the local terrain has helped boost the gain at the medium angles more than a similar antenna 120 feet over flat ground. The gain is even greater at lower angles, say at 1° elevation, where most signals take off, statistically speaking. Putting the antenna up higher, say 150 feet, will help the situation at this location, as would adding an additional Yagi at the 70-foot level and feeding both antennas in phase as a vertical stack.

Although the preceding discussion has been in terms of the transmitting antenna, the same principles apply when the antenna is used for reception. A high antenna will receive low-angle signals more effectively than will a low antenna. Indeed, amateur operators know very well that "If you can't hear them, you can't talk to them." Stations with tall towers can usually hear far better than their counterparts with low installations.

The situation becomes even more difficult for the next lowest amateur band at 3.5 MHz, where optimal antenna heights for effective long-range communication become truly heroic! Towers that exceed 120 feet are commonplace among amateurs wishing to do serious 3.5-MHz long-distance work.

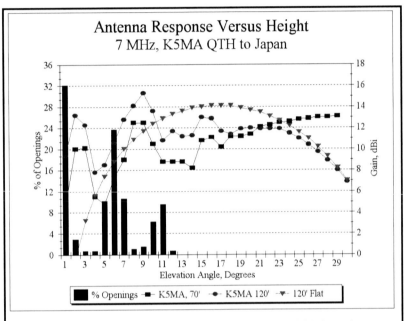

Fig 10—Elevation response on 7 MHz from K5MA location towards Japan on 7 MHz. The 120-foot high Yagi is definitely superior to the one only 70-feet high.

The 3.5 and 7-MHz amateur bands are, however, not always used strictly for long-range work. Both bands are crucial for providing communications throughout a local area, such as might be necessary in times of a local emergency. For example, earthquakes, tornadoes and hurricanes have often disrupted local communications—because telephone and power lines are down and because local police and fire-department VHF/UHF repeaters are thus knocked out of action. Radio amateurs often will use the 3.5 and 7-MHz bands to provide communications out beyond the local area affected by the disaster, perhaps into the next county or the next metropolitan area. For example, an earthquake in San Francisco might see amateurs using emergency power providing communications through amateurs in Oakland across the San Francisco Bay, or even as far away as Los Angeles or Sacramento. These places are where commercial power and telephone lines are still intact, while most power and telephones might be down in San Francisco itself. Similarly, a hurricane that selectively destroys certain towns on Cape Cod might find amateurs in these towns using 3.5 or 7.0 MHz to contact their counterparts in Boston or New York.

However, in order to get the emergency messages through, amateurs must have effective antennas. Most such relatively local emergency situations require towers of moderate height, less than about 100 feet tall typically.

Antenna Height and Interference

Extensive Federal Regulations cover the subject of interference to home electronic devices. It is an unfortunate fact of life, however, that many home electronic devices (such as stereos, TVs, telephones and VCRs) do not meet the Federal standards. They are simply inadequately designed to be resistant to rf energy in their vicinity. Thus, a perfectly legal amateur-radio transmitter may cause interference to a neighbor's VCR or TV because cost-saving shortcuts were taken in the design and manufacture of these home entertainment devices. Unfortunately, it is difficult to explain to an irate neighbor why his brand-new $1000 stereo is receiving the perfectly legitimate transmissions by a nearby radio operator.

The potential for interference to any receiving device is a function of the transmitter power, transmitter frequency, receiver frequency, and most important of all, the proximity of the transmitter to the potential receiver. The transmitted field intensity decreases as the inverse square of the distance. This means that doubling the height of an antenna from 35 to 70 feet will reduce the potential for interference by 75%. Doubling the height again to 140 feet high would reduce the potential another 75%. Higher is better to prevent interference in the first place!

Recently enacted Federal Regulations address the potential for harm to humans because of exposure to electromagnetic fields. Amateur-radio stations rarely have problems in this area, because they use relatively low transmitting power levels and intermittent duty cycles compared to commercial operations, such as TV or FM broadcast stations. Nevertheless, the potential for rf exposure is again directly related to the distance separating the transmitting antenna and the human beings around it. Again, doubling the height will reduce potential exposure by 75%. The higher the antenna, the less there will any potential for significant rf exposure.

THE WORLD IS A VERY COMPLICATED PLACE

It should be pretty clear by now that designing scientifically valid communication systems is an enormously complex subject. The main complications come from the vagaries of the medium itself, the Earth's ionosphere. However, local terrain can considerably complicate the analysis also. The main points of this paper may be summarized briefly:

The radiation elevation angle is the key factor determining effective communication distances beyond line-of-sight. Antenna height is the primary variable under control of the station builder, since antenna height affects the angle of radiation.

In general, placing an amateur antenna system higher in the air enhances communication capabilities and also reduces chances for electromagnetic interference with neighbors.

Appendix A2: Importance of Antenna Height at George S. Ham's Location, Anywhere, MA

   As explained in the white paper "Antenna Height and Communications Effectiveness," the height of an antenna over the surrounding terrain has a profound affect on the ability to communicate effectively. The following information in this exhibit is a customized analysis of the terrain at the location of George S. Ham in Anywhere, MA, in the critical direction towards Europe, the most densely populated area for amateur-radio communications. Unfortunately, this direction is also one of the most challenging for Mr. Ham's antenna system because of the hilly local terrain. **Fig 1** plots the height of the terrain towards Europe against distance from the base of his antenna system. The terrain data was taken off an official US Geodetic Survey topographic map.

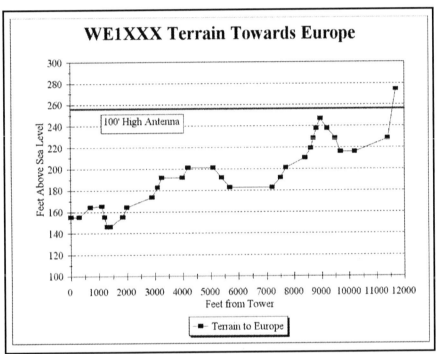

Fig 1—This terrain is rather challenging, since there are several significant hills about two miles away in the all-important direction towards Europe.

   A 100-foot high antenna aimed at the horizon would almost, but not quite, clear the obstructing hill. This would mean that direct line-of-sight communication necessary for repeater or packet-radio operation on the VHF/UHF frequencies in that direction would be marginal, if even possible. Luckily, there are repeaters in other directions that Mr. Ham could use for VHF/UHF work from his location.

   The real problem, however, is the effect the intervening terrain has on the ability to contact Europe by means of HF ionospheric propagation. The blockage would be most keenly felt at the lower amateur-radio frequencies, such as 3.5 and 7 MHz. These frequencies are necessary for nighttime operation. **Fig 2** shows the computed response (using the ARRL computer program Y7) for a 7-MHz antenna at a height of 100 feet in the direction of Europe.

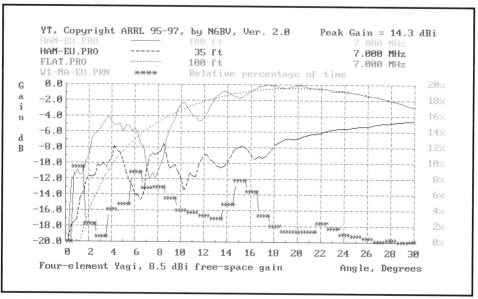

Fig 2—Operation on 7 MHz into Europe from WE1XXX location in Anywhere, MA. A 100-foot high antenna (blue solid line) over this terrain suffers in comparison to an identical antenna mounted over flat ground (violet dotted line) at intermediate elevation angles. For an extreme comparison, a 35-foot high antenna (black dashed line) at WE1XXX shows markedly poorer performance.

The green asterisks in Fig 2 represent statistics showing the elevation angles versus the relative percentage of time that the 7-MHz band is open for communications to Europe. These angles vary from 1° (occurring 10% of the time) to 30° (for less than 1% of the time). These statistics are true for the entire 11-year solar cycle, for all months in the year. For example, look at an elevation angle of 6°, which is the elevation angle needed 8% of the all times when communication is possible to Europe from Massachusetts on 7 MHz.

Note that at elevation angles between 6° to 9°, Ham's 100-foot high antenna suffers a performance degradation compared to an identical antenna mounted over flat ground. Interestingly, due to the effects of diffraction off the hilltop peaks, the performance at lower elevation angles is actually enhanced slightly compared to the flatland antenna.

For stark comparison, a 35-foot-high antenna would show an even more marked dip in performance because of the effects of the rugged local terrain. Note that the performance degradation compared to the 100-foot high antenna is 8 dB at 6° elevation. It would be possible to raise the transmitting power from, say, 100 W to 630 W to make up the deficit, but there is no way to make up the loss in *receiving*. Merely raising the transmitter power might lead to the embarrassing and frustrating situation of being an "alligator"-all mouth and no ears.

Fig 3 shows another comparison of three antennas at Ham's location in the direction of Europe. The response of the 150-foot high antenna is without question superior to the one at 100 feet and overwhelming superior to the one at 35 feet. This is because the 150-foot high antenna can "see over" the hill tops in the direction of Europe.

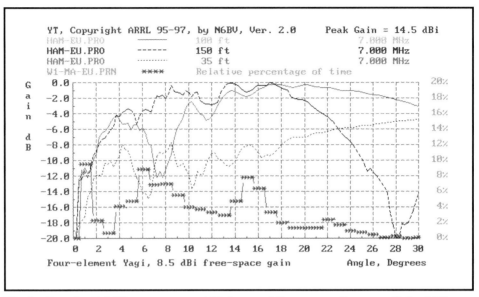

Fig 3—Put the 7-MHz antenna at 150 feet and it can now "see over" the hilltops in the direction of Europe.

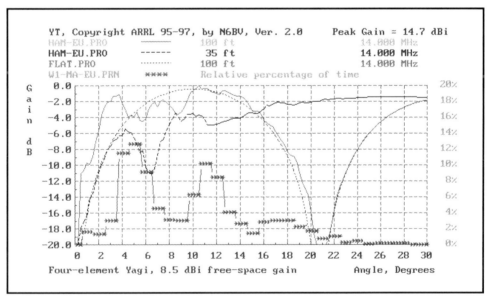

Fig 4—Comparison of 14-MHz antennas at WE1XXX location in Anywhere, MA, in the direction of Europe. The 35-foot antenna suffers rather dramatically at 6° elevation.

Now, let us examine how George Ham's terrain towards Europe affects the present antennas he has installed-a vertical stack of triband Yagis at the 100, 70 and 35-foot levels on his antenna support. **Fig 5** shows the computed response at 21 MHz into Europe. Above the dip in response at the 6° elevation point (where the hilly terrain again adversely gets into the act), the stack (blue solid line) has appreciable gain over a single 100-foot high antenna over flat ground (violet dotted line). The net effect of the two lower antennas in the stack is to extend outwards the "footprint" of the elevation response, while the highest antenna still sets the lower boundary, covering the lower elevation angles. This ability of a stack to enlarge the elevation footprint yields more reliable performance for all possible ionospheric conditions.

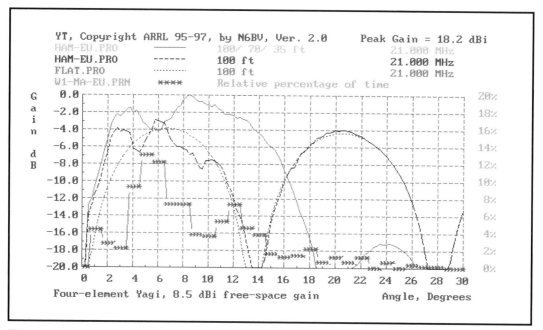

Fig 5—Computed response towards Europe for Ham's location, for three identical Yagi antennas in a vertical stack at 100/70/35 feet on a single tower (blue solid line). Compare the stack's response to that of the top antenna by itself (black dashed line), which would be too high for good performance at medium elevation angles.

Conclusion

In the very important direction towards Europe, this location is partially blocked by a hill. In order to achieve minimally acceptable results on the HF bands, a tower height of 100 feet is necessary. A height of 150 feet would actually be far preferable, but Mr. Ham is sensitive to the desires of his neighbors and is willing to compromise on a height of 100 feet.

APPENDIX B: POTENTIAL FOR RADIO-FREQUENCY INTERFERENCE

*[Available on CD-ROM as filename: **Potential for RF Interference Sample.DOC**.]*

The question for potential radio-frequency interference has been completely preempted by Federal law on the matter. In amending the Communications Act of 1934 in 1982, the Congress clearly expressed its opinion:

"The Conference Substitute is further intended to clarify the reservation of exclusive jurisdiction to the Federal Communications Commission over matters involving RFI [radio frequency interference]. Such matters shall not be regulated by local or state law, nor shall radio transmitting apparatus be subject to local or state regulation as part of any effort to resolve an RFI complaint.

[T]he Conferees intend that regulation of RFI phenomena shall be imposed only by the Commission."

H.R. Report No. 765, 97th Cong., 2d Sess. 33 (1982), reprinted in 1982 U.S. Code Cong. & Ad. News 2277, referring to amendments to Section 302(a) of the Communications Act.

In a private letter opinion to the American Radio Relay League, Inc., dated February 14, 1990, Robert L. Pettit, General Counsel of the Federal Communications Commission (FCC) adopts the position of the Congress as the position of the FCC, writing:

"State laws that require amateurs to cease operations or incur penalties as a consequence of radio interference thus have been entirely preempted by Congress."

These opinions have been confirmed repeatedly by the courts. See, for example, *Broyde v. Gotham Tower*, 13 F.3d 994 (6th Cir., 1994) **http://pacer.ca6.uscourts.gov/cgi-bin/getopn.pl?OPINION=94a0007p.06**. *[Also available on the CD-ROM as **Broyde v. Gotham Tower.PDF**.]*

For an excellent discussion, and a wealth of cases, see *Southwestern Bell Wireless, Inc. v. Johnson County Board of County Commissioners*, No. 98-3264 (10th Cir. Dec. 27, 1999) **http://www.kscourts.org/ca10/cases/1999/ 12/98-3264.htm**. *[On the CD-ROM, as filename: **SW Bell Wireless.PDF**.]* Another well-written and thorough discussion states plainly: "We conclude that allowing local zoning authorities to condition construction and use permits on any requirement to eliminate or remedy RF interference 'stands as an obstacle to the accomplishment and execution of the full purposes and objectives of Congress.'" *Freeman v. Burlington Broadcasters, Inc.*, No. 97- 9141 (2d Cir. February 23, 2000) **http://www.tourolaw.edu/2ndCircuit/February00/97-9141.html**, 2000 U.S.App. LEXIS 2672. *[Also on the CD-ROM as filename: **Freeman vs Burlington Broadcasters.PDF**.]*

Furthermore, please see "The Ghost in the Computer: Radio Frequency Interference and the Doctrine of Federal Preemption" by Ralph H. Brock, appearing in the *Computer Law Review and Technology Journal*, Volume 1999, No. 1 (Fall 1998 – Spring 1999), Southern Methodist University School of Law, **http://www.sbot.org/docs/RFI.pdf**. Section V, Conclusion reads:

> Although home electronic equipment is immersed in a sea of radio frequency energy from myriad sources, most of it functions as intended. The FCC has the authority to virtually eliminate RFI problems by requiring manufacturers to implement design features and filtering that would make all home electronics equipment "bullet proof." Instead, it has chosen to require such equipment to accept any interference it receives, while relying on the marketplace to compel manufacturers to produce serviceable merchandise.

> Historically, local authorities have attempted to regulate RFI as a common-law nuisance or trespass. But as courts have consistently concluded, Congress has completely preempted the field of RFI regulation, thus precluding local regulation and state-law claims. Although legislation has been proposed that would yield some limited authority to local governments to regulate illegal CB operations, such legislation has not been enacted.

> City, county, and private attorneys who understand how federal preemption applies in RFI matters can prevent potential litigants, beset by RFI problems, from filing ineffective lawsuits. Attorneys should also help their clients to understand that under current law, RFI is properly viewed as the equipment's inability to reject unwanted signals, not as transmitter interference. The focus of eliminating RFI can then properly shift to improving the filtering capabilities of home electronic equipment. Unless the law changes, this approach is the only reliable method of exorcizing the ghost in the computer.

Nonetheless, amateurs generally, and this Applicant in particular, are prepared to offer aid beyond the requirements of law. Should it be necessary, the Applicant pledges to cooperate with any individual, whether or not an abutter, who owns equipment that might be affected.

At least one study by the FCC Field Operations Bureau has shown that amateurs are responsible for less than 1%

of all interference complaints (400 of 42,000 complaints during a fiscal year in the early 1970s) filed with the Commission. (Source: FCC data, as reported in *QST*, July 1974, p 10) Part of the preparation for licensing involves studying how to minimize and correct such problems, if they should ever occur.

Furthermore, many home entertainment electronic devices, including portable telephones, bear the following label, in accordance with 47 CFR 15.19(a)(3):

> This device complies with part 15 of the FCC Rules. Operation is subject to the following two conditions: (1) This device may not cause harmful interference, and (2) this device must accept any interference received, including interference that may cause undesired operation.

For information on resolving problems, the FCC's *Interference Handbook* is available on the Internet. The 22 page booklet, available from the Compliance and Information Bureau via the FCC World Wide Web home page. (It includes the same information and illustrations contained in the recently published *Interference to Home Electronic Entertainment Equipment Handbook.*)

The FCC booklet includes information about equipment installation, identifying interference sources, curing interference problems and filters. It also contains a list of home electronic equipment manufacturers and telephone numbers. Pictures illustrate different TV interference problems, including ham or CB transmitter interference." See **http://www.fcc.gov/cib/Publications/tvibook.html**. *[Also available on the CD-ROM, under filename: FCC Interference Handbook.PDF.]*

For telephone interference, see **http://www.fcc.gov/eb/Publications/phone.html**. *[Also available on the CD-ROM, under filename: FCC Phone RFI.PDF.]*

The Consumer Electronics Manufacturer's Association (CEMA) publishes a pamphlet available on the World Wide Web: "What to Do If You Have An Electronics Interference Problem." See **http://www.cemacity.org/gazette/files/whattodo.htm**. *[Also available on the CD-ROM as filename: Simple RFI Booklet.PDF.]*

Actually, the erection of this antenna system will have a tendency to *decrease*, not increase, the likelihood of television interference, as higher antenna systems (with directional arrays) are farther away from neighboring television sets and transmit over nearby homes. Lower, wire antennas, erected in trees, or from a house to a tree, for example, have a greater likelihood of interference, since they would direct more energy toward a neighboring TV set.

This is exactly the position that was taken by the FCC's Chief of the Private Radio in a letter to the Board of Zoning Appeals of Hempstead, NY (October 25, 1994):

"(A)ntenna height is inversely related to the strength, in the horizontal plane, of the radio signal that serves as a catalyst for interference in susceptible home electronic equipment. It is a matter of technical fact that the higher an amateur antenna, the less likely it is that radio frequency interference will appear in home electronic equipment.

For information on resolving problems, the FCC's *Interference Handbook* is available on the Internet. The 22 page booklet, available from the Compliance and Information Bureau via the FCC World Wide Web home page, includes the same information and illustrations contained in the recently published Interference to Home Electronic Entertainment Equipment Handbook. It includes information about equipment installation, identifying interference sources, curing interference problems, and filters. It also contains a list of home electronic equipment manufacturers and telephone numbers. Pictures illustrate different TV interference problems, including ham or CB transmitter interference."

http://www.fcc.gov/Bureaus/Compliance/WWW/tvibook.html
[Available on the CD-ROM as filename: FCC Interference Handbook.PDF.]

APPENDIX C: ENVIRONMENTAL EFFECTS

[This sample document is available on the CD-ROM as filename: Environmental Effects Sample.DOC.]

The proposed transmitter output is 1500 watts. The maximum legal limit is 1500 watts. As an Amateur-Radio station, and a hobby of the Applicant, the transmitter will be in intermittent service. Even when an amateur is active, transmissions occupy less than 50% of the time of activity, as amateurs listen more than half the time.

By contrast, typical FM broadcast or AM broadcast stations use from 5,000 to 50,000 watts, continuous duty. Think of it another way—the energy of a ham radio station, at maximum power output, is about the same as a kitchen toaster. Nonetheless, using the output power at the antenna, after feed-line losses, and calculating the energy per square cm, the standard unit of measurement in these matters, this amateur station, in a worst-case scenario, will produce only 0.036 milliwatts per square centimeter of power, or 16.3% percent of the American National Standards Institute (ANSI) safety standard at the worst-case frequency, measured at 50' away from the tower *[the property line / the nearest home].*

*[If you are going to use the above paragraph, see **http://www.utexas.edu/students/utarc** or use the program **Pwr_Dens.EXE** by Ed Parsons, K1TR. This software is included on the CD-ROM, courtesy of K1TR.]*

In this case, if the Applicant were to put up the antenna at a lower height, the power required for the same reliability of the communications would increase significantly. Thus, a lower antenna would be closer to a neighbor and increase exposure (although exposure would still remain well below the regulatory threshold).

See the computation below for the engineering calculations supporting the statements above. Under the Environmental Policy Act of 1969 (NEPA), 42 U.S.C. 4321 et seq. (1976) at 4332 (2)(c), and as allowed by regulations of the Council on Environmental Quality (CEQ), 40 C.F.R. 1508.4, the FCC has ordered categorical exclusion of Amateur Radio stations from the need to do Environmental Assessments, FCC Gen. Docket No. 79-144, adopted February 12, 1987.

[For Massachusetts applicants only: Under Massachusetts law, neither notification nor approval is necessary for "amateur intermittent single source emitters of less than 1 KW average output" (average values over any 0.5 hour period). 105 CMR 122.021 (a more stringent test as it applies to the general public and not occupational use).]

Furthermore, a search of the literature fails to find a single example in the history of radio in which an Amateur Radio station has caused injury or death from exposure to Amateur Radio signals at any power level.

POWER DENSITY COMPUTATIONS

Far Field Power Density Calculation
From PWR_DENS V3.2 by E. S. Parsons, K1TR

SITE: WE1XXX with antenna at 100 feet — neighbor's house 50' away.
INPUTS:
      Output Power from Transmitter is 1500 Watts.
      Antenna Gain Over a Dipole is 6.0 dBd.
      Frequency of Operation is 28.5 MHz.
      Total System Losses are 2.7 dB.
      Distance to Antenna is 112 feet.
OUTPUTS:
      Power at Antenna Feedpoint is 805.5 Watts.
      Effective Radiated Power is 5259 Watts.
      IEEE C95.1-1991 Maximum Limit is 0.22 mW/sq cm.
      Computed Power Density is 0.036 mW/sq cm (0.360 W/sq meter).
      (Power density calculated along antenna boresight in free-space;
         no assumptions made about antenna pattern.)
      Hence: 1. The Computed Power Density is 16.3% of the C95.1-1991 Limit.
             2. The Computed Power Density is −7.89 dB from the C95.1-1991 Limit.
             3. Transmitter output power must be increased by
                at least a factor of 6 to exceed the C95.1-1991 Limit.

Far field power density is a measure, in units of milliwatts per square centimeter (mW/cm^2), of the radio frequency power to which a human or animal is exposed. To put this in context and add meaning, the power density at the point specified (usually the home closest to the amateur's antenna) is compared to the Maximum Permissible Exposure (MPE) for uncontrolled environments set forth by the FCC in their 96-326 Report and Order.

An uncontrolled environment is an area where people would not normally be aware of potential RF exposure.

A neighbor's home is an example of an uncontrolled RF environment. The FCC 96-326 Report and Order adopted the standards set forth in IEEE C95.1-1991 for uncontrolled RF environments.

This analysis assumes that the antenna is pointed at the nearest dwelling. For rotary antenna systems, the antenna is often pointed in other directions, resulting in much lower power densities at the nearest dwelling.

APPENDIX D: NOISE

*[Available on the CD-ROM under filename: **Dinman No Noise Letter.PDF**.]*

April 22, 1999

Atty. Fred Hopengarten
Volunteer Counsel, American Radio Relay League
Six Willarch Road
Lincoln, MA 01773-5105

Dear Mr. Hopengarten:

You have asked if amateur radio antenna support structures, at any height below 200 feet, create noise problems for neighbors. I am pleased to respond that the short answer is: No.

There are several potential sources of noise in an amateur radio antenna system—but none that are bothersome, or perhaps even within the ability of the human ear to detect a few feet away. These sources are an antenna rotator, the antennas, guy wires, and the support structure.

The Antenna Rotator. This is normally in the shape of an inverted bulb, about ten inches across and one foot high. When activated, it typically turns the antenna at a pace of one revolution per minute. The typical rotator uses a highly geared, small fractional horsepower motor (similar to an oversized electric clock motor) and emits a small hum, which is the sound of the motor and gears turning. I have never heard the hum of a rotator motor more than five feet away.

The Antennas. Typically made of 6061-T6 aluminum tubing, amateur radio antennas are rarely made of tubing greater than one inch, with booms (cross-piece supports) rarely greater than two inches in diameter. In my experience, when the wind is blowing hard enough so that sound is created in the vortex behind the elements, the sound of the wind itself is much louder than that of the wind shed by the antenna. This is why I have never heard such a sound and doubt that anyone has. They do not flap like a flag on a flag pole, as they do not present enough wind loading and are firmly attached to the boom supports. The ends of the properly maintained antenna are sealed with caps to prevent them from whistling in high winds. Even if the caps were no longer in place, any whistle produced by the wind would not be audible more than a few feet away from the structure.

Guy Wires. Guy wires are typically 1/4 or 3/16" steel cable, similar or identical to the guy wires that support telephone poles everywhere. No matter the wind, they never produce detectable sounds, even when long.

The Structure. Amateur radio antenna support structures, whether lattice or monopole, also shed the wind effectively. I know of no case where any steps had to be taken to reduce sound. Besides, the support structure is firmly fastened to a base at ground level, usually embedded in concrete below ground level, and presents no resonance possibilities from any vibrations that may be induced in the structure from very high winds.

Given the above analysis, I know of no reason that any Town board, or the neighbors of any radio amateur, should be concerned about acoustic noise from an amateur radio antenna system. There will be no objectionable noise.

I received a BS degree in Electrical Engineering from the Pennsylvania State University in 1959, and have practiced as a professional engineer for over 35 years. I am licensed in the state of Massachusetts, having also been registered in four other states at various times. I have been involved with the erection of over 50 amateur radio antenna systems and hold the FCC Amateur Advanced Class license. I have been a licensed Amateur for 45 years.

A list of publications and further curriculum vitae information is available on request.

Sincerely,
Saul B. Dinman, PE
MA PE License #19566

APPENDIX E: SETBACK

*[This document is available on the CD-ROM as filename: **Setback Example.DOC**.]*

The careful reader of this application will note that the height of the proposed antenna structure is greater than the distance from its base to the nearest property line. Despite this fact, the site was carefully chosen with the best interests of the Town in mind.

Accidents involving such structures are rare. They are so rare, in fact, that ARRL Volunteer Counsel Fred Hopengarten, of Lincoln, Massachusetts, reviewing 20 years of literature in amateur radio, was able to discover only a few published photographs, out of thousands of antenna photographs, showing how an antenna structure falls. In conjunction with these several photos, further discussions with mechanical engineers have yielded a better understanding of the failure modes of antenna structures.

The most likely method of failure occurs when, as a result of a storm, a nearby tree falls on a guy wire. The tower is then pulled in the direction of the guy wire that was struck. As it comes down, the antenna system and the tower catch on trees and branches of trees; and the antenna structure remains up, but at a 20° to 40° degree tilt.

Since the antennas atop the tower are likely to have a turning radius 10 to 25 feet, this is the most likely scenario. Something will catch, with the system never reaching the ground.

The other failure mode, which may occur when an antenna system is completely out in the open, involves a tower twisting and buckling. In effect, the structure corkscrews onto the ground. Towers do not fall the full length of their height, like a pencil. Instead, a failure occurs at a point of particular stress. This phenomenon is well known in physics, and is usually demonstrated in physics textbooks with a photograph of a falling chimney. As an example, see *Fundamentals of Physics*, 2nd Edition, by Halliday and Resnick, page 174, published by John Wiley & Sons:

When a tall chimney is toppled by means of an explosive charge at its base, it will often break near its middle, the rupture starting at the leading edge. The top part will then reach the ground later than the bottom part.

We note that as the chimney topples, it has at any instant an angular acceleration [A] about an axis through its base. The tangential acceleration [At] of its top is given by [At = Ar].

As the chimney leans more and more, the vertical component of At comes to exceed g [gravity, or 9.8 m/s squared], so that the bricks at the top are accelerating downward more than they would in free fall. This can happen only as long as the chimney is a rigid body. As the chimney continues to fall, internal tension stresses develop along its leading edge. In nearly all cases rupture occurs, thus relieving those stresses.

Instances of damage caused by a falling antenna system are so rare that the presence of an amateur radio antenna system has no impact on the cost or availability of insurance for the homeowner. In addition to the reasons founded in physics as to why concern about the proximity to a property line is unnecessary, the neighbor concerned has been consulted, and has authorized the applicant to represent that there is no objection to the proposed placement of the antenna system.

Although the casual observer might think that a setback to lessen visual impact is always better, this would be wrong. Take the example of a self-supporting tower placed one foot from a rear lot line. If the lot to the rear has four square miles of woods, then the least visible siting for the antenna system would be the site closest to a lot line. As a result, rigid application of standard setback rules least serves the purposes of the Town's zoning bylaw.

The Public Hearing— Your Big Moment in the Spotlight

PURPOSE

The Public Hearing serves several purposes. Among these is that, in the words of Supreme Court Justice Brandeis, "Sunshine is the best disinfectant." The Public Hearing is the very essence of democracy. It is supposed to guarantee that all sides are heard. But there are rules and common procedures—formal and informal. Here are some thoughts on getting through the evening.

ADVERTISING

Newspaper

You will probably be required to pay for the advertisement in the local weekly, or bi-weekly newspaper where legal notices appear. This will cost $35-65, as it is usual for the notice to appear twice. If there is a continuance, it is unlikely you will be required to pay again. The notice will probably parrot the opening paragraph of the application you make. You can save yourself some grief if you work with the secretary who puts the ad in the paper.

Try to make sure that the notice says "antenna-support structure" and not "tower." Try to make sure it says "Amateur Radio" antenna-support structure, as opposed to "radio tower." The latter conjures up all the wrong images, and may confuse the public into thinking you are going to erect a cellular telephone tower on a piece of residential land.

The newspaper advertisement will appear in the "Legal Notices" section of your local weekly, in very small type. It may look something like this:

J. Ham
LEGAL NOTICE
TOWN OF BELMONT
BOARD OF APPEALS
The Board of Appeals of the Town of Belmont hereby gives notice that it will consider an APPLICATION TO ERECT AND MAINTAIN AN AMATEUR-RADIO ANTENNA-SUPPORT STRUCTURE on the property at 123 HAMLY LANE, under Section 6.2(f) of the Zoning Bylaw, at a Public Hearing in the conference room, Town Hall, 76 Main Street, on Wednesday, October 8, 2001, at 7:30 pm. Those wishing to be heard should be present.
Nancy Jones, Clerk
Board of Appeals

Posting

In some jurisdictions you are required to post a sign or two on your front lawn about the upcoming Public Meeting. Don't get cute and hide it behind a bush. The temptation may be great, but you will regret it, because opponents will use your hiding strategy to argue that you can't be trusted to conform your other actions to the requirements of the law. See **Fig 8-1** for an example of such a posting.

The Public File

Just before your "big night," be sure to drop by Town Hall and examine the public file on your case. You might be amazed at what is there. For example, in the case of *Bodony v. Sands Point (NY)*, 681 F. Supp. 1009, EDNY 1987, K2LE was nosing through the public file at Town Hall when he discovered papers that showed that the Board of Zoning and Appeals intended to deny his application, well in advance of

Fig 8-1—Photograph of posted notice for a Public Meeting, courtesy of Jim Parise, W1UK.

parties outside of the Public Hearing, but trying to do so right then and there, for the first time, will make Board members nervous and suspicious.

If the meeting hasn't begun yet and you haven't done so previously, go up and introduce yourself to the Board. Hand a business card to the Board Secretary. You want to help the Chairman by informing him or her how to pronounce your name (correcting him/her later is bad form).

You want to help the Board Secretary by providing the spelling of anyone who will be appearing with you (lawyer, witness, neighbor, another ham) so that their names will appear correctly in the minutes. You could even prepare this information in advance on paper (call it "Potential Participants"). The Secretary will appreciate that.

If there are hearings before yours, do not leave the room. Stick around and see how they go. See if this Board likes a touch of humor or whether it shows a profound distaste for a light touch. See if they are formal or informal. See if they ask questions as proponents talk, or only after a presentation is made. See if they vote right then and there. Get comfortable with the process.

If you are reading this section a long time before your own hearing, go to a Board meeting and sit through one evening session. If asked: "Is there anything we can do for you?" Reply: "No, thanks. I'll have an application coming in soon and I wanted to see how things work, so that I can be more helpful to the Board when my time comes." They'll appreciate that. It is a sign of respect. In addition, sitting through a session from start to finish really will help you prepare and you'll feel more comfortable when your time comes.

Take a seat near the front and near an aisle. This reduces the amount of stumbling and fumbling when you rise. Personally, I like the front row, as it allows you to step to the side and make your presentation so that both the Board and members of the audience can hear you.

Now let's assume the Chairman or Secretary announces your item on the agenda. You will be expected to stand to make your case. Begin with your name and the purpose for your presence.

his hearing. His lawyers used that information about the Board's prior intent very effectively.

Another thing you may learn from examining the file before the hearing is that someone has circulated and submitted a petition or that there are letters on file against you. The petition or letters may make false claims. This gives you a chance to prepare exhibits to counter such claims. You don't want to be surprised.

YOUR BIG NIGHT

The Public Hearing is typically held on only one of four nights, Monday through Thursday. Friday nights are not favored because it is difficult to ensure that members of the Board will attend that night. A Friday night hearing may also conflict with some members who are celebrating the Sabbath. For similar reasons, there are no hearings on Saturdays or Sundays.

It will be held in Town Hall, a municipal building or a school. The hearing room typically uses some long tables, sometimes called "catering tables." The members of the Board will face the audience, while the audience has no table and sits on uncomfortable folding chairs looking back at the Board.

If you arrive early (and you should), volunteer to help set up the room. It is a nice thing to do as a citizen. It shows that you observe common courtesies. It allows you to introduce yourself. Do *not* use the time for lobbying a member or two, as this is seen as impolite, and may well be illegal as *ex parte* communications (communicating to a Board member without the presence of others, especially opposing parties). This is not to say that Board members have never spoken with

Your Presentation

Good evening. My name is <u>George S. Ham</u> and I live at <u>1234 Anywhere Street</u>, which is near the intersection of <u>1st</u> and <u>Main</u>. I'm here tonight on an application for a Special Permit under section <u>123.456</u>. Cite the exact section of the bylaw in excruciating detail, since this tells them that you are prepared.

At this point, at least one member of the Board is going to

reach for his own copy of the bylaw and start reading it while you continue. Other members will be rustling papers so that they can be sure that it is your application in front of them. Don't let this seeming inattention distract you.

Your application may be anywhere from 2 to 60 pages long. Under no circumstance should you read from it. Furthermore, the best presentations are made from outlines and are not read. But you knew that. Unless you have Ronald Reagan's speech-reading skills (and you don't), you will be much, much better off speaking from an outline.

Despite whatever you've been told about having a full opportunity to answer questions later, make sure that this presentation has a beginning, a middle and an end. Make it complete unto itself. But make it brief. If you go over ten minutes, you'd better have a good reason. A really good reason. A really, really good reason.

Nonetheless, show what you intend to do, why it meets all the requirements of the bylaw or ordinance, why the site you've chosen is the best site, what the total height is going to be, that you've spoken to the neighbors you could find, and then ask for exactly what you want from the Board.

At this point it is important for you to have read the state statute on municipal hearings. Few people do. You might be surprised to learn that you are entitled to cross-examine opposing witnesses. On the other hand, this may not be permitted.

Expect to have some nasty, accusatory questions put to you; some relevant, some not so relevant. Practice your answers to the tough questions in advance by rehearsing the hearing with friends and other hams from town with whom you get along. Always answer by addressing the Chairman of the Board, not the questioner.

Here is a sample list of some difficult questions, and suggested answers. (A full set of answer cards, formatted to fit on 4 × 6″ index cards can be found on the CD-ROM as filename: **Answer Cards.DOC** and **Answer Cards.PDF**.) Remember what you were taught in customer-service school: Validate the concern and answer the question.

- "I'm a doctor and I rely on my beeper/cell phone. Lives are at stake. What if you interfere with my beeper/cell phone?"

Suggested answer: "Given the doctor's responsibilities, she has every right to be concerned. However, I've been using the same transmitter, with antennas that are wires in the trees for many weeks/months now and I've had no reports of interference. I would point out to the Board that this topic is entirely outside of the Board's jurisdiction, as it is completely pre-empted by Federal law. Nonetheless, whether it is a television, VCR, cable TV, beeper or whatever, should a problem arise, I pledge to work in good faith with anyone concerned to resolve the problem. However, you should know that a higher antenna is LESS likely to cause interference than a low one, because it is further away. If interference is a concern, you should ask me to put my antenna up 300 feet high to be really far away."

- "When you came around, you misled me. I didn't realize that what you were planning was going to be so monstrous."

Suggested answer: "Ladies and Gentlemen (remember to address the Board, and do not respond directly to a person in the audience). I am very sorry that anyone feels he was misled. If Mr ___ feels that way, then I failed in my mission to make my plan clear. When I walked around to meet with my neighbors, I carried a copy of the application you have before you tonight. If someone remembers my presentation differently, I assure you I had no intention to mislead. The proposal then was the same one before you tonight. I've tried to explain the project to my neighbors before this evening."

- "Isn't this ham radio stuff really old technology that's going to be replaced by the Internet and satellite communications or cell phones? Why do we have to have one of these things in our neighborhood?"

Suggested answer: "Members of the Board, I'm also a big fan of new technologies. But just because you don't need a dog to hunt for food anymore does not mean that the pleasure of owning a dog should be forbidden. Furthermore, when a disaster comes, will the Internet or cellular phone be there for emergency communications? Even today, experience shows that experienced communicators who have their own equipment—and who regularly practice their communications skills on the air—are necessary to man the Civil Defense network. If it would be useful to you, I'd be happy to provide piles of newspaper articles showing that this is true. Nonetheless, we're not talking about a permanent change here. Antenna systems go up and antenna systems come down. In fact, I'll be erecting an antenna here that I brought with me from my former home. I do believe that this proposal qualifies for a Special Permit under the bylaw and that it should be granted, despite whatever other methods of communications are available."

- "It's going to ruin our nice neighborhood."

Suggested answer: "Ladies and gentlemen, if it were true that my antenna system would ruin the neighborhood, I wouldn't propose it, because I have to live there too. However, as the photos in my application demonstrate, it will not be visible at all from several directions, even in winter, and from the one or two spots from which it can be seen, the antennas will just look like a pencil line against the sky (that's what a piece of one-inch tubing looks like from 150 feet away). The largest part of the antenna is only a three-inch diameter boom. The largest part of the support structure visible above the trees is only a $1^1/_2$-inch diameter tube. The whole structure together has an equivalent size of a $4^1/_2$-inch diameter flagpole, and less visibility, because the lattice construction is "see through." *[Change the above statements to match your facts.]* Finally, as you can see from examples of similar antennas located in (name a fancy neighborhood or town), Western Civilization as we know it will not end if this permit is granted. It will not change the character of the neighborhood or the zoning district, which was residential and will remain residential. This is not a commercial use, a commercial tower or any such thing."

- "I've been a radio ham for 35 years and I was always able to contact England and to make other exciting contacts, with just a dipole hanging from my garage at 18 feet."

Suggested answer: "I'm pleased to see you here, and I hope we'll have a chance to get together afterward to chat about ham radio. I'm sure that you've made those contacts and enjoyed them very much. But the ability to make such a contact now and again, when conditions are just right, is no argument against my need for effective communications on a more reliable basis, which is what the Federal preemption in this area is all about."

- "Nobody really needs this, right? It's just a hobby, right?"

Suggested answer: "This is a public-service hobby, like the Civil Air Patrol or being a Red Cross volunteer. Amateur Radio is the one hobby that offers the opportunity to experiment and to create and test new communications technologies. Hams were in the forefront of developing the early mobile radios that led to cellular telephones. Hams were pioneers in packet-radio techniques that led to the ability of police to check your license plate from the front seat of a patrol car, and hams have been involved in satellite communications from the start. The State Legislature and the US Congress agree that we as a society need Amateur Radio."

SUBSTANCE

During the course of your presentation, you must never assume that all of the members of the Board have read your written presentation. If you get a question that can be answered straight out of the written proposal, simply begin: "Good question. I apologize for not covering it earlier in my oral presentation. May I call your attention to page 12, where I show that this is true."

Don't smirk. Don't even *think* about implying that a better-prepared Board member would have spotted it. Here are a few more tips.

- Don't talk about what they allow in a neighboring town. You can be sure that the Board members here in your new town feel that they'd never stoop that low.
- Do stress that you've tried to be thorough and that you've tried to seek out the placement of the antenna system on your property that is the least visible to the most families, not because it is ugly (it isn't), but because you want to be a good neighbor.

Eventually, it will be time to sum up. If things have been going well, use just one sentence. "Members of the Board, I've put a proposal before you that meets all the requirements of the bylaw, shows consideration for the neighbors and deserves your support. I ask that you grant *[exactly what you are seeking]* under Section 123.456 of the bylaw."

If you've been getting slammed, emphasize everything you've done to prevent what they've witnessed. "Members of the Board, I'm more than a little stunned by the opposition to this proposal. I assembled it over weeks and months, with consultations from *[name the other hams and town fathers, as well as neighbors with whom you consulted]*. I came here proposing an antenna system with limited visual impact. It deserves an affirmative vote under the ordinance, state and Federal law."

WHAT I BRING TO THE HEARING

If you should find yourself packing up to appear before a Planning Board, Board of Appeals, Architectural Review Board or the like, perhaps you will find it useful to know what I keep in my permanently packed three-ring binders. These details are shown below.

In addition to my permanent three-ring binders, I bring a copy of the local zoning code (bylaws), which can be bought at Town Hall for a nominal cost (in 2000, this is usually $7 to $20). This permits you to respond to specific questions on how that code applies (or fails to apply) to the project. I also bring the ARRL *Continuing Legal Education* book, because it has photocopies of some relevant cases. (You, on the other hand, can just print out from this book's CD-ROM the legal cases you think are relevant to your situation.)

FEDERAL LAW

Public Law 103-408, October 22, 1994

See CD-ROM, filename: **Public Law—HamRadio.PDF**.

"Congress finds and declares that:
(3) reasonable accommodation should be made for the effective operation of amateur radio from residences, . . . and that regulation at all levels of government should facilitate and encourage amateur radio as a public benefit."

Use: To counter claims that neighbors should not be hurt for a private benefit; ie, a hobby.

47 CFR § 97.1
Basis and Purpose

"voluntary non-commercial communications service, particularly with respect to emergency communications"

Use: To allay concerns that the tower is going to be used for a commercial purpose. This is useful where an ordinance against towers is badly written, but where you can forcefully argue that it was intended to regulate commercial uses, not Amateur Radio.

47 CFR §97.15(b)

See CD-ROM, filename: **FCC PRB-1 (1985).PDF**.

This is the actual Federal regulation and delivers the rule of PRB-1. PRB-1, 50 FR 38813.

I hesitate to use the full text, and don't recommend giving it to a zoning authority. You can also find this on the ARRL web page at **www.arrl.org/field/regulations/prb-1.htm**.

DA 99-2654

See CD-ROM, filename: **FCC PRB-1 (1999).PDF**. Also see:**www.fcc.gov/Bureaus/Wireless/Orders/1999/da992569.txt**.

Released November 19, 1999, this is the denial of RM-8763. However, it delivers the FCC's answer to "balancing" vs. "accommodation" and says regulations must not "impinge on the needs of amateur operators."

Use: Along with the <u>Pentel</u> case, shows that a town *may not balance* its interests with those of the radio ham.

Which Structures Must Be Registered with the FCC?

See CD-ROM, filename: **FCC-Registering Antennas. PDF** and **http://www.fcc.gov/wtb/antenna.what.html**. This includes the 200-foot height rule, airport rules and exemptions.

Use: Shows that what you propose will not require stripes and lights (if that is so in your case).

Compliance with Commission's Rules Implementing the National Environmental Policy Act of 1969

See CD-ROM, filename: **FCC & National Environmental Policy.PDF**. Also see **http://www.fcc.gov/wtb/siting/npaguid.html**. An environmental assessment (EA) is required only in eight environmentally sensitive situations (47 CFR 1.1307(a)), or for radiation in excess of OET 65 guidelines (47 CFR 1.1307(b)).

Use: To show that no EPA filing is necessary.

STATE LAW

(Substitute documents applicable to your own state law.)
- Massachusetts General Laws, Chapter 40A, Section 3— the Massachusetts statute that adopts 47 CFR §97.15(b).
- Code of Massachusetts Regulations (780 CMR Relevant Sections)
- 780 CMR 3108.0 Radio and Television Towers
- 780 CMR 3109.1 Radio and Television Antennas
- 780 CMR 1611 Wind Load (Specifies mph by zone, and psf by height, zone and exposure), including Table 1611.4
- The entire text of every section of Massachusetts building code dealing with antennas and towers, roof mounted or freestanding. (Only a few sections are needed, but Building Inspectors keep this on their desks. He probably brought his with him.)
- MGL Ch. 112, Sec. 81R (Exemptions from need for a MA seal, (b) permits IL seal.)
- MGL Ch. 143A, Sec. 54A (Seal required unless...)
- MGL Ch. 112, Sec. 60L (Permits non-resident seal)

Other Massachusetts Town Bylaws

- Concord
- Lincoln
- Sudbury
- Wayland

This is to show that a favorable local bylaw is not a quirk. These very wealthy towns with unusually high property values also favor ham-radio antenna structures.

RADIO FREQUENCY INTERFERENCE (RFI)

Letter from Massachusetts Assistant Attorney General

See CD-ROM, filename: **Mass Attorney General Letter.PDF**. From Henry F. O'Connell to the Town of Andover (September 8, 1981). It states that "A local community may not legislate in this area."

Letters from FCC

- See CD-ROM, filename: **Petit-Haller-MacNamara Letters.PDF** from Ralph Haller, Chief, Private Radio Bureau, to Hempstead, NY (25 October 1994). This states that towns "may not. . . base their regulation of amateur service antenna structures on the causation of interference to home electronic equipment . . ." and "there is no reasonable connection between requiring Mr. Nadel to reduce the height of his antenna and reducing the amount of interference to his neighbors' home electronic equipment. On the contrary, antenna height is inversely related to the strength, in the horizontal plane, of the radio signal. . ."
- See CD-ROM, filename: **Petit-Haller-MacNamara Letters.PDF** from Robert L. Petit, General Counsel, to Pierre, SD (February 14, 1990). This states that "Congress has preempted any concurrent state or local regulation of radio interference pursuant to the provisions of the Communications Act."

Cases

- *Broyde v. Gotham Tower, Inc.*, 13 F. 3d 994 (6th Cir. 1994). See CD-ROM, filename: **Broyde v. Gotham Tower.PDF** or see: **http://pacer.ca6.uscourts.gov/cgi-bin/getopn.pl?OPINION=94a0007p.06**. This holds that an action against a radio station for nuisance was preempted by the Federal Communications Act, since Congress had clearly removed regulation of radio transmitting apparatus from state or local law.
- *Southwestern Bell Wireless, Inc. v. Johnson County Board of County Commissioners*, No. 98-3264 (10th Cir. Dec. 27, 1999). See CD-ROM, filename: **SW Bell Wireless.PDF** and **www.kscourt.org/ca10/cases/1999/12/98-3264.htm**. This has an excellent discussion and a wealth of cases.
- *Freeman v. Burlington Broadcasters, Inc.*, No. 97- 9141 (2d Cir. February 23, 2000), 2000 U.S.App. LEXIS 2672. See CD-ROM, filename: **Freeman vs Burlington Broadcasters.PDF** and **www.tourolaw.edu/2ndCircuit/February00/97-9141.html**. This states plainly: "We conclude that allowing local zoning authorities to condition construction and use permits on any requirement to eliminate or remedy RF interference 'stands as an obstacle to the accomplishment and execution of the full purposes and objectives of Congress.'"

- An illustration showing the Inverse Square Law ($1/R^2$) to demonstrate that power is reduced as the square of the distance.

NOMENCLATURE

I bring a pictorial to help a Board understand the various parts of an antenna: the mast, the boom, the elements, the support structure, the guy wires and so forth. See **Fig 8-2**. (CD-ROM Filename: **Antenna Nomenclature.PDF**)

ANTENNA HEIGHT

- *Antenna Height and Communications Effectiveness*, by N6BV and K1TD (Latest Version: 1999). This is important to counter idea that low antennas work "well enough." See **http://www.arrl.org/field/regulations/local/ antplnr.pdf** and CD-ROM, filename: **Antenna Height and Communications Effectiveness.PDF**.

PUBLIC SERVICE

Generic letters from people who have been helped in emergencies by local hams, pointing out that were it not for effective communications made possible by high antennas, bad things would have happened to a them or a relative. (You must, of course, sometimes draft these for those people. Keep it to one page if you can.)

BIOEFFECTS OR HAZARDS

- FCC OET 65

A printout of information showing various sample situations from:
http://n5xu.ae.utexas.edu/rfsafety/ and on the CD-ROM, filenames: **FCC OET-65.PDF** and **FCC OET-65 Supplement B.PDF**.

- 440 CMR 5.04 (1)(b)

The Massachusetts blanket exemption from RF safety rules for Amateur Radio stations licensed or authorized by the FCC.

SCREENING

- *Sight Lines and Screening of Towers by Trees*, a graphic prepared for K1VR. See CD-ROM, filename: **Tree Screening.PDF**.

PROPERTY VALUES

- "Electric Transmission Lines and the Selling Price of Residential Property," *The Appraisal Journal*, October 1979, pp 490-499. See CD-ROM, filename: **Electric Power Study.PDF**.

Shows no effect on prices of homes more than 50 feet away from power line towers. (Be sure to point out that, unlike

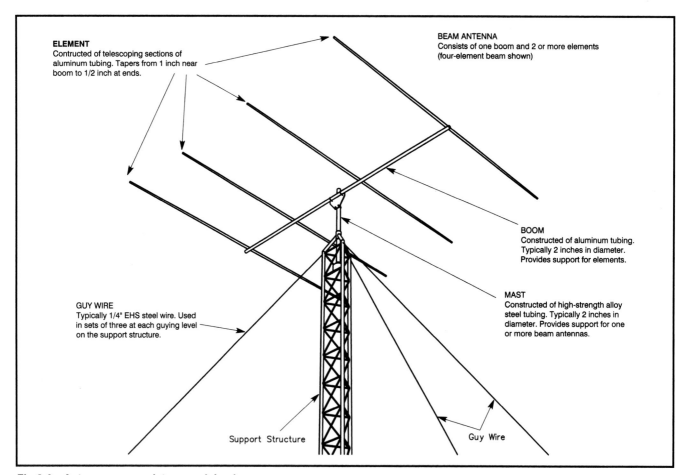

ELEMENT
Contructed of telescoping sections of aluminum tubing. Tapers from 1 inch near boom to 1/2 inch at ends.

BEAM ANTENNA
Consists of one boom and 2 or more elements (four-element beam shown)

BOOM
Constructed of aluminum tubing. Typically 2 inches in diameter. Provides support for elements.

MAST
Constructed of high-strength alloy steel tubing. Typically 2 inches in diameter. Provides support for one or more beam antennas.

GUY WIRE
Typically 1/4" EHS steel wire. Used in sets of three at each guying level on the support structure.

Support Structure

Guy Wire

Fig 8-2—Antenna nomenclature explained.

power company transmission lines, ham radio antennas go away when the ham moves, so there is no possible permanent effect. *Note*: If anyone finds an article later than 1979 in a serious appraisal journal, please let the rest of us know.)

- "Communications Tower Site Specific Impact Study" (November 10, 1997, Eastern Massachusetts) prepared for a Sprint PCS special permit application. "...the construction and operation of the Project will not have any adverse affect upon the property values in the surrounding neighborhood." Shows no effect on prices of homes in several high-value towns near major radio and TV tower clusters.
- "Market Analyses to Determine Impact of Property Values in Proximity to Tower Sites" prepared for BellSouth Mobility (April 21, 1996, Gwinnett County, Georgia): "...the construction and on-going presence of BellSouth Mobility cellular towers have no adverse effect on surrounding and adjoining residential property values." See the CD-ROM, filename: **BellSouth Mobility Property Value Study.PDF**.
- "Impact Study of Two Communication Towers/Three Subdivisions, Cordova, Shelby County, Tennessee 38018" prepared for Contel Cellular (March 14, 1995, Memphis, Tennessee): "...no negative impact exists from a communication tower and its relationship to single-family properties as tested." See CD-ROM, filename: **Memphis PCS Towers-Summary.PDF**.
- The Study prepared for NQØI's law case (from ARRL CLE materials). See CD-ROM, filename: **NQØI Boulder CO Assessment.PDF**.

BIRDS

- MA Audubon Society letter. See CD-ROM Filename: **Audubon Letter.PDF**. From Field Ornithologist saying "those of us who love birds are not concerned about small towers" (less than 200 feet).
- Wild Bird Center letter (CD-ROM Filename: **Wild Bird Center Letter.PDF**). From a retail bird feed and supplies store, saying towers "do not present an unusual or increased risk to birds."

CASELAW.DOC

A summary of the relevant cases that I have prepared for myself in the hope that I won't be caught flat-footed, not remembering a particular case that an adversary may cite. I want to know what distinguishes that case.

[Query to Readers: If you think of a document that is not on this list, could you please tell me about it, and why you'd bring it?]

YOUR OPPORTUNITY TO MAKE (OR BREAK) YOUR CASE

Your oral presentation will make, or break, your case. If you are calm, respectful, professional and prepared for all the usual questions, you will do well in most circumstances. But you knew that. If you are unprepared for the inevitable questions

and angry when you answer them, you will be hurt.

A few tips on what can really hurt you.

- Do not tell the Board that they *have to* give you this permit because you are entitled to it under Federal law. That's not what PRB-1, 47 CFR §97.15(b) and your state statute (if your state has one) say. Accommodation and a full, unlimited right to build are not the same thing.
- Do not tell the Board that you could do this easily in another town you name. The Board members don't care. In fact, the Board members truly and sincerely believe that the reason their town is better than that other town is that this town exerts more control.
- Do not tell the Board that what you propose will be invisible, unless it is really true. How could it be truly invisible? It could be, if it is below the tops of trees, if it is blocked by trees, or if it is set against a backdrop of trees that go higher up a slope. On the other hand, you can always say that people really don't spend time looking up, that it will quickly become a routine feature, that it will go away when you move (a condition you'll gladly accept), and that the impact is limited. All construction has some impact and this proposal has an acceptable impact, within the bylaw or ordinance.

On the other hand, the following is true and can help you:

- Be respectful (not belligerent)—even when asked a question that is designed to enrage you (such as: "Nobody really needs this, right? It's just a hobby, right?").
- Amateur Radio, while it may not be familiar to the Board, does offer a public service, and your station will be available as a resource in times of public emergency.
- Amateur Radio has a legal position that is favored by the legislature and the Congress.
- Your activities are in the public interest.
- All elements of the bylaw or ordinance for this request have been met.
- It will be safe.

Here are some words of wisdom from Jim Idelson, K1IR, concerning zoning for tower(s):

> A few comments on my experience in dealing with the town authorities and the value of having the right attitude . . . When I faced the local Zoning Board of Appeals with my tower permit application, the whole room was filled with neighbors who were opposed to it. We [K1VR, Esq and I] won the permit under very difficult conditions for the following reasons:
>
> 1. Our homework was done. We had answers prepared for every potential question. As each question was asked during the hearings, a carefully written document was submitted to the record in response. No information was omitted or exaggerated in any way. Every fact presented was supportable.
>
> 2. We listened carefully to the specific concerns raised by the opponents—and responded to every issue. We demonstrated a high degree of flexibility. We did not, however, compromise our most

important requirements—the height and the types of antennas to be installed.

3. We cooperated fully with the members of the Zoning Board of Appeals. We considered every question carefully. We showed respect for each individual and his position. We provided every piece of information requested immediately. When the Board members came to the house for a site visit, they were treated to a complete tour of the property, which included clearly marked locations of several potential tower sites and guy anchors as well as trees marked with their measured heights for reference.

4. Our primary opponent made us look good. The most vociferous opposition came from one of my neighbors. He is an attorney. Fortunately, not a very good one. His attitude was extremely offensive to the Board. After making many unreasonable arguments and showing a lack of respect for the Board and its process, he was asked to be seated because his " . . . input was no longer needed . . ." The other neighbors were somewhat embarrassed at this point because they had chosen to allow him to lead their opposition to my application. He essentially showed that a bad attitude can drive your case in exactly the wrong direction.

5. I extended an olive branch to the entire neighborhood in my closing remarks—letting them know that I didn't hold their opposition against them, and that whatever the outcome, I would continue to be a good neighbor—and that I would expect the same of them. I believe the Board saw this as a mature gesture, which only added to the long list of positives for our case.

Bottom Line:

During deliberations, Board members commented on the "quality of the presentation by the applicant." They were also impressed with the fact that I had dealt directly and honestly with the neighbors.

Had we presented the same case and all the facts with "an attitude" we would most certainly have been *denied*. Instead, I now have both an 80-foot tower in my backyard and a neighborhood that gets along just fine.

Thanks to K1VR for outstanding legal advice, and to my family and the local ham community for moral support.

From Bill Sohl, K2UNK, ARRL Local Government Liaison (and Councilman for Mt. Olive Township, NJ), here is some solid, positive advice:

A little free advice for those working with municipal government officials: "You'll catch more flies with honey than with vinegar." Be nice. Be agreeable. As someone very knowledgeable once said, "Be wise as serpents, gentle as doves." Know your stuff, but don't throw it in their faces.

I am an elected official myself. Remember, like it or not, the officials hold all the cards and even if you

are right, you can waste much time, effort and $$$ fighting to get your way if you take an acrimonious attitude. You don't have to kiss up— just be polite, open and willing to listen.

Show them (as early in the process as you can) how you can offer a workable compromise that allows them to save face, yet preserve the local resources of Amateur Radio. Show them what a resource it is, and give them just a taste of the depth of technical, electronic considerations that go into an efficient, non-interfering amateur station. Be sure they are the ones who "figure out" the solution for your tower or antenna needs that you are trying to lead them towards. Don't force them (by your abrasive attitude) to dig in their heels.

Remember, they are political and trying to represent those who will keep them in power. Living with your neighbors means compromise for everyone, except maybe a dictator. Most officials are willing to consider alternatives. Be sure you are too. Don't try to be a bully. It won't work!

Mike Lazaroff, K3AIR, adds:

Like Bill Sohl, I also am a local elected official and agree wholeheartedly with the advice given. We try to be reasonable and fair with all applicants, no matter what they want to do, but everybody is much more satisfied with the outcome when people don't come in with an arrogant, "know-it-all" attitude. You'll find that most people are a lot more reasonable than you'd expect if you make an honest effort to be co-operative.

Finally, some notes from Jim Idelson, K1IR:

November 3, 1998
Lessons Learned from the Sudbury, MA Experience:

- The nomenclature sheet was useful. [Fig 8-2 and CD-ROM, filename: **Antenna Nomenclature.PDF**—*Ed.*]
- It would be nice to have articles to hand out when the question comes up in which ham radio is described as quaint, or perhaps unnecessary in this era of modern technology and the Internet.
- *Recent* articles, showing what hams did in the most recent crisis or hurricane or flood are necessary to prove that the emergency aspects are still vibrant.
- It would be a good idea to include one triband Yagi as an example of the antenna—so that specifics such as 2-inch boom and 3/4-inch elements will always be in front of the Board, but emphasize that you are applying for what the tower will hold, as experimentation is inherent in Amateur Radio.
- Get a number as to how many towers there are nationwide. Include TV antenna towers. This would help to show that they are in all sorts of neighborhoods.
- Be prepared to show that certain people have no sight line.
- Don't screw around with the height. Tell them the height of the tower and the height to the top of the mast. Otherwise it will come out painfully.
- Only photos of the woods in winter will ultimately satisfy questioners as to whether it will be a problem in winter.
- Always close with the bylaw test to be applied and exactly what you are asking for.
- In the closing, emphasize that, with time, the offensive-

ness evaporates.
- Offer to plant evergreens as appropriate to block view of base.
- Always volunteer the anti-climbing device, and bring a photo.
- The best use of hams in town is to have them show up and not say anything. Just put them up front and tell them to keep quiet.

Inviting other hams to attend has its pros and cons.

- You don't want to be seen as the guy who brought a riot to the meeting.
- You don't want an invited ham to sing off key; ie, to say something which contravenes the very carefully thought-out position that you've put together.
- Out-of-town observers (speakers are usually asked to say their names and addresses) are heavily discounted, unless such a person is an expert. Boards tend to look on this hearing as a town matter.

Thus, the following good ideas:

- If hams come, ask that they leave the call letter hats at home. It is disrespectful to wear a hat indoors anyway. Other indicia attire may only look, to the untrained eye, like they are members of a motorcycle gang.
- Most hams will not help your legal arguments. Ask them to do their best to remain silent.
- Ask your friends to get there early and take seats. This forces the NIMBYs (a NIMBY is a person who is there to say: "Not in my back yard") to stand, to tire and to leave early.
- Hams who live in town are, however, usually useful, as they may actually know the bylaw, the Board members and some history.

CONTINUANCES

There are several reasons why a Board may decide to continue your hearing until the next session. This is called a *continuance*. There are some subtleties to consider.

- The Board may want the continuance because you submitted a big pile of information at the last minute (within a few days of the hearing or that very evening). In this case it is perfectly reasonable for them to continue the hearing to absorb the material. You can sometimes avoid this situation by submitting your ton of information well in advance. Yet this is sometimes impossible. So you must live with the continuance.
- If you have retained a lawyer, the continuance will add to your expense. You are now asking your lawyer to show up twice. This is another reason to get your materials in early.
- Some states have a maximum number of days between the date of the original submission of the Building Permit application, or the date of the original appeal to the Board, and the date by which the board must render a decision in writing, or else the appeal is granted. This creates an interesting dynamic.
- You may be asked to agree to the continuance. If you do, the number of days until the hearing continues will be "tacked onto" the present end date. The tension here is that if you refuse to agree to a continuance, the Board can

become irritated with you and not give you any breaks.
- If the continuance is due to your late submission of information, or because you want to supplement the record, you should agree to it. If the continuance is because they are going to ask Town Counsel for ways to torpedo your application, you should not agree to it.
- In particular, if you hear the Board discussing the real meaning of the Williams decision (the Federal Circuit Court case that held that a town may balance the interests of the town with the interests of the radio ham), and they appear to be looking for time to solicit advice from Town Counsel on how to use the Williams case against you, *do not* agree to the continuance. It will just extend the time and you are going to lose. Make them decide more quickly, as this increases the likelihood that they will write something in the opinion that will make it easy to appeal and win! The Williams case was wrongly decided and it is pretty easy to see that the FCC had this particular case in mind when it issued DA 99-2565 to make the intentions of the FCC even more plain.
- If the continuance is to allow a site visit so that they can resolve for themselves a fact situation, then you must stress that you are only agreeing to the continuance for the purpose of the site visit, but the public comment portion of the hearing should be closed. This can be good, if the facts are in your favor. A typical example: You say that your antennas will not be visible from the neighbor's bedroom window, because there is 200 feet of thick forest in between. The neighbor says that your antennas will dominate his view. By all means, agree to a continuance for the purpose of a site visit. Let the Board see that the neighbor is a liar.
- You could also agree to a continuance solely for the purpose of submitting additional written materials. If possible, try to avoid a continuance of the public portion. This gives your neighbors a chance to organize and develop a real head of steam—by getting petitions, dragooning neighbors to appear and testify against you and so forth. Since you don't want an angry mob of neighbors appearing the next time, if they weren't there the first time, do your best to avoid a continuation of the public portion of the hearing. Here are some arguments you may use:
  1. You've assembled a team of experts to appear on your behalf, the meeting had fully published notice and it is simply not fair for you to be forced to bring your witnesses back again. This is especially true because your lawyer, engineer, professor, whatever, came in from out of town and cannot be there to rebut testimony the next time, due to the distance or a scheduling conflict, or both. Even hostile Boards want a fair hearing, since it makes it harder to overturn their decision against you.
  2. Everything they need can be submitted in writing. There is no need for a further Public Hearing.
  3. Amateur Radio is a public service. You get no revenue from this use. It is unfair to make you pay your lawyer for an additional hearing. Can't any additional

information required be obtained by a site visit or submitted in writing?

SUBMITTING A PROPOSED DECISION AND ORDER

It is hard to understand why, in cases such as this, Boards do not simply ask the Applicant, who is going to be granted a permit anyway, to submit a proposed decision and order. But they don't. However, if the Board has decided in your favor and is fumbling with the question of who is going to write the opinion and order, you should volunteer to submit a proposed decision and order. Here's a sample based on a real decision, with only the names changed. It is included on the CD-ROM, as **Proposed Decision & Order.DOC**.

DECISION OF THE BOARD OF APPEALS UNDER
ZONING BYLAW §_____
TOWN OF FRIENDLYVILLE, STATE
UPON THE PETITION OF APPLICANT
#0016SP GRANTED

A meeting of the Board was held in Town Hall, commencing at 6:00 PM on ___day of week_____, ___month___ __, 200_. There were present: Name 1 , Chairman; Name 2, Clerk; Name 3, Name 4 and Name 5, Members.

Pursuant to public notice in the ___ [name of newspaper], a newspaper of general circulation in the Town of Friendlyville, published on __Month 19 & 26, 200 , and pursuant to notice sent by mail, postage prepaid, to all interested parties in accordance with the provisions of State General Laws, a Public Hearing was held on the petition of *Harry Ham* filed on __Month_____, 200_, for a variance from the requirements of Article ___, Section ____ of the Zoning Bylaw and a special permit under Article ____, Sections _____ of the Zoning Bylaw to allow the Applicant to erect and maintain an Amateur-Radio antenna-support structure and appurtenant antennas.

Premises affected are located at _____address____, Friendlyville, ___, in a Single Residence A District, shown on Assessor's Map #_____ as Lot #_____.

Attorney Fred Hopengarten of Lincoln, MA, represented Petitioner at the Public Hearing. Dr. Ham seeks a special permit under Section _____ of the Friendlyville Zoning Bylaw to construct an Amateur-Radio antenna-support structure and appurtenant antennas. Due to the proposed siting, the Applicant also needs a variance from the setback requirements of Section _____ that requires that the structure not be erected nearer to any property line than a distance equal to its vertical height.

Attorney Hopengarten and Dr. Ham submitted extensive documentation by way of maps, path profiles, plans, photographs and technical data in support of the application. Dr. Ham is an experienced (he has been licensed by the FCC for ____ years) amateur-radio operator and he holds the highest-class license for a non-commercial operation. The structure will be sited in the rear yard (what is technically the side yard, although to all appearances it would look like it is in the rear yard). Dense, mature trees envelop the site. The nearest neighbor's house is at least ___ feet away. Only two (2) trees will be removed, leaving hundreds left.

Dr. Ham explained that the structure would be anchored by three (3) sets of ³/₄″ guy wires and that in the event of failure, such a structure collapses within the radii of the guy wires. Even if the structure were literally to fall over, it would not strike any abutters' houses because it is too short and because it would most likely be "caught" by the thick tree

growth. *[If applicable, add that it will fall entirely within the Applicant's yard, that no house is within a distance equal to the height, or other facts that are in the Applicant's favor.]*

The variance has been requested because the most favorable location for the structure does not quite meet the setback requirements referred to above and is about _____ feet, (__) feet short of the bylaw's mandate. When asked why he needed a ____ foot high structure, Dr. Ham explained that to reduce the height would reduce and negate his ability to effectively communicate by amateur radio. He reminded the Board that the current by-law allows for support structures of up to ____ feet, and that FCC and FAA law generally allow heights of up to 200 feet before special procedures must be followed, but that he is requesting a support structure with the minimum height necessary to accomplish his goals.

In all other respects, the proposed antenna-support structure complies with the design standards set forth in the applicable bylaw.

Petitioner submitted a letter of support from the Friendlyville Chief of Police *[Director of Civil Defense]* as well as several abutters and neighbors. Some neighbors opposed the application, citing what they felt would be a negative visual impact and reduced property values. In that regard, Mrs. _____, a licensed and experienced real estate broker, *[alternative: the Applicant]* produced and submitted hard data which indicate that the existence of this type of structure does not impact negatively on property values or resale prices.

It must also be kept in mind that both state and Federal law restrict a municipality's ability to arbitrarily ban or restrict these structures.

The Board voted to continue the hearing to its October meeting and it took a view of the site on ____month_____, 200_ after which it deliberated.

Finding that the proposed facility would not be detrimental to the town or neighborhood and that it could actually serve the public interest, the Board unanimously voted to grant the special permit.

The Board also found that there exists a hardship to the Petitioner owing to the shape and topography of his lot and the location of the existing structures and that such hardship especially affects his property but not generally the neighborhood in which it is located. Further, the Board determined that it could grant the requested relief without substantial detriment to the public good and without nullifying or substantially derogating from the intent or purpose of the Zoning Bylaw. Accordingly, the Board unanimously voted to grant the application for a variance from the setback requirements of the Bylaw.

The structure must be sited and constructed in substantial conformance with the plans and specifications submitted with the application and shall otherwise comply with the letter and spirit of Section _____.

Member 3 was not present at the deliberation meeting so did not vote.

Name 1, Chairman
Name 2, Clerk
Name 3, Member
Name 4, Member
Name 5, Member

Dated: ____Month_____, 200_

THE VIEWING

The Board may decide that, before making a decision, it wishes to visit the site and see for itself how tall the trees may be, how good or bad the view may be, etc. There are several things about "the Viewing" or the "Site Visit" that you should know.

Opportunity for Argument

Yes, when the Board shows up on your property, you may think that you will have that extra moment to show just what a brilliant orator you are, holding forth with a captive audience while waving your hands. Dream on.

First, the visit is likely to last only a few minutes. Unless your Board is different from most, they will not be there long enough to have a cup of coffee. Furthermore, they don't want your cup of coffee—for reasons of the appearance of impropriety, delay or whatever.

Second, this is not part of the Public Hearing, so they shouldn't want to hear any argument. The most you can do is point and say: "This is north." "Mr. Jones lives there." "The property line is marked by that pin with the blue cap." "The piece of wood stuck in the ground with the top painted orange is the proposed site." And so forth.

Furthermore, if you start to engage in oral argument on the spot, and an opposing neighbor is present (as the opposing neighbor has every right to be under your state's "government in the sunshine" act, even though it would otherwise be trespassing on your land), you've really opened up the chance for the neighbors to start arguing all over again. This will remind the Board just how much your project is opposed. Arguing at the viewing is rarely in your best interest.

What do you do if an opponent starts arguing first? First, point out that this is not part of the Public Hearing and that the Board should not be hearing argument. This accomplishes the point of making it plain that you are law abiding and the opponent is not. Second, ask the Board members present if you should respond. From there, if you are asked to respond, or you just can't help yourself, speak briefly. Since this is a viewing, these are daylight hours and the Board is composed of volunteers who would rather be at home mowing the lawn or watching a football game. They want to get out of there.

However, here are some tips on preparing for the viewing.

- Get rid of "slash." You may have moved in recently, you may have cut some branches recently. No matter how all those dead branches came to be in your back yard, get rid of them. There is no need to remind the Board that you may cut down some more trees or branches to accommodate the structure or guy wires. The presence of slash would do that.
- Clean up the yard so that no one could get hurt. You are arguing that you will construct the project safely. Why would you want to leave out ladders, shovels or other tools that someone could trip over?
- Cover any holes. You wouldn't leave an open hole into which someone could fall, would you?
- Take the trash to the dump before they arrive. Some people equate neat construction with safe construction. While the essential truth of this equation may be tested, there is simply no need for it to become an issue.

- Plant flags or wooden sticks (a pointy 1 × 3-inch pine stick often used by builders to show boundaries or mark a driveway is a useful tool) to show where the support structure will go, where the guy wires will go, and if not otherwise marked, to show where boundaries are located. This will allow you to just say: "The orange painted 1 × 3 is where the structure will go. The unpainted 1 × 3's are where the guy wires will go." Thus you can do less talking, which is generally good, especially if a neighbor is blathering on and repeating himself or herself.

THE PRESS

The Interview

At some point a reporter may approach you. Prepare for it now by asking yourself the questions that a reporter will ask you: Who? What? Where? When? Why? Figure out the answers you want to give and stick to them. But first, a story:

One cold morning, two boys were playing hockey at the Frog Pond on Boston Common, when all of a sudden a pit bull appeared out of nowhere and attacked one of the boys. The second boy, thinking quickly, stuck his hockey stick under the dog's collar and twisted it, breaking the dog's neck and killing it.

A reporter who happened to be walking by saw this event and hurried over to get the story. "Young Bruins fan saves friend from vicious dog!" he began writing in his notebook.

"But I'm not a Bruins fan," protested the boy. "Oh, I'm sorry," replied the reporter, scratching out his initial headline. "Brave Red Sox fan heroically rescues friend from horrific attack!" the reporter wrote anew.

"But I'm not a Red Sox fan either," the boy protested again. "My mistake," said the reporter, "I just assumed that here in Boston everyone was either a Bruins or Red Sox fan. Never mind, though. What team do you like?" "I'm a Yankees fan," the boy said proudly.

The reporter disgustedly turned the page in his notebook and wrote furiously, "Little bastard from New York kills beloved family pet."

Now what is the point of this story, besides a gratuitous slap at the fourth estate? It is that there is a strong likelihood that you are from out-of-town (moving in and seeking to erect an antenna system) and that you are a minority (hams are only about 400,000 of the 270,000,000 people in the USA, or way less than 1%). You cannot rely on a reporter to put *your* best face forward. A local weekly newspaper is usually the place where young, inexperienced reporters get a start. In addition, always remember that they became reporters because they were good with words, not science. Keep that in mind. Now, on to the usual questions.

Who?

Decide how you would like to be called in the article. The reporter is likely to ask you how to spell your name. If you spell L-A-W-R-E-N-C-E, you will be called Lawrence in the article. It will also avoid an entire article in which you are called Laurence. If you spell L-A-R-R-Y, you will be called Larry in the article. Don't insist on getting your call sign into the article. It will only make the reporter think you are even more of a geek than he or she already thinks.

What?

The building code calls it an "antenna-support structure." Call it a *structure* for short. Don't call it a "tower." It doesn't much matter whether you call it "ham radio" or "Amateur Radio." The reporter will probably use both, just to vary the text. Call what's on top an "antenna," not a "beam." Beam conjures up the idea of being zapped or transported, as in "Beam me up, Scotty." Not a good phrase.

Where?

If it is the truth, keep talking about the location as "in the woods," not "in my backyard."

When?

If you are an experienced ham, licensed for a long time, use that to convey that this is not a novel experiment and that you know what you are doing.

Why?

Emphasize public service. Sorry, my reporter friends, but that's mostly what the public will understand. DXCC on 40 meters just isn't easily understandable to outsiders. But your need for a good antenna for reliable communications with sailboats at sea is understandable.

Finally, remember that reporters have deadlines. Delay, and the story will feature your opponents, if you have them, without your side. "The applicant could not be reached," does not help your cause.

The Photos

If your case has stirred up a local storm, the paper will want a photo of an existing structure. We are now on dangerous ground, for technical reasons. There is a chance that your own 4 × 6-inch color photos of your former structure (if you had one erected at your former home) will be rejected because they don't scan well. This excuse is, however, also a reason to reject your photos because they "don't tell an interesting story."

Closer to the truth is that the paper employs photographers, and your own photos were "not invented here." Nonetheless, it is in your best interest to suggest where to find an antenna-support structure in your area, rather than letting the paper's photographer loose to run wild. If that happens, the paper may run a photo accompanying your story of the local 1400-foot broadcast tower, eight-feet wide all the way up and visible for miles. The caption could be: "The WBZ-TV tower, similar to the one Joe Ham seeks to erect in his backyard." You don't want that.

So, if you are going to erect a Tri-Ex, Rohn SSV or Rohn 25G structure, tell the newspaper where to find a similar antenna—in the woods if possible—and give them an exact address and directions. If you have applied for a second or subsequent structure on your own property, point out that the controversy is not how it looks from your backyard but how

it looks from the home of a particular complaining neighbor. Send the photographer to that neighbor. The farther away the photo is taken, the better off you are, due to the granularity of reproduction of a halftone. (This means that the farther away the photographer gets from those thin tower legs, the more they will look like a pencil line in the photo.)

Whatever you do, do not agree to pose in front of an existing structure. When the photo of you in the foreground is taken, the camera will be almost on the ground. You will look like The Jolly Green Giant™, and the structure will loom large, with a bad view. This is a view not available to members of the public and is not the view about which anyone will complain.

That's totally unfair. Don't let them do it to you! One way to avoid such a photo is to say that you will not pose "in front of" your existing structure or outdoors at all. That's your privilege.

The Letter to the Editor

OK, the first hearing is over, the article has come out and the editorial has railed against you. What do you do? The temptation is to write a letter to the editor in which you tell the editor that the reporter:

- Is a poor excuse for a human being.
- Promised to tell your side of the story with compassion.
- Misrepresented something you said.
- Got your call sign wrong.
- And so forth.

Resist that temptation. If the article was small, had no photo and only a few neighbors are raging against you, leave it alone. The result of your letter may be a follow-up article and a photo, because now the newspaper has a genuine controversy and a guarantee that even more people will come out to the second hearing. You don't want that.

If it is a small fire, keep it a small fire. Furthermore, you will find that some neighbors just wanted to vent against you. Perhaps your kid bit their dog, or they once had TVI from a CBer at a former home. It doesn't matter. Once having had the chance to "vent" their feelings, Mr and Mrs Neighbor will go home and not return to a second hearing—because they've had their say. You may also be able to placate them between a first and a second hearing.

However, what you don't want to do is to cause your application to become a *cause celebre*. If you absolutely must write a letter to the editor, do not tell him:

- That this is newsworthy (this brings out the photographer)
- That his reporter is a lying dog (this brings out staff loyalty)
- That the Editor is trying to rule the world from the editorial page (of course he is).

The old expression is: "Never get into an argument with someone who buys ink by the barrel."

So what do you do? Make one or two, not more, affirmative points that are part of the story you are trying to sell. For example:

- "For those who wonder what such an antenna system will look like, there is an existing one on Old County Road, two blocks west of Main. Though your readers may have never noticed it, it has been there for 20 years."
- "Concerning claims that such a system will lower property values, I suggest that they drive by Old County Road, two blocks west of Main. Every home in the neighborhood sells for more than $350,000, so it will probably come as a surprise to people that their homes have been negatively impacted in price."
- "While the claim has been made that Amateur Radio is just a hobby, I call your attention to ____ *[name a recent public-relations triumph for Amateur Radio by watching W1AW Bulletins or the ARRL Web "Amateur Radio News"*

column], where the storm took out power, cell phones and 911 were jammed, and the Governor of that state cited radio hams for their excellent work supporting disaster-relief teams."

This is an old story that is always renewed when the next disaster strikes. The best ways to get a story printed are to keep it short, to add something to the discussion and not to attack any person. A long letter will be edited for length anyway.

So, before you send it off, ask your wife and a friend to review the letter. Make them move quickly, however, because if you are dealing with a weekly local paper it is easy to miss the deadline and become "old news."

9

Deliberations and Decisions

Whew, the Public Hearing is over. The tradition is that you gather somewhere—down the hall or out in the parking lot—out of earshot of the other side. You may want to call someone a liar or describe someone else as playing fast and loose with the facts. It's natural. You want to replay the ballgame.

Don't do it within earshot of anyone else. Nothing good can come of that. The local newspaper reporter could report what you say. You could give away an essential fact that is against your interest to disclose. You could threaten someone. (Don't do that!)

Another possibility is that the reporter from the local newspaper, who covers week after week of dull meetings, is all excited and rushes over to you to ask some questions. If you have a lawyer, let your lawyer answer the questions. If you don't have a lawyer, be pleasant and do not say anything that you did not say during the hearing. A real danger is that you could say something that could wind up in the paper before the Board has met to vote on its decision.

Back at your group meeting, remember that your lawyer charges by the hour. He's human and is only too happy to replay the game too, but you aren't going to get much benefit from his thinking after the first 20 minutes or so. However, there is one exception. Let's say you have gathered a team—an engineer, surveyor, a close friend who has been useful and the lawyer. Let's say that you need to map another strategy, perhaps to reapply for a different site on your property or perhaps to strategize your appeal. It will be hard and expensive to get them together again. If you need to talk, leave town hall immediately and go to some place

where you can have coffee and take notes—perhaps at your own home.

The next day, people are going to ask how it went. People who were there may ask what you are going to do next. It is really easy to say something inappropriate responding to these questions, so be careful.

IF YOU WON

If you won, don't gloat. Don't tell the newspaper reporter that the folks on the other side were a bunch of idiots, or that they lied or misrepresented things. You don't want to say such things because it is never a good idea to anger your enemy.

Be gracious. If you don't know how, here is a sample sound bite: "I'm pleased that the Board supported the application. I understand that in an adversary situation they have to make tough decisions. Now, I just want to put up my antennas and do what I've always done, preparing for and handling emergency communications—only this time with a better antenna system. I'll bet that in a year or two from now, the neighbors will have forgotten that my antenna system is even there."

Don't say anything that will cause the Board to rewrite the favorable decision that is coming. Here is an example of something stupid that you could do. "Now that I've got the permit, I'm going to cut down all the trees in the yard and pave it over."

If you say such a thing and the Board hears about it, they may decide to add a condition requiring you to come back to them every time you need to cut the grass. Of course the remark and the response are exaggerations, but you get the idea.

Another thing: Please don't walk out of the hearing saying: "Boy, we really pulled the wool over the eyes of those dummies." Do I have to explain why?

Well, I will explain. Remember: "It ain't over until it's over." The actual decision isn't written yet. That will be done by one member, or perhaps by the secretary to the Board. The Board must still reconvene to sign the decision. In some jurisdictions the Board may have 30, 60 or even 90 days to issue a decision. They'll have a lot of time to figure out a way to pay you back for any belittling remarks that filter their way back to them.

IF YOU LOST

Don't insult the Board and don't insult your opponents. Don't insult the Board because it is likely that you are going to be back in front of them again sometime. You may have to come up with a different plan and then go back to them. When you do, you'd like to be treated courteously and you'd like to be successful.

Or you may appeal, win that appeal and get a "remand" order that sends you back to the Board with instructions for them to reconsider in the light of the new court decision. Should that happen, you could wind up again in front of the same people you insulted three months ago.

Remember, these people are volunteers. They are not paid to take insults. They don't work in the NBA, where referees are paid to listen to hoots, whistles and catcalls. Unlike the referee, who can't take it out on the man who is booing him, the Board can and will find a way to vent their anger on an arrogant and ungrateful applicant. So be nice. Be respectful, just like your mother taught you to be.

Also, be kind to your neighbors. After all, you still have to live with them. If you must return to the Board with another plan or appeal, you don't want your neighbors to be so angry that they really do a lot of homework, hire a lawyer and try to crush you in the next Public Hearing.

In victory or defeat, it always pays to be nice to your opponents. Remember that.

10

Now Get the Permit and Build Your Antenna System!

Congratulations! You've been granted a Special Permit or perhaps a Variance. Can you put up your tower now? No. What you really have now is permission to go to the Building Inspector (your new best friend). If you never needed a Special Permit or Variance, you still need to read this chapter.

THE PROCESS

The Application

The typical Building Permit application is fairly simple, normally demanding no more than you have already assembled for any Public Hearing. If you didn't have to go through a Public Hearing and you are applying directly for a Building Permit, you will still find that you must supply many of the same items found in the generic permit application found in Chapter 7.

If you haven't already done so, it is now time to make a formal call on the Building Inspector to discuss what he or she needs before signing the permit. Assemble what is requested and file it, pronto! Be sure to get a date stamp on the filing, and keep a copy of the stamped filing.

After the Building Permit is granted, do not lose it! The original is very important, since typically the Building Inspector wants to see it posted by the work so s/he can sign the original at each inspection.

Posting

Now that you have the permit, you'll notice that it says something like: "Post at worksite." Let's consider this requirement. Should you post it in your front yard, near the street where passersby can see it? Or should you post it near the work in your backyard, deep in the woods?

If you have the luxury of a place to put the Building Permit where it is less likely, or unlikely, to be seen by the public, that's what you should do. Do what is required and no more. There will always be someone who never knew about your Special Permit or Variance proceeding. Reduce the chances that this person can learn about the project until the *fait accompli* stage, if possible.

At the start of your project, you cannot hang it from the structure, since you haven't even dug the first hole in the ground yet. So step about eight feet away from the proposed base site, and pound a 1×3 or 2×4-inch post into the ground. The post should be tall enough to go down one foot and up two or three feet above the highest snow you expect during the winter.

Mount the Building Permit on the post in a plastic bag, a page protector or the like (open side *down*). This will keep it from getting wet. Many Building Inspectors like to make efficient use of their field time and they will not necessarily schedule a visit with you. Instead, the Building Inspector may just drop by after you've told him that you are ready for the next inspection. Thus, the Building Inspector wants to drop by, take a look, sign the posted permit and leave. For this reason, *do not keep the permit indoors*.

Inspections

Since few Building Inspectors have a great deal of

experience with the construction of antenna-support structures, you'll have to negotiate a bit on exactly what inspections will be required. Ask the Building Inspector to cross out and initial several of the boxes, such as "plumbing" or "electrical." Why be so formal? Sadly, the Inspector could get hit by a bus or fired. You want the next Inspector to know exactly where to pick up the ball. See **Fig 10-1**, which shows my original Building Permit issued in 1982.

The usual permit calls for inspections:

- To see holes at the correct depth (for a guyed structure, that's four holes—the base and three anchors), the stones at the bottom, the "Dobie Bricks" (usually available at Home Depot in the section near the concrete mixers) so that your rebar won't stick down into dirt and the rebar (neatly tied with wire).
- To see that the concrete has been poured and finished. This means going about six inches up for the base, and staying below grade and backfilling for the anchors—but follow the directions of your structure's manufacturer.
- To see the finished structure and to see that it is properly grounded. For this inspection, you should have the safety wires on the anchor turnbuckles, the anti-climbing device (if one is required) and so forth.

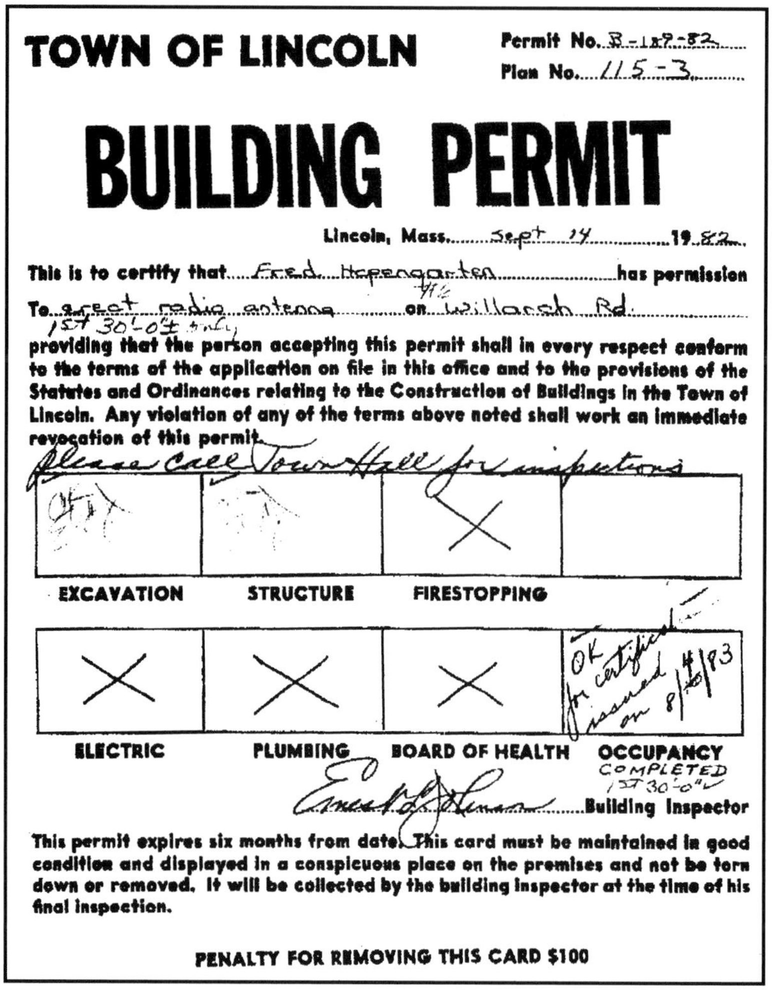

TOWN OF LINCOLN

Permit No. B-189-82
Plan No. 115-3

BUILDING PERMIT

Lincoln, Mass. Sept 14 1982

This is to certify that Fred Hopengarten has permission To erect radio antenna on Willarch Rd. 1st 30'-0" only providing that the person accepting this permit shall in every respect conform to the terms of the application on file in this office and to the provisions of the Statutes and Ordinances relating to the Construction of Buildings in the Town of Lincoln. Any violation of any of the terms above noted shall work an immediate revocation of this permit.

Please call Town Hall for inspections

EXCAVATION | STRUCTURE | FIRESTOPPING

ELECTRIC | PLUMBING | BOARD OF HEALTH | OCCUPANCY

OK for certificate issued on 8/4/83
COMPLETED 1st 30'-0"

Building Inspector

This permit expires six months from date. This card must be maintained in good condition and displayed in a conspicuous place on the premises and not be torn down or removed. It will be collected by the building inspector at the time of his final inspection.

PENALTY FOR REMOVING THIS CARD $100

Fig 10-1—K1VR's original Building Permit.

At each inspection the Building Inspector should simply initial and date the appropriate box. After the last inspection, the Building Inspector may let you keep the permit or he may want it for his file. In any event, you want a copy for your file, to prove dates. Since you may not be there when he makes the last inspection, make a photocopy before you invite the Building Inspector to make the last inspection, then go to work on securing a Certificate of Completion.

Construction Tips

Don't give your unfriendly neighbors a reason to go screaming to the Building Inspector. This is another way of saying: "Don't give the Building Inspector a reason to doubt your good faith or ability to build the project correctly and safely." Here are some tips:

- When you cut down trees, get the slash out of the way. You don't want the neighbors to go complaining that you are raping the forest. Make neat piles of firewood. Don't leave any wood where it could later interfere with the pouring of concrete or the handling of ropes during construction (as you go vertical).
- When you dig a hole in the ground, cover it before leaving the site—even just overnight. If you are going to bury cables in PVC pipe (or conduit), close up the trench as you go so that no one twists an ankle.
- When you pour concrete in the winter, cover it with straw and a tarpaulin, to aid proper curing. When you pour concrete in the summer, spray it with water to help the cure.
- When you install ground rod(s), make sure there are no sharp bends in the ground wire(s). When you run the guy wires to the anchor points, either protect them with guy guards (see Chapter 6) or plant bushes, so that no one will run into them accidentally. Before the bushes are planted, put construction orange tape on guy wires as flags, to make them visible.
- Don't leave rotator cable or feed lines dangling across your yard at a height that could catch someone in the neck or face, should he be outdoors walking at night.
- Don't run 110 V ac to the base of the tower without an electrical permit (and inspection). If you decide to run 110 V ac to the base of the tower, use a GFI socket to detect a ground fault interruption.

The Certificate of Completion

When the project is completed, invite the Building Inspector back for the final inspection. This is a point in the process where it can be easy to let a few things slip. These things are so easy to do that now is not the time to get sloppy. I'll explain why in a minute.

Don't let it slide. Keep a signed copy and be sure it has a

date on it to prove that the structure was built within two years from the grant of the original permit (or whatever your state requires), and to prove that it was built before the Town may have changed a bylaw—to grant you the status of a *prior existing structure*. Remember that we have always insisted you call it a structure? This is one of the reasons. The law surrounding this subject matter is called the law of prior existing structures.

If, for whatever reason, you must get a renewal, or a subsequent inspection a year later (or two or three), this is the time to get an agreement from the Building Inspector about when that subsequent renewal or inspection should take place. Will it be on the anniversary of the grant of the permit, the anniversary of the Certificate of Completion or some other time? Put it in a memo to yourself and write it in your calendar. It is very embarrassing not to know when your permit is up for renewal. It can also be devastating.

If your renewal date comes and goes and the bylaw has changed, you could wind up with a prior existing structure for which you no longer have a permit. This could require you to reapply and, if everything is going badly for you in this life, you might be forced to reapply under any new bylaw that may have passed since you were granted your original permit. This is not a good thing.

When the blessed day comes that you have completed your construction for the purposes of the building permit (this awkward phrase represents the fact that no ham has ever completed his antenna installation—as there is always another experiment to perform), it is time for you to seek out from the Building Inspector a Certificate of Completion. Similar to a Certificate of Occupancy, this certificate serves several purposes:

1. It tells your insurance company that you built the project according to the building code, and if the system should ever suffer, for whatever reason, it could prove helpful in filing your insurance claim. Among other reasons, it tells the adjuster that you did not have a "phantom" system upon which you are now trying to make a fraudulent claim.
2. It serves to show that you had completed construction and your system had become a prior existing use before any subsequent bylaw changes.
3. It can be shown to any neighbor who wants to know if what you've put up is "safe." Should you need it for this purpose, however, be gentle. It never pays to make an enemy of your neighbor. Some readers may have passing familiarity with the expression: "Love thy neighbor."

Here are some real life examples of Certificates of Completion, issued in letter form, where only the identifying information has been changed. If your building department doesn't have a form, type up something based on the concepts below and ask the Building Inspector to sign it. These form letters are on the CD-ROM, under filename: **Building Inspector Form Letters.DOC**.

Dear Mr. Ham:

Construction under Building Permit # _____ having been completed in accordance with its terms and conditions, this Certificate of Use is hereby granted on _____(date)_____.

(Signature)
Name
Building Commissioner/Inspector

or

Mr. Ham,

It is my opinion, as Building Commissioner for the Town of xxxxx, that the antenna-support structure located on the approved site plan and constructed on your property at [address] Street conforms to the xxxxx Zoning By-Laws and the [name of state] State Building Code regulations.

This letter is the final affidavit for the tower as permitted.

Sincerely,

(Signature)
Name
Building Commissioner

Once you've got that Certificate of Completion in hand, make a photocopy and put it in your file. In addition, you might consider taking a photograph of the structure with a child or two (or three, or four would be even better) around the base. This makes it easy to demonstrate later *when* the structure was erected, should an argument ever erupt. You could even mail such a photograph to yourself as a postcard, to get a postmark. Put the originals in your safety deposit box. Relax, smile, and enjoy your hamming.

After a few days of hamming, make up your mind to reestablish relationships with your neighbors. You'll want to do this for several reasons:

- It is the right thing to do—after all, you will still be neighbors. You don't want them to poison your children at Halloween, do you? It is also what your religion tells you to do.
- You don't want them to go running to the Building Inspector every time you change from a triband Yagi to a log periodic antenna. Permanent war is no fun.
- You may one day want to erect a satellite dish, a second tower, a swimming pool cabana, a tennis court—who knows? You don't want to go to war all over again because you never smoothed those feathers.
- And finally, there is always the possibility that your town requires a renewal at some point in the game. That will be covered in detail in the next chapter.

The point? Make your enemy your friend. It may sound like Zen, but the concept will permit you, your spouse and children to return to a state of neighborhood tranquility.

Awkward Post-Permit Situations

CONSTRUCTION PROBLEMS

In towns where a ham-radio antenna system may be constructed without a special exception, special-use permit or the like, a neighbor may first find out about construction of your system when you begin constructing it. This can sometimes cause a flurry of activity on his/her part. If you are afraid that a neighbor may go ballistic when you start construction, there are several principles you can use to reduce distractions to the construction of your antenna system.

- Work fast.
- Work neatly.
- Work thoughtfully.
- Work safely.

Work Fast

Have you ever noticed that hostile corporate takeovers often begin on a Friday afternoon after the market closes? Have you ever noticed that when the President of the United States is about to do something unpopular, it is usually announced on Friday night, after the national newscasts, or early on Saturday morning?

It is more difficult, although not impossible, to assemble a corporate-takeover defense team if they've gone away for the weekend. Similarly, if bad news is released and published in the Saturday papers, by Sunday morning it is old news and may no longer warrant a headline.

Similar thinking suggests that if you have a permit in hand, you should begin construction after the Building Inspector goes home on Friday afternoon, and finish before he comes in on Monday morning. Why would you do that? For one thing, it becomes more difficult, if not nearly impossible for the Building Inspector to issue a *stop work* order over the weekend. The neighbors may not know how to reach him and the police will consider it to be a civil matter that can wait until Monday morning.

Building over the weekend is not impossible, if you have an existing set of holes in the ground, with a concrete base that has cured (allow 10 to 21 days, depending on local construction requirements) and the first section or pier pin plus anchors—all ready to go. Do the rest of your preparation in the garage to avoid creating a stir.

Preparation for fast construction should include putting each section of a lattice structure together on the ground, filing off burrs and reaming out boltholes as necessary, marking matching legs with colored tape and so forth. It would also include building guy sets, or as much of them as possible, in advance in the garage.

A heavy equipment contractor who specialized in building golf courses first introduced me to this concept. Over an Egg McMuffin one day, he described to me how he once found himself in a situation where a privately owned woods was going to be converted into a golf course. He checked with the Building Inspector to see if any special permits would be required to clear the land and was (correctly) told that no special permits would be required. So he lined up a huge crew of forest workers and machinery.

They went to work on Friday afternoon and worked almost continuously until Sunday night. On Monday morning, the neighbors were banging on the Building Inspector's door, demanding that he find a way to stop the construction. Lacking authority to stop the construction, but wishing to appear responsive to the neighbors, the Building Inspector called the contractor and asked him to hold off a while so that the town Conservation Commission could consider the situation. To this request, the builder replied: "Of course, but perhaps you should drive over here to better understand the situation."

Eighteen acres had been cleared over the weekend. Ever hear of the French expression "*fait accompli*" (translated literally: accomplished fact)? In the Middle East, this is known as "creating facts on the ground." The *fait accompli* is a well-established principle of international relations and can be employed by radio hams too.

Work Neatly

It sounds odd but it is a fact of life: Your neighbors may not know whether you have designed your support structure well or badly. But they can tell if you are sloppy or neat. So if you work neatly, they will think you have designed well. Whether this is rational or not is debatable. Yet it is still an oft-experienced fact. Thus, you can instill confidence in your neighbors by doing a few simple things.

- If you must store things outdoors (although you'd be better off strategically with indoor storage), stack support sections and antenna parts neatly.
- Build your rebar cages in the garage.
- Cover holes with plywood, so no one falls in.
- Cover outside piles of materials with tarpaulins.
- Cut guy wire ends to length and tape them.
- Coil excess cables neatly.
- Use a wood chipper to get rid of slash. Rake the construction area and plant grass as soon as possible.

In other words, don't leave your construction site looking like a construction site.

Work Thoughtfully

Be considerate of your neighbors. Don't stack things along the property line. Don't store antennas along the property line. Plant bushes to block the view where guy wires meet your guy anchors.

Work Safely

Never leave an open hole. Get that anti-climbing device on the structure as fast as possible. Wear safety glasses. Wear hard hats. Use handy-talkies instead of shouting. Keep nosey kids away, nicely of course, for their own safety.

Tree Removal

The golf-course story above reminds me of a ham who became the victim of irate neighbors. Intending to install both a swimming pool and an antenna-support structure the following year, he had about an acre of his backyard forest cleared. With a whole year to organize, and bare stumps to point at, the neighbors built up a full head of steam before

the ham went to the permit-granting authority for his Special Permit to erect and maintain an Amateur Radio antenna system. The neighbors organized and fought, raising the grief factor substantially for the ham and requiring him to retain a lawyer. If he'd built the antenna-support structure in the woods, and cleared the land later for the pool, his situation might have been different.

Think hard about the phases of construction, so you can improve your chances of obtaining a permit. There will always be neighbors who hold to a simply expressed view: "We love trees." For some reason, they believe that this view also entitles them to require you to forego the use of your own land. He may be legally wrong, but a determined neighbor who holds this view can make your life miserable. Think very hard about your land-clearing strategy.

How much of a clearing do you need to start your project? Can you live with "alleys" for guy wires instead of a cleared acre? Can you live with an alley created by discrete limbing of trees? Can you leave trees standing that can limit the ability of a neighbor to even see your antenna system?

Please remember that if tree cutting or limbing is part of your project (and especially if you don't live in a rural area), get rid of the "slash" quickly. Do this before neighbors can take photos, however irrelevant, of trees and branches all over your yard. Rent a chipper or have a landscaper chip up the slash. If your yard looks like a wreck, your neighbors will be upset. Nothing good happens when the neighbors are upset.

Holes in the Ground

Don't leave any open holes in the ground. This will upset the Building Inspector and give the neighbors a reason to complain. It makes good sense anyway to cover holes with two by fours and plywood, so that no child (or adult!) can fall in. Also, your insurance company wants you to do that. The issue you are attacking is an outcrop of an old Latin expression: *"Falsum in unum, falsum in omnium."* (Verbatim translation: "False in one, false in all.") This is a line of argument that holds that if you can be false about any one fact, you can be false about all facts.

(Courtesy, *The Westford Eagle* (Community Newspaper Corporation), April 25, 1996, Editorial page. Cartoon reprinted with permission of Ed Colley.)

The problem with this line of argument is, of course, that it is not true. For example, is it necessarily true that you would falsely represent the visual impact of a communications antenna just because you once told your wife that you liked that hideous dress she'd just bought?

However, you can be sure that neighbors who oppose you will stand up at a public hearing and say: "He left open holes in the ground. This is dangerous construction. How can we believe that he'll build a safe antenna-support structure?"

So be a good neighbor and make sure you build anything you build safely. This way, when you later stand up at the hearing and say that you are going to build this antenna system yourself and it will be safe, you will be more believable.

Anti-Climbing Devices

Some hams are reluctant to include their plans for an anti-climbing device in the Special-Permit application. They may feel it is not necessary. They may feel that any kid who climbs the tower and gets hurt is just a trespasser who gets what he deserves. They may think of this as yet another unnecessary government intrusion.

Yes, a ham may think any or all of those things. But he will still be asked about it during the course of the hearing, unless the support structure is a push-up pole or something like a crank-up round pole—inherently unclimbable.

For your typical lattice structure, however, a device to prevent curious children from climbing it is often a requirement of municipalities. There is always some member of the Board who is re-enacting in his mind the scene from the movie *Kindergarten Cop*, where Arnold Schwarzenegger must climb a tower to save a frightened child who has climbed a huge, self-supporting microwave link tower to get away from something scary. Of course such a tower is no doubt wider and taller than most ham radio installations, but such is the power of modern cinematic illusion—that's what sticks.

So don't fight it. Include your method in the application and assure the Board that at least this element will not be a problem. Remember, health and safety regulations are specifically exempted from the "accommodation" required by PRB-1 (47 CFR §97.15(b)).

There are several common approaches. One is to wrap the bottom ten feet in hardware cloth and mount a ladder to begin your climb above the cloth fencing. See **Fig 11-1A** for the method developed by K1ZM and Fig 11-1B for the method used by K1HT, who uses neat construction with pine boards, painted gray in this case.

Yet another situation uses either pine board or plywood. Start with a thick (one inch is good, $^3/_8$ inch may not stand up to the animals) plywood sheet, 4 × 8 feet. A sheet yields three panels just under 16 inches in width, each eight feet

Fig 11-1—Tower anti-climbing techniques. At left, K1ZM's technique, using "hardware cloth." At right, K1HT's technique, using plywood panels U-bolted to the tower.

tall. A 16-inch panel is adequate for Rohn 25G or other structures with a 12-inch face. It is just a bit too small for Rohn 45G or 55G, as those models have an 18-inch face. Start the panel at two or three feet above ground and it will end 10 to 11 feet above ground. This is above the grasp of all but the most determined trespassers.

Danger: High Voltage Signs

If the town asks you to put up a sign saying "Danger: High Voltage," you should resist. Your position is: "If it were true, I'd be happy to put it up. But it is not true, and the Board doesn't want me to lie, right?" In addition, any sign at all is like inviting teenagers to defy the "sign of authority," and climb the structure. However, in the end, if they just absolutely, positively insist, put it up. If you can, put it on the face of the structure facing the backyard, where it is least likely to be seen by curious teenagers.

Phillystran

This book cannot resolve controversies about costs, or the influence of metallic guy wires on radiation patterns. However, if guy-wire visibility is going to be a complaint against you, it is hard to imagine anything less visible than a guy wire made so that the outer covering is black and uninterrupted. Grey galvanized steel quickly dulls and becomes hardly visible, but black guy wire is almost impossible to see at any time. If you install insulators in your guy wires to avoid parasitic resonances, those insulators do increase visibility if they appear above the tree line. Below the tree line, both galvanized steel and Phillystran are almost impossible to spot.

In the interest of compromise with respect to cost, use Phillystran for guy wires above the tree line and convert to steel at the tree line. This is perfectly safe (even recommended by the manufacturer of Phillystran, who would rather not have Phillystran be too close to the ground, where a vandal or a small brush fire could attack it).

THE TVI/RFI COMPLAINT

Before wading into the discussion of how to respond (in the sense of letters and legal actions), to an RFI (radio frequency interference) complaint, see **http://www.arrl.org/tis** for some good information packages on various aspects of RFI. *The ARRL RFI Book* (see **http://arrl.org/catalog/**) is another good source of help for all types of RFI problems. There's nothing like curing an RFI problem to quiet the situation.

TVI/RFI Complaint by a Town Official

It is with uncanny freakishness that hams wind up living across the street from the sister of the Chairman of the Board of Appeals. This creates all kinds of problems. To deal with the most important one first, if your Board of Appeals (or other permit-granting authority) has no alternate members available should a member be forced to recuse himself/herself, you could wind up requiring *unanimous approval* from the remaining members of the Board. For example, you might find yourself needing all four votes on a five-member panel, where the fifth member cannot vote. While your presentation may be

brilliant, winning unanimously is always hard.

Second, RFI is a possibility in today's world of poorly designed VCRs or wireless 49-MHz telephones that are leftovers from another era. Once someone has experienced RFI, she just doesn't want to hear your logic. She will complain to her brother, the Chairman of your permit-granting authority. This will happen even though putting your antenna higher in the sky will improve not only your Amateur Radio enjoyment, but will also reduce interference, simply because the antenna is further away.

The best way to deal with this is to be proactive and *ask your neighbor* if he or she has experienced any interference. If there is interference, immediately consult the ARRL's web page for RFI tips. In any event, get the ball rolling. Prove that you are technically competent and try to ameliorate the problem. Employ or create a local RFI Committee. Show yourself to be a good neighbor. It will help later.

TVI/RFI Complaint by a Homeowners Association

This is a tricky situation. Jim Altman, W4UK, an ARRL Volunteer Counsel in Atlanta, GA (**http://www.altlaw. com/**) was kind enough to contribute the following story on the topic of a Homeowners Association (HOA) and RFI, from a case where he represented a ham.

This involved a neighbor who was experiencing telephone RFI. The neighbor complained to the Homeowners Association and the lawyer for the Homeowners Association wrote a "nasty-gram" to the ham, threatening to sue him over the covenant of "no nuisance" (one of those paragraphs in a typical CC&R). In a telephone call between the two lawyers, the Homeowners Association lawyer said that he was going to set up an Emergency Restraining Order hearing. Altman picks up the story:

> I told him that he should go ahead, conference me with the Court and we'll pick a mutually convenient time. I said I would acknowledge service, together with the Georgia equivalent of the Rule 11 warning. I also FAXed him a whole slew of case law and told my client to stay completely off the air for two weeks. Well, it appears that the strong arm worked and there will be no suit by the Homeowners Association over the covenant of no nuisance. I (eventually) got a letter stating that none of the other neighbors had a problem and that the Association considered it a matter between the two neighbors.
>
> The Association lawyer suggested binding arbitration. I rejected that, noting that Arbitrators have no obligation to follow the law and their decisions are unappealable on legal grounds. I said we have a clear legal right to be "judged" by the FCC and that no procedure other than the FCC's procedure was acceptable to us.
>
> The President of the Association told the client last night that they had spent enough time with their lawyer and the matter was concluded.

All's well that ends well. Here's a letter that Altman has found to be successful—once in the case of the HOA above and the other time in an inter-neighbor harassment situation. This second situation was one where the HOA's counsel wrote to Altman threatening sanctions against the amateur, after forcing compliance with a CC&R rule regarding antenna visibility. (This is available on the CD-ROM, under filename: **Altman Letter.DOC**.)

Dear Atty. ***:

The Amateur Family intends to abide by all reasonable provisions of the recorded Covenants, Conditions, and Restrictions ("CC&Rs") and Bylaws of the Association.

The Amateur Family retains the right to erect any and all antennas which do not violate CC&R § [nnn] by being "visible to the public view" with the understanding that this is interpreted in terms of a reasonable observer using reasonable means to make the observation from a place where the observer has a right to be without requesting permission from the Amateur Family to be there.

The Amateur Family retains the right to operate their licensed radio station(s) in accordance with the terms of their license(s) and applicable statutes and regulations. Said operation, by virtue of holding a current license, will, therefore, be presumed to be in the public interest, convenience and necessity, absent a specific ruling to the contrary from the Federal Communications Commission ("FCC") [See 47 U.S.C.A. § 309(a)] and will be presumed to be in compliance with all FCC rules and regulations, absent a specific determination to the contrary by the FCC.

The Amateur Family will handle issues of unwanted reception caused by improper technical operation of their equipment by bearing the responsibility to take the required steps to bring their equipment into compliance with FCC regulations and will cease operations while it is in non-compliance, with the exception of reasonable tests to determine the effectiveness of attempted adjustments, repairs or remedial measures.

If unwanted reception is caused by conditions beyond their control, they will assume the obligation to reasonably cooperate with the affected party or parties to determine how to prevent such unwanted reception and to make a reasonable number of tests to assist the affected party or parties in determining the effectiveness of any remedial measures, but they have no obligation to, and will not attempt to, repair or replace any home entertainment or other electronic equipment of the affected party or parties nor are they obligated to cease operations as long as they are in compliance with FCC regulations and technical standards.

We regard any unilateral attempts by the Association to impose restrictions on the Amateur Family's operations beyond the parameters outlined above as unreasonable and an interference with the Amateur Family's own "right of enjoyment" in the use of their property, especially where the correction of the problem is in the hands of the complainant, and we are prepared to secure and defend their rights as necessary.

We trust that the situation will not come to that point. As you stated in your letter "I am hopeful that this matter has been resolved and no further action will be necessary." I echo that stance.

Sincerely,

James Altman, Esq.

C: Amateur Family

TVI/RFI Complaint by a Neighbor

[Note: A much deserved "thank you" is due to Greg Becker, JD, PhD, NA2N, and a former policeman, for advice contained in this section.]

The first rule to remember when confronted by an angry neighbor is to let him say his piece. Don't try to interrupt. Let him get it all out.

Yet venting works *only* when the situation is relatively calm, even within the nature of a confrontation. The *instant* it rises to the point where you feel that you may no longer be in control of the situation, *end it* if you possibly can. Close the door. Ask him to leave and come back when you can both be calm. Don't know what to say? Try: "Listen, it's late and we're both a little upset. Can we talk about this another time when we're both calm?"

If it is late at night and no drinking is involved, ask if he can shut off his motion-sensor lights, TV, stereo, or whatever, and you can work on the problem after work Monday. Nothing is going to get settled right then and there. If it is late at night and he's been drinking, don't try to settle anything right then and there.

Here's a further tip from Greg Becker: If he starts yelling, tell him, "I'll be happy to work with you to resolve this, but the way you're acting is frightening me. Please leave. We can talk about this when we're both calm."

The "frightening" part places language into the situation evincing your state of mind, should the situation escalate. Should the neighbor persist in that behavior, it strengthens the position that his threatening conduct was *intended* to place you in fear of your safety (or that is a negligent result), and gives the law-enforcement officer or District Attorney grounds for criminal action (at least in New York).

If he threatens to call the cops, don't be afraid to hand him a phone. If he calls the cops, you should thank your lucky stars. Now you have a neutral party with a District Attorney on call to be an arbiter. You are lucky because the neighbor who does not call the cops could be thinking of taking things into his own hands; see below.

On the other hand, if he has really frightened you, even without threats, or is in any way acting in what might be perceived as a threatening manner, *you* call the police—do not wait for him to do it.

Worried that the police won't pay attention if it is just a phone call, and it's just swearing ("Get the hell off the air, right now!!") with no *words* conveying a threat, just a menacing voice? Should you file a complaint?

You could be really scared, yet lack the words or act that amounts to a threat or an unwanted touching to form the basis of a complaint. Should you still file a report?

If you are asking that question, you are assuming that nothing much happens when the cops get the first filing—as it lacks a criminal act. However, the mere filing means that the second time it happens, cop nostrils should flare.

Yet the ugly neighbor could now make lawsuit noises (defamation). Don't worry too much, as the ham would likely win any lawsuit against the ham by taking the position that filing a police report fails the "publication" test and is privileged. But the ham still winds up hiring a lawyer and defending in court. Thus, the question is really interesting.

Here's something to consider. There can be a number of crimes that are less than an assault. ARRL Volunteer Counsel Brent H. Gourley, KE4MZ, **bgrly@ala.net**, of Klemm & Gourley, PC, Dothan, AL, provided information on the Alabama situation below.

Put briefly, in Alabama,

Class A misdemeanors = $2000 fine and one year with the sheriff

Class B misdemeanors = $1000 fine and six months

Class C misdemeanors = $500 fine and 90 days

Sentence is usually suspended upon payment of the fine and good behavior.

Here are the crimes that may be involved.

Sec. 13A-6-23. Menacing. *[that is, threaten with a weapon]*
(a) A person commits the crime of menacing if, by physical action, he intentionally places or attempts to place another person in fear of imminent serious physical injury.
(b) Menacing is a Class B misdemeanor.

Sec. 13A-6-24. Reckless endangerment. *[usually motor vehicle, but ...]*
(a) A person commits the crime of reckless endangerment if he recklessly engages in conduct which creates a substantial risk of serious physical injury to another person.
(b) Reckless endangerment is a Class A misdemeanor.

Sec. 13A-11-8. Harassment or harassing communications. *[verbal, physical, e-mail, telephone]*
(a)(1) HARASSMENT.— A person commits the crime of harassment if, with intent to harass, annoy, or alarm another person, he or she either:
a. Strikes, shoves, kicks, or otherwise touches a person or subjects him or her to physical contact.
b. Directs abusive or obscene language or makes an obscene gesture towards another person.
(2) For purposes of this section, harassment shall include a threat, verbal or nonverbal, made with the intent to carry out the threat, that would cause a reasonable person who is the target of the threat to fear for his or her safety.
(3) Harassment is a Class C misdemeanor.
(b)(1) HARASSING COMMUNICATIONS. — A person commits the crime of harassing communications if, with intent to harass or alarm another person, he or she does any of the following:
a. Communicates with a person, anonymously or otherwise, by telephone, telegraph, mail, or any other form of written or electronic communication, in a manner likely to harass or cause alarm.
b. Makes a telephone call, whether or not a conversation ensues, with no purpose of legitimate communication.
c. Telephones another person and addresses to or about such other person any lewd or obscene words or language.
Nothing in this section shall apply to legitimate business telephone communications.
(2) Harassing communications is a Class C misdemeanor.

SOME SAMPLE RFI LETTERS

In any event, here are some "RFI letters" for you to use as a guide in responding to your jerky neighbor. After reading a few, you should have the confidence to compose an appropriate one for yourself. For ease of use, they are also on the CD-ROM accompanying this book.

A Sample RFI Letter from a Ham to a Neighbor, by Scott Neader, KA9FOX

Here's the way Scott Neader, KA9FOX, approached a problem, using information supplied in this book. It is available on the CD ROM as filename:
KA9FOX RFI Letter.DOC.

Dear ***,
I am really sorry that you are having problems with your motion-detecting lights picking up Amateur Radio transmissions. As you know, your lights should not be doing this. If you would be willing to cooperate in some experiments, I am hopeful your interference problem could be resolved by the application of standard engineering techniques. As a good neighbor, I am willing to assist in applying these techniques to your specific situation.

I do want to clarify that Federal law does not require me to assist with interference problems such as the one you are experiencing, as long as my station meets all applicable FCC regulations. I am confident my station meets and even exceeds all regulations. My power output is always within specified limitations and I spent considerable time and money to be sure that my station is properly installed with better than average grounding and filtering.

While I don't have to help, I want to help, as I want to be a good neighbor. But it will take cooperation to cure any interference problem. I cannot do it alone. If you want my help in curing your interference problem, all you have to do is call me at (telephone number) and, while I cannot make any promises, I will do the best that I can to help you solve the problem.

I do not have any experience with solving interference problems with motion-detection lights, but I am a member of several local, regional and national Amateur Radio associations, and I have already contacted two of them for assistance.

I have attached some additional information regarding Radio Frequency Interference issues that you may find useful. However, I believe the best solution is neighborly cooperation and I await your phone call.

Sincerely,

Scott Neader

Attachment

Attachment

Can local or state authorities or laws be involved in matters of Radio Frequency Interference?
No. RFI matters are handled exclusively by the Federal Communications Commission (FCC). In amending the Communications Act of 1934 in 1982, the Congress clearly expressed its opinion:
"The Conference Substitute is further intended to clarify the reservation of exclusive jurisdiction to the Federal Communications Commission over matters involving RFI [radio frequency interference]. Such matters shall not be regulated by local or state law, nor shall radio transmitting apparatus be subject to local or state regulation as part of any effort to resolve an RFI complaint. . . . [T]he Conferees intend that

regulation of RFI phenomena shall be imposed only by the Commission."

H.R. Report No. 765, 97th Cong., 2d Sess. 33 (1982), reprinted in 1982 U.S. Code Cong. & Ad. News 2277, referring to amendments to Section 302(a) of the Communications Act.

In a private letter opinion to the American Radio Relay League, Inc., dated February 14, 1990, Robert L. Pettit, General Counsel of the Federal Communications Commission (FCC) adopts the position of the Congress as the position of the FCC, writing:

"State laws that require amateurs to cease operations or incur penalties as a consequence of radio interference thus have been entirely preempted by Congress.

These opinions have been confirmed repeatedly by the courts. See, for example, *Broyde v. Gotham Tower*, 13 F.3d 994 (6th Cir., 1994)."

Whom should I call when I have RFI problems?

While RFI matters are handled exclusively by the FCC, Amateur Radio operators generally are prepared to offer aid beyond the requirements of law, working closely with neighbors who may be affected by radio transmissions and scientific experiments.

The Consumer Electronics Manufacturer's Association (CEMA) publishes a pamphlet available on the World Wide Web that may also be of assistance: "What to Do If You Have An Electronics Interference Problem."
http://www.cemacity.org/gazette/files/whattodo.htm

For information on resolving problems, the FCC's *Interference Handbook* is available on the Internet. The 22-page booklet, available from the Compliance and Information Bureau via the FCC World Wide Web home page, includes the same information and illustrations contained in the recently published *Interference to Home Electronic Entertainment Equipment Handbook*. It includes information about equipment installation, identifying interference sources, curing interference problems, and filters. It also contains a list of home electronic equipment manufacturers and telephone numbers. Pictures illustrate different TV interference problems, including ham or CB transmitter interference. FCC's *Interference Handbook* can be found at:
http://www.fcc.gov/Bureaus/Compliance/WWW/ tvibook.html

Is RFI from Amateur Radio operations common?

At least one study by the FCC Field Operations Bureau has shown that Amateur Radio operations are responsible for less than 1% of all interference complaints (400, of 42,000 complaints during a fiscal year in the early 1970's) filed with the Commission. (Source: FCC data, as reported in *QST*, July 1974, p 10). Part of the preparation for licensing involves studying how to minimize and correct such problems, if they should ever occur.

Would a smaller Amateur Radio antenna system help?

Actually, the higher the antenna, the better! The erection of a taller antenna system will have a tendency to decrease, not increase, the likelihood of television interference, as higher antenna systems, with directional arrays, are farther away from neighboring electronic devices, and transmit over nearby homes. Lower, wire antennas, erected in trees, or from a house to a tree, for example, have a far greater likelihood of interference, as they would direct more energy toward a neighboring TV set.

This is exactly the position that was taken by the FCC's Chief of the Private Radio in a letter to the Board of Zoning Appeals of Hempstead, NY (October 25, 1994):

"(A)ntenna height is inversely related to the strength, in the horizontal plane, of the radio signal that serves as a catalyst for interference in susceptible home electronic equipment. It is a matter of technical fact that the higher an amateur antenna, the less likely it is that radio frequency interference will appear in home electronic equipment."

Sample RFI Letter from a Ham's Lawyer to a Neighbor, by Phil Kane, K2ASP

This is the typical TVI/RFI situation where the neighbor has refused to cooperate with the amateur in resolving the problem and has started to harass the amateur and his family. This letter is on the CD ROM as filename: **K2ASP RFI Letter.DOC**.

Dear Mr. Neighbor:

The Amateur has related that since the spring of 1990, you have alleged that your television receiver, VCR, and telephone have been receiving the radio signals from his station, and that not only have you refused to apply the necessary corrective measures (filters) to your home electronic/entertainment equipment ("HEEE") which would reduce or eliminate the effects of that unwanted reception, you have been abusive to his family and have made threats of further abuse.

The Amateur is licensed to operate that station by the Federal Communications Commission ("FCC"), which has sole jurisdiction and authority in connection with any complaints of this nature. The particular problem which you are experiencing is, unfortunately, the most common complaint from the general public with which the FCC deals.

FCC engineers have looked into this type of problem, its causes, and its solutions for literally decades, and their research, both in the laboratory and in the field—the homes and offices of folks like yourself—has shown that the overwhelming cause of the problem is the lack of effective shielding and filtering of the affected HEEE devices to prevent the interception and detection of such radio signals. Indeed, the Amateur is able to operate his HEEE devices such as television receivers, VCRs and telephones in his own home without experiencing the effects you complain to him about.

We live in an era where radio transmitters of all types—cellular radiotelephones, electronic baby monitors and other types of wireless communicators, mobile radios, and business and personal communications devices and services such as Citizens Band and Amateur Radio transmitters—are proliferating in the effort to bring the benefits of wireless communications to the public. This has resulted in increasing technical incompatibility with HEEE devices that have not been designed with the interception resistance needed to coexist in that environment.

Most people such as yourself are never aware of this sort of deficiency and the proper methods of curing it until being exposed to a nearby radio signal causes the unwanted interception, and then your natural reaction is "I never had the problem before, why should I have to deal with it? It must be someone else's problem." The analogy, which has been used all over the country and for many years is: "Why does my roof leak when it rains—it didn't leak before it started raining." The solution of the problem, though, is in your own hands, not the Amateur's.

The FCC will send to you an "Interference Handbook" which will explain the steps which have to be taken for you to restore the proper operation of your equipment. You may write to them at:

[Insert local FCC Public Service address]

The Amateur's obligation is to operate his radio transmitter upon mutual pre-arrangement for you to see whether the things that you do are effective in restoring the proper operation of your equipment. He is not obligated to stop operation in the interim. He is not obligated to provide the necessary filters or technical repairs to your equipment, nor will he.

With the above as a background, then, we are insisting that you cease harassing the Amateur about a problem the solution of which is in your own hands, and we reserve the right to take necessary legal action to restrain such harassment should you continue to do so.

Phil Kane, K2ASP
Principal Attorney
Communications Law Center
ARRL Pacific Division Assistant
Director

A Sample RFI Letter from a Ham's Lawyer to a Neighbor Who is a Policeman, by Fred Hopengarten, K1VR

(This is available on the CD ROM as filename: **K1VR Lawyer to Cop RFI Letter.DOC**.)

December 7, 1988

Name Neighbor
Address
Town

Dear Mr. Neighbor:

I am an attorney with a particular interest in communications law. It is the only area in which I am active. In addition, I act as volunteer counsel, providing free legal services to Radio Amateurs who may encounter problems with neighbors or municipalities. I write to you today on behalf of Radio Ham, a neighbor of yours, who resides at (# same street).

Mr. Ham's Concern

He has recorded, in notes made at the time, that you phoned his home, on November 30, 1988. In the course of a call at approximately 6:00 PM, you said to him that an interference problem from which you now suffer, was his fault, and that if he does not stop it, you would get a court order to arrest him for disturbing the peace.

As you are a police officer employed by the Town of Town, Mr. Ham was very concerned, and asked for my help.

Escalation is Undesirable

If this matter escalates, it will involve all sorts of claims by Mr. Ham, based on actions you have taken attempting to restrain his First Amendment right of free speech, and attempting to deprive him of equal protection under the law. In that case, I would advise you to retain a lawyer to defend yourself, and it would become necessary to call in Town Counsel to defend the Town, due to your role as a police officer. The matter would then become protracted, expensive for you and for the Town, and would likely not solve your essential problem.

If I understand the situation correctly, you suffer from some interference. Frankly, your concerns are best solved by engineering, not litigation.

A Helpful Publication

The law on interference to a television set or intercom is clear. As a help to consumers, the Federal Communications Commission publishes a booklet: "How to Identify and Resolve Radio-TV Interference Problems." Copies are for sale for only a few dollars at the government bookstore at the Kennedy Building in downtown Boston, or from the Superintendent of Documents, U. S. Government Printing Office, Washington, DC 20402. In addition, a book, including the FCC pamphlet, can be purchased at the Heath Zenith store on Route 9 in Wellesley, or You Do It Electronics in Needham.

Allow me to quote from the introduction, written by the FCC, in that pamphlet.

Interference from a radio transmitter (CB, Amateur or Police) can occur, even when the radio transmitter is properly operated. One or all of the following may be a contributing factor:

• Technical deficiencies in a radio transmitter, or improper operation of the transmitter.
• Design deficiencies in the device receiving the interference (television, telephone, stereo, or AM/FM radio).
• Inadequate antenna system (rabbit ears versus a well-maintained outside antenna system).
• Distant TV or radio signal being received (referred to as fringe area reception).
• Booster amplifier installed on TV receiving antenna.

Action Steps

Mr. Ham is a degreed electronics engineer, who has worked in the electronics industry all his life. He suffers no interference at home, and he has no word from other neighbors that they have problems. Therefore, it is highly unlikely that the problem is with his transmitter or antennas. Furthermore, it is likely that the problem in your home can be easily remedied.

By letter of December 5, 1988, Mr. Ham has offered written suggestions, and has provided, at his own expense, some materials (0.002 mfd capacitors with alligator clips for your telephone line, and snap-on filter chokes for your TV feed line) which may be of help to you. Furthermore, if you have cable TV, and the problem continues, you may contact me or Mr. Ham, and we will be happy to coordinate with the local cable TV company, to see what further steps can be taken. Furthermore, as I understand it, no one has yet tried a "high pass filter" (which may be appropriate after you have taken the first steps Mr. Ham suggested) in your home.

Mr. Ham's Antenna

Mr. Ham has reason to believe that you have complained to the Town Building Inspection Department about his antennas, perhaps in the hope that without an antenna up in the sky, your problem would go away. Unfortunately, that concept is faulty. If it were true that an antenna caused the problem, which isn't true, you would not want a low antenna (which would be closer to your house), but rather the highest antenna known to man (which would be farther away from your house). Let's put it another way. If the antenna caused the problem, you'd want the antenna five miles up, not 50 feet up.

Due to the physics of signal dispersion, each additional foot of height in the antenna actually makes the potential interfering signal increasingly weaker and less likely to present a problem. Here is an example we can all relate to:

If you shine a flashlight at a wall from a distance of one foot, you will see a strong light in a narrow spot on that wall. Now move the flashlight back four feet, and any one spot on the wall will now have only one-sixteenth as much light, as the light disperses over a broader area and gets weaker.

Any requirement to lower Mr. Ham's antenna, taken alone, would therefore actually increase any problem, which you may suffer, not decrease the problem.

The Zoning Bylaw

I have examined the zoning bylaw of the Town of Town, and find that it does not meet the strict requirements of the limited Federal preemption of such bylaws created by a recent FCC ruling, found at 47 CFR §97.15(b), and commonly referred to as PRB-1. If you feel that it is important, I would be happy to provide you with a copy of the preemption ruling by the FCC, and citations to cases in which zoning bylaws have been struck down and attorney's fees awarded to the radio amateur affected. Thus, use of the Town's Zoning Bylaw will not reduce your interference.

Your Equipment Manufacturer

While I do not know which brand of equipment you use, many manufacturers of equipment provide free technical help and are anxious to aid their customers. The FCC publication I mentioned earlier contains a list of contacts and telephone numbers.

Conclusion

Officer Neighbor, it seems that you have a technical problem that is susceptible to a technical solution. I know that Mr. Ham, and other local radio hams, who have a long and proud tradition of public service, would be willing, even anxious, to help out. I urge you, in the strongest terms, not to make a law case out of this situation. Instead, I ask you to help create a "win/win" situation here.

With cooperation, you can be rid of your interference problem, and Mr. Ham can be relieved of his concerns about any possible action you may take. Are you willing to take a chance on cooperation? It could solve your problem, and avoid a confrontation in which no one wins, except the attorney for the radio ham who is awarded his fees by the Court at the conclusion of litigation.

I hope that you and Mr. Ham can work this thing out. If I can be of assistance in any way, on questions of engineering (I am the President of a cable TV company), or law (and General Counsel), please feel free to contact me at work (617 xxx-xxxx), or at home (781 259-0088).

Sincerely,

Atty. Fred Hopengarten

FH/lbe

File: Interference Correspondence

cc: General Counsel, American Radio Relay League
  Mr. Ham

Sample RFI Letter from a Ham's Lawyer to a Neighbor's Lawyer, by Fred Hopengarten, K1VR

(This is available on the CD ROM as filename: **K1VR Lawyer to Lawyer RFI Letter.DOC**.)

November 14, 2000

Attorney Robert C. Robert
Robert and Robert, P.C.   e-mail: rcrobert@xxxxxx.net
PO Box 1234   Tel.: (508) 123-1234
Town, MA 02134   FAX: (508) 123-1235

In re: Your letter to Mr. & Mrs. Ham dated November 7, 2000

Dear Atty. Robert:

I represent Joe T. Ham of (street address), Town, MA with respect to matters of Federal law governing radio frequency interference. Mr. Ham has provided me with a copy of your letter to him dated November 7, 2000. Your letter advised Mr. Ham that "a CB tower installed on your property has caused a substantial interference with the electronics within the Neighbor's home. This interference includes, but is not limited to, audio interference with their telephone, stereo and TV sound systems."

On behalf of Mr. & Mrs. Neighbor, you wrote: "I must respectfully request that you cease and desist from using your CB radio until you have acquired the technology necessary to stop this interference." You advised Mr. Ham that should he not comply with your request, that you have been authorized by your clients to take appropriate legal action including, but not limited to, a restraining order to stop this condition deemed a nuisance.

Mr. Ham is a Federally Licensed Radio Amateur

Mr. Ham is a federally licensed Amateur Radio Operator, holding an Amateur Extra Class license issued by the Federal Communications Commission (FCC). The FCC licensed Amateur Radio Service is separate and distinct from the FCC licensed Citizen's Band (CB) Radio Service. The FCC has sole jurisdiction and authority in connection with any complaints of radio frequency interference (RFI).

Applicable Law

Congress has preempted any state or local regulation of radio frequency interference (RFI) pursuant to the provisions of Section 302(a) of the Communications Act of 1934, as amended. I refer you to 47 U.S.C. §302(a)(1) of the Act, which provides that the "Commission may, consistent with the public interest, convenience, and necessity, make reasonable regulations (1) governing the interference potential of devices which in their operation are capable of emitting radio frequency energy by radiation, conduction, or other means in sufficient degree to cause harmful interference to radio communications . . . " 47 U.S.C. §302(a)(1).

The legislative history of Section 302(a) explicitly provides that the Federal Communications Commission has exclusive authority to regulate radio frequency interference. In its Conference Report No. 97-765, Congress declared:

> The Conference Substitute is further intended to clarify the reservation of exclusive jurisdiction to the Federal Communications Commission over matters involving RFI. Such matters shall not be regulated by local or state law, nor shall radio transmitting apparatus be subject to local or state regulation as part of any effort to resolve an RFI complaint. The Conferees believe that radio transmitter operators should not be subject to fines, forfeitures or other liability imposed by any local or state authority as a result of interference appearing in home electronic equipment or systems. Rather, the Conferees intend that regulation of RFI phenomena shall be imposed only by the Commission.

H.R. Report No. 765, 97th Cong., 2d Sess. 33 (1982), reprinted at 1982 U.S. Code Cong. & Ad News 2277.

In a private letter opinion to the American Radio Relay League, Inc, dated February 14, 1990, Robert L. Pettit, General Counsel of the Federal Communications Commission adopts the position of the Congress as the position of the FCC, writing:

"State laws that require amateurs to cease operations or incur penalties as a consequence of radio interference thus have been entirely preempted by Congress."

These opinions have been confirmed repeatedly by the courts. See, for example, *Broyde v. Gotham Tower*, 13 F.3d 994 (6th Cir., 1994), **http://pacer.ca6.uscourts.gov/cgi-bin/getopn.pl?OPINION=94a0007p.06**. For an excellent discussion, and a wealth of cases, see *Southwestern Bell Wireless, Inc. v. Johnson County Board of County Commissioners*, No. 98-3264 (10th Cir. Dec. 27, 1999). See **http://www.kscourt.org/ca10/cases/1999/12/98-3264.htm**. Another well-written and thorough discussion states plainly: "We conclude that allowing local zoning authorities to condition construction and use permits on any requirement to eliminate or remedy RF interference 'stands as an obstacle to the accomplishment and execution of the full purposes and objectives of Congress.'" *Freeman v. Burlington Broadcasters, Inc.*, No. 97- 9141 (2d Cir. February 23, 2000) **http://www.tourolaw.edu/2ndCircuit/February**, 2000 U.S. App. LEXIS 2672.

Furthermore, many home entertainment electronic devices bear the following label, in accordance with 47 CFR §15.19(a)(3):

This device complies with part 15 of the FCC Rules. Operation is subject to the following two conditions: (1) This device may not cause harmful interference, and (2) this device must accept any interference received, including interference that may cause undesired operation.

Finally, and for all of the above reasons, as well as the fact that the solution is in the hands of the complainant, claims on grounds of nuisance do not succeed.

A Helpful Publication

The law on interference to telephones, television, and audio systems is clear. As a help to consumers, the Federal Communications Commission (FCC) publishes a booklet "How to Identify and Resolve Radio-TV Interference Problems". Copies are for sale for only a few dollars at the government bookstore at the Kennedy Building in downtown Boston, or from the Superintendent of Documents, US Government Printing Office, Washington, DC 20402, Stock No. 004-000-0345-4. In addition, a book on this topic by the American Radio Relay League (ARRL), including the FCC pamphlet, can be purchased through the ARRL web page (**http://www.arrl.org/**), or at You Do It Electronics in Needham.

You can also download the publication without charge from the Internet at this site: **http://www.fcc.gov/cib/Publications/tvibook.html**. For telephone interference, see: **http://www.fcc.gov/eb/Publications/phone.html**.

As this booklet states, "Telephones, stereos, computers, electronic organs and home intercom systems can receive interference from nearby radio transmitters. When this happens, the device improperly functions as a radio receiver. Proper shielding or filtering can eliminate such interference." The FCC clearly puts the responsibility for interference to home electronics interference devices on the manufacturer. Most manufacturers respond appropriately if contacted about consumer RFI.

The Consumer Electronics Manufacturer's Association (CEMA) also publishes a pamphlet available on the World Wide Web: "What to Do If You Have An Electronics Interference Problem." **http://www.cemacity.org/gazette/files/whattodo.htm**.

Technical Solution and Responsibility

We live in an era where radio transmitters of all types—cellular radiotelephones, electronic baby monitors and other types of wireless communications, mobile radios, and business and personal communications devices and services such as Citizens Band and Amateur Radio transmitters—are proliferating in the effort to bring the benefits of wireless communications to the public. This has resulted in increasing technical incompatibility with home electronic/entertainment devices that have not been designed with the interception resistance needed to coexist in that environment.

Most people, such as your client, are never aware of this sort of deficiency and the proper methods of curing it until exposure to a nearby radio signal results in the unwanted interception. Your client's reaction is natural, "I never had the problem before, why should I have to deal with it?" The analogy, which has been used for years, is: "Why does my roof leak when it rains—it didn't leak before it started raining?" The solution to the problem, however, is in the hands of the homeowner, not those of the Amateur.

Mr. Ham would be pleased to operate his radio transmitter by mutual pre-arrangement, for your client to see if there are steps Mr. Ham can take that may be effective in restoring the proper operation of your client's equipment. Mr. Ham is not obligated to stop operation in the interim. If there is nothing further Mr. Ham can do thereafter, Mr. Ham is not obligated to provide the necessary filters or perform the technical repairs to your client's equipment.

Conclusion

In conclusion, I refer you to an excellent article entitled "The Ghost in the Computer: Radio Frequency Interference and the Doctrine of Federal Preemption" by Ralph H. Brock, appearing in the *Computer Law Review and Technology Journal*, Volume 1999, No. 1 (Fall 1998 – Spring 1999), Southern Methodist University School of Law, **http://www.sbot.org/docs/RFI.pdf**. Section V, Conclusion reads:

Although home electronic equipment is immersed in a sea of radio frequency energy from myriad sources, most of it functions as intended. The FCC has the authority to virtually eliminate RFI problems by requiring manufacturers to implement design features and filtering that would make all home electronics equipment "bullet proof." Instead, it has chosen to require such equipment to accept any interference it receives, while relying on the marketplace to compel manufacturers to produce serviceable merchandise.

Historically, local authorities have attempted to regulate RFI as a common-law nuisance or trespass. But as courts have consistently concluded, Congress has completely preempted the field of RFI regulation, thus precluding local regulation and state-law claims. Although legislation has been proposed that would yield some limited authority to local governments to regulate illegal CB operations, such legislation has not been enacted.

City, county, and private attorneys who understand how federal preemption applies in RFI matters can prevent potential litigants, beset by RFI problems, from filing ineffective lawsuits. Attorneys should also help their clients to understand that under current law, RFI is properly viewed as the equipment's inability to reject unwanted signals, not as transmitter interference. The focus of eliminating RFI can then properly shift to improving the filtering capabilities of home electronic equipment. Unless the law changes, this approach is the only reliable method of exorcizing the ghost in the computer.

Although the law does not require Mr. Ham to 'solve' your client's problem, I know that Mr. Ham, and other local Amateur Radio operators, would be willing, even anxious, to help out. I urge you, in the strongest terms, not to make a law case out of this situation. Instead, I ask you to help create a "win/win" situation here. Cooperation could solve Mr. Neighbor's problem, and avoid a confrontation in which no one wins, except the attorney for the radio amateur who is awarded his fees by the Court at the conclusion of frivolous litigation.

Sincerely,

Atty. Fred Hopengarten

C: Mr. Ham

Sample RFI Letters from a Ham's Lawyer to Town Counsel, by Jim O'Connell, W9WU

These are available on the CD ROM as filename: **W9WU RFI Letters.DOC**.

Letter 1:

Date

James H. Knippen, II
Walsh, Knippen, Knight   Via FAX (630) 462-1984
    & Diamond
601 West Liberty Drive
Wheaton, Illinois 60189

Dear Mr. Knippen:

As you may recall, I am a Volunteer Counsel for the American Radio Relay League, a national organization representing amateur radio operators throughout the United States. I have received a copy of the complaint filed by you in *City of Wheaton, etc. v. Leonard Fumarolo, Jr.*, 96 CH 0814. The Complaint alleges that Mr. Fumarolo, by the operation of his citizens band radio has caused numerous complaints from residents in his neighborhood regarding radio frequency interference to their televisions, radios, telephones and other home electronic equipment. The Complaint also seeks an injunction and damages for both alleged violations of various city ordinances and private nuisance caused by the alleged interference. While I do not represent the Fumarolo family, I am concerned that similar actions could be brought in the future against Amateur Radio operators residing in Wheaton.

The purpose of this letter is to bring to your attention both Federal law and case law applicable to a radio frequency interference nuisance complaint. Congress has preempted any state or local regulation of radio frequency interference (RFI) pursuant to the provisions of the Communications Act of 1934, as amended, 47 U.S.C. §301. Section 302(a)(1) of the Act provides that the Commission may, consistent with the public interest, convenience, and necessity, make rea-

sonable regulations (1) governing the interference potential of devices which in their operation are capable of emitting radio frequency energy by radiation, conduction, or other means in sufficient degree to cause harmful interference to radio communications . . . 47 U.S.C. §302(a)(1). Section 302(a)(2) of the Communications Act authorizes the Federal Communications Commission to establish . . . minimum performance standards for home electronic equipment and systems to reduce their susceptibility to interference from radio frequency energy.

The legislative history of Section 302(a)(2) explicitly provides that the Federal Communications Commission has exclusive authority to regulate radio frequency interference. In its Conference Report No. 97-765, Congress declared:

"The Conference Substitute is further intended to clarify the reservation of exclusive jurisdiction to the Federal Communications Commission over matters involving RFI. Such matters shall not be regulated by local or state law, nor shall radio-transmitting apparatus be subject to local or state regulation as part of any effort to resolve an RFI complaint. The Conferees believe that radio transmitter operators should not be subject to fines, forfeitures or other liability imposed by any local or state authority as a result of interference appearing in home electronic equipment or systems. Rather, the Conferees intend that regulation of RFI phenomena shall be imposed only by the Commission."

H.R. Report No. 765, 97th Cong., 2d Sess. 33 (1982), reprinted at 1982 U.S. Code Cong. & Ad News 2277.

Case law from other jurisdictions is particularly instructive in this situation. In *Blackburn v. Doubleday Broadcasting Company, Inc.*, 353 N.W. 2d 550 (Minn. 1984), plaintiffs brought a nuisance action against five radio stations which broadcast from a Minneapolis building, alleging the defendants' transmissions interfered with plaintiffs' reception of other stations. The Minnesota Supreme Court held that the Communications Act preempted plaintiffs' claim that defendants' radio transmissions constituted an actionable nuisance by distorting their reception of other desired signals.

In *E.G. Helm, Jr. v. Louisville Two-Way Radio Corporation*, 667 S.W. 2d 691 (Ky. 1984), the Jefferson County Police Department filed suit against a commercial radio paging service, seeking injunctive relief for interference with police communications. The police chief alleged that the interference was a dangerous nuisance and threatened the public safety. The Kentucky Supreme Court held that Congress and the federal government were the sole regulators of radio interference, and that a common law nuisance action was not sufficient to confer jurisdiction on the state court.

Finally, the Illinois Supreme Court has held that a claim for interference with television reception simply does not state a cause of action for nuisance. *People ex rel. Hoogasian v. Sears, Roebuck and Co.*, 52 Ill.2d 301 (1972). See also *Public Service Co. of New Mexico v. Catron*, 98 N.M. 134 (1982) (claim that construction of a high tension transmission line would cause interference to television and radio reception failed to state a cause of action for nuisance).

Finally, most of the home electronic equipment set out in Paragraph 8 of the Complaint is sold subject to FCC regulations which require the manufacturer to label the equipment with the following warning:

This device complies with FCC Rule Part 15. Operation is subject to two conditions: (1) it may not interfere with radio communications; and (2) it must accept any interference received, including that which may cause undesired operation.

47 C.F.R Ch. I, §§15.236 and 15.624.

Based on the foregoing, I believe that, with the possible exception of Count III, the Complaint simply fails to state a cause of action or is preempted by the Supremacy Clause of the United States Constitution. Please call me at your convenience to further discuss our mutual concerns.

Very truly yours,

James C. O'Connell

Letter 2:

September 30, 1996

James H. Knippen, II

Via FAX (630) 462-1984

Walsh, Knippen, Knight & Diamond
601 West Liberty Drive
Wheaton, Illinois 60189

Re: *Wheaton v. Fumarolo*

Dear Mr. Knippen:

As we discussed, I am enclosing the following materials from the Federal Communications Commission regarding interference to home electronics equipment, as well as some additional correspondence related to the Commission's views on preemption of any effort to regulate radio interference complaints at the local level.

Both the Commission's April 5, 1996 Public Notice "FCC Policy for Handling Complaints of Interference to Home Electronics Equipment," and August, 1995 "Telephone Interference Bulletin" CIB-10 make clear that the cause of this type of interference is the design or construction of home electronic products and not a violation of any FCC rule.

Also enclosed are several letters from Federal Communications Commission officials to various municipalities or individuals concerning attempted regulation of radio interference complaints. These letters clearly state the Commission's position in regard to this issue.

Let me know if you have any questions regarding this material, or need other information in order to determine the validity of the Fumarolo Complaint.

Very truly yours,

James C. O'Connell

Letter 3: Chase the Police Chief!!

Date

Ben K. Blake
Chief of Police
Village of Carpentersville
1200 L.W. Bensinger Drive
Carpentersville, IL 60110

Dear Chief Blake:

I represent Mr. XXXXXX, XXXXXX Avenue, XXXXXXX. Mr. XXXXX has provided me a copy of your December 22,

1994 letter addressed to him. Your letter advised Mr. XXXXX that the Police Department had received numerous complaints from residents in his neighborhood regarding interference to their televisions, radios, telephones and other home electronic equipment, allegedly caused by Mr. XXXXXX operation of his radio equipment. You advised Mr. XXXXXX to cease operation of his Amateur Radio equipment within 5 days, and threatened further unspecified "necessary and appropriate action to ensure compliance" with your demand.

Please be advised that Mr. XXXXX is a federally licensed Amateur Radio Operator, holding an Advanced Class license issued by the Federal Communications Commission. Congress has preempted any state or local regulation of radio frequency interference (RFI) pursuant to the provisions of Section 302(a) of the Communications Act of 1934, as amended. 47 U.S.C. § 302(a)(1) of the Act provides that the "Commission may, consistent with the public interest, convenience, and necessity, make reasonable regulations (1) governing the interference potential of devices which in their operation are capable of emitting radio frequency energy by radiation, conduction, or other means in sufficient degree to cause harmful interference to radio communications . . ." 47 U.S.C. § 302(a)(1).

The legislative history of Section 302(a) explicitly provides that the Federal Communications Commission has exclusive authority to regulate radio frequency interference. In its Conference Report No. 97-765, Congress declared:

> The Conference Substitute is further intended to clarify the reservation of exclusive jurisdiction to the Federal Communications Commission over matters involving RFI. Such matters shall not be regulated by local or state law, nor shall radio-transmitting apparatus be subject to local or state regulation as part of any effort to resolve an RFI complaint. The Conferees believe that radio transmitter operators should not be subject to fines, forfeitures or other liability imposed by any local or state authority as a result of interference appearing in home electronic equipment or systems. Rather, the Conferees intend that regulation of RFI phenomena shall be imposed only by the Commission.

H.R. Report No. 765, 97th Cong., 2d Sess. 33 (1982), reprinted at 1982 U.S. Code Cong. & Ad News 2277.

Any further action by your department or continued harassment of Mr. XXXXX by your officers or employees of the Village of Carpentersville in an attempt to regulate radio frequency interference is illegal and preempted by federal law. I suggest you so advise Trustee XXXXX or other neighbors of the XXXXX's.

I have advised Mr. XXXXX of his rights in this matter, including the right to file a suit in the United States District Court for the Northern District of Illinois seeking declaratory and injunctive relief against the Village of Carpentersville and its agents should further action be taken against him or his family. See *Borowski v. City of Burbank*, 101 F.R.D. 59 (N.D. Ill. 1984).

I trust such action will not be necessary now that you are aware of the applicable law.

Very truly yours,

James C. O'Connell

Letter 4:

Re: *Wheaton v. Fumarolo*

Dear Mr. Knippen:

Thank you for your letter of October 1, 1996. In the future, please address any correspondence to me at the above address. I have forwarded a copy of your letter to the Fumarolo's attorney, Mr. Gary Evans, who I understand will be contacting you to further discuss his clients' position.

Attached to this letter, please find a copy of an Amendment to the Communications Act proposed by Senator Feingold of Wisconsin on August 2, 1996. Senator Feingold's remarks upon introduction are instructive, and clearly demonstrate that municipalities are presently preempted from regulating radio frequency interference complaints, whether caused by CB or Amateur Radio operators. (Congressional Record, S9564-65, August 2, 1996).

As additional authority for this proposition, see *Broyde v. Gotham Tower, Inc.*, 13 F.3d 994 (6th Cir. 1994) holding that a homeowner's state law action against a radio station for nuisance was preempted by the Communications Act of 1934. The Court stated that when Congress gave the FCC power to establish performance standards for home appliances to reduce their susceptibility to interference from radio frequency energy, it clearly removed regulation of radio transmitters from state or local law.

In *Still v. Michaels*, 791 F. Supp. 248 (USDC AZ, 1992), the Court held that the law of nuisance in the area of radio frequency interference was preempted by the Communications Act since it would obstruct the FCC's ability to regulate such matters. Plaintiffs' state law action for nuisance had been previously dismissed on the grounds that state courts were precluded by federal preemption from remedying an alleged private nuisance caused by interference from the operation of a radio transmitter. 166 Ariz. 403, 803 P.2d 124 (App. 1990).

Please call me if you have any questions in regard to this information.

Very truly yours,

James C. O'Connell

TVI/RFI Complaint by a Neighbor with a Gun

[Note: Again, a much deserved "thank you" is due to Greg Becker, JD, PhD, NA2N, and a former policeman, for advice he gave me contained in this section.]

The author once received a 10 pm phone call from a very shaken ham. It seems that a neighbor had just come calling, carrying a gun. The essence of the message delivered by the neighbor was: "Shut that damn thing off or I'll use this."

Was this a direct threat against the life or property of the ham? I don't know, and I didn't care. I advised the ham to file a written report with his town's police department right then, by leaving the house and driving down to the station. And that's what I'd advise you.

Don't be a namby-pamby, filled with "I don't want to cause hard feelings or make things more difficult by talking to the police" crap. If your neighbor was concerned about hard feelings or making things more difficult, chances are he would have stayed in bed, and not be present at your front door.

However, there are two schools of thought about this situation. The Hopengarten school of thought is that by driving to the Police Department you are removing yourself from the physical situation. It is hard to get knifed or shot if you aren't there. On the other hand, Greg Becker would *call* the police and have them come to your house. By bringing a marked unit to your house, you make a visible statement to the neighbor that you will not tolerate that behavior, and give the officer(s) the opportunity to deal with the situation right then and there (that is, arrest, chat, etc).

Nonetheless, when you place the 911 call, say that you are frightened for your safety. Now it's on tape. When the patrol car arrives, remember to mention that you are "frightened for your safety," and make sure it gets written down. It may sound like a little thing, but it gives law enforcement a bigger stick should it become necessary to do more than "speak softly."

Threats with guns are just not neighborly. They amount to a criminal offense, not just a civil concern. That's what the police are for: To protect and defend. In the "neighbor with gun" case mentioned above, the police took the issue seriously. In essence, they told the offending neighbor: We don't care about your interference, *Don't Do That*. After the police report was filed, the neighbor was never heard from again and moved a little while later.

This does not mean that the ham was not shaken. Both the ham and his wife didn't sleep easily for a while. But if I had to do it again, I'd escalate again. Start a paper trail immediately by filing a police report.

By the way, don't say or write: "He threatened me." That's a conclusion. Report the words of the threat or your best memory of what was said. If he said: "Cut it out or I'll use my trusty rifle," report those words. And if it is true, be sure to say: "I'm frightened and concerned for my safety." Those words, if not overplayed, will normally make a police department jump.

Someone who shows up at your door with a gun should be in handcuffs, at least for criminal trespass, menacing, and potentially some weapons charges. Let the judge sort it out when everything has calmed down. You can't "un-arrest" someone, but it's much more difficult to resolve the situation with the rest of your family is sitting in the hospital (or God forbid in the funeral parlor) saying "If only we'd called the police..."

My view of the world is that threats of physical violence are not to be ignored. Whether the caller mentioned a gun, or another weapon—and even if the caller did not mention a weapon—if you felt threatened, you should take action. Call the police. This is not 1835, and this is not the Wild West.

THE CB INTERFERENCE STATUTE

There is always the possibility that a law-enforcement official may believe that a new Federal statute has changed things. This new law, PL 106-521, an act entitled "State and

Local Enforcement of Federal Communications Commission regulations on Use of Citizens Band Radio Equipment," amends the Communications Act of 1934, making it legal for a State or local government to enact a statute or ordinance prohibiting unauthorized operation of citizens-band radio equipment from 24-35 MHz.

Such a statute is sometimes called "an enabling statute." This means that it doesn't immediately empower the police to assume jurisdiction in the area of RFI, where once only the FCC could act. A state or local government must still first create legislation under this statute, and the legislation "shall identify the [Amateur Radio] exemption…" So even the local law must tell the police that as a licensed Radio Amateur you are exempt.

Note that an appropriately licensed ham could, indeed, use converted CB gear on 10 meters, even if such a local statute or ordinance exists, because the ham would *not* be "unauthorized." However, as most law-enforcement officers cannot be expected to know the difference between Citizen's Band radio and Amateur Radio, you may need to be informed about the following law, signed by President Clinton in late 2000, just before the end of his term.

SECTION 302 OF THE COMMUNICATIONS ACT OF 1934

SEC. 302. DEVICES WHICH INTERFERE WITH RADIO RECEPTION.

(f) (1) Except as provided in paragraph (2), a State or local government may enact a statute or ordinance that prohibits a violation of the following regulations of the Commission under this section:
    (A) A regulation that prohibits a use of citizens band radio equipment not authorized by the Commission.
    (B) A regulation that prohibits the unauthorized operation of citizens band radio equipment on a frequency between 24 MHz and 35 MHz.
    (2) A station that is licensed by the Commission pursuant to section 301 in any radio service for the operation at issue shall not be subject to action by a State or local government under this subsection. A State or local government statute or ordinance enacted for purposes of this subsection shall identify the exemption available under this paragraph.
    (3) The Commission shall provide technical guidance to State and local governments regarding the detection and determination of violations of the regulations specified in paragraph (1).
    (4) (A) In addition to any other remedy authorized by law, a person affected by the decision of a State or local government enforcing a statute or ordinance under paragraph (1) may submit to the Commission an appeal of the decision on the grounds that the State or local government, as the case may be, enacted a statute or ordinance outside the authority provided in this subsection.
    (B) A person shall submit an appeal on a decision of a State or local government to the Commission under this paragraph, if at all, not later than 30 days after the date on which the decision by the State or local government becomes final, but prior to seeking judicial review of such decision.
    (C) The Commission shall make a determination on an appeal submitted under subparagraph (B) not later than 180 days after its submittal.
    (D) If the Commission determines under subparagraph (C) that a State or local government has acted outside its authority in enforcing a statute or ordinance, the Commission shall preempt the decision enforcing the statute or ordinance.
    (5) The enforcement of statute or ordinance that prohibits a violation of a regulation by a State or local government under paragraph (1) in a particular case shall not preclude the Commission from enforcing the regulation in that case concurrently.
    (6) Nothing in this subsection shall be construed to diminish or otherwise affect the jurisdiction of the Commission under this section over devices capable of interfering with radio communications.
    (7) The enforcement of a statute or ordinance by a State or local government under paragraph (1) with regard to citizens band radio equipment on board a "commercial motor vehicle", as defined in section 31101 of title 49, United States Code, shall require probable cause to find that the commercial motor vehicle or the individual operating the vehicle is in violation of the regulations described in paragraph (1). Probable cause shall be defined in accordance with the technical guidance provided by the Commission under paragraph (3).

For a radio amateur, the heart of the statute is found at 47 USC § 302(f)(2): "A station that is licensed by the Commission pursuant to section 301 in any radio service for the operation at issue shall not be subject to action by a State or local government under this subsection." You are exempt. You are not required to produce your Amateur Radio license in order to be exempt.

THE RENEWAL

Occasionally you find a town that requires *renewal* of the Special Exception, or Special-Use Permit. The renewal may be required by the general bylaws or the town, the zoning bylaw, or it may be an invention of the permit-granting authority (this means that they just made up the requirement, all by themselves).

A renewal requirement is *very* dangerous and must be treated with great respect, taking every opportunity to soften its requirements, while trying to eliminate the periodicity or to elongate the period. A renewal is basically bad public policy, because as time passes and the tower becomes part of the neighborhood, it will be forgotten by the majority of inhabitants and will never be noticed by passersby. Why stir up passions and animosities unnecessarily?

Should someone on the Board say that a renewal is necessary because of a concern for safety, there is a simple reply: "This is construction like all other construction. You don't require renewals on a Building Permit for a free-standing garage, do you?" If a neighbor really fears that your structure may become dangerous, it can be treated like any other dangerous construction. Using his police power (which is why most Building Inspectors are issued a badge), a Building Inspector may come onto your property without your permission if she/he has a reason to believe there is a danger to the public's health or safety.

Furthermore, if he/she does find a danger, and the homeowner doesn't correct the problem, the Building Inspector has the power to put a lien against the property to pay for repair or removal. The Town always gets paid back, because the property cannot be sold without clearing that lien. A mortgage company or bank would see to that. Thus, a renewal is totally unnecessary.

Frequency of Renewal

There are many different towns and many different Boards, with many different applicants. A Variance is permanent and runs with the land. This means that you can record it in your local registry of deeds and any subsequent owner of the land may take advantage of the Variance. However, a Special Permit may be made *personal*. When you are no longer there to use that permit, it will expire.

It is not unusual to find Boards that take the position that the Town must be *protected*. One of the ways that such Boards seek to protect the town is by not issuing permanent Special Permits for antenna-support structures. Of course, this begs the very real question: "From what are they protecting the town once a permit is granted?"

Nonetheless, as a form of harassment to hams—because no other logical explanation can be put forward for renewal requirements except to hasten the removal of a support structure by harassing the ham—some towns will add periodic renewal requirements to a Special Permit. In many cases they do so because they can, not because it makes any sense. I feel that such towns don't think the process through completely.

If your ordinance, or Board, absolutely, positively insists that a Special Permit for an Amateur Radio antenna-support structure must have periodic renewals, there are several strategies, some with variations, the Board may try. Expressed briefly, they are:

- One year, then permanent,
- Three years, then permanent, and
- Some years, then to coincide with License Renewal.

One Year, Then Permanent

In this scenario, the Board issues a one-year permit, then reexamines the issue. Actually, this is silly. Things may not yet have gelled in a year. Assume that twenty days, or some number of days must pass before the Special Permit becomes valid, to allow the passing of the appeal deadline. Then one applies to the Building Inspector for a Building Permit, which has a time frame all its own.

Only after the grant of a Building Permit can construction actually begin. If construction is interrupted by bad weather (more properly known as *winter* in Northern climates), the structure may not be up, populated by antennas and eligible for a Certificate of Completion for six to nine months. Thus, a one-year period before renewal is really bad public policy, because you could wind up in a situation where it is time to renew a Special Permit before construction has concluded.

Three Years, Then Permanent

If a Board feels compelled to revisit the situation after construction, allowing three years after the grant of a Special Permit makes more sense (four or five years would make even more sense). This time period allows for construction of the antenna system and a period of time for grass to grow back around the base of the structure (where it may have been bothered by the pouring of concrete). It also allows time for neighborhood hotheads to cool off. Presentations to the Board, if there are any, will be much more levelheaded in three or more years, and they can be accompanied by photographs of the actual installation.

However, there is little or no benefit to further hearings after this "post-construction" hearing. Thereafter the only matters are matters of safety, because no matter what changes may come in zoning bylaws, the antenna-support structure has achieved the status of a "prior existing structure."

There are Boards that have claimed that they cannot and will not delegate matters of public safety to the Building Inspector. This is total nonsense, since the job of the Building Inspector is to be the person to whom matters of public safety arising out of construction are delegated.

After the three (four or five) year hearing, the renewal should be made *permanent*. Well, actually not permanent, as that would then be a Variance. In this case permanent really means that the permit should expire when the radio amateur, or a successor radio amateur, no longer has a substantial ownership and use interest, direct or beneficial, in the land.

Why is it necessary to write such a convoluted expiration date? For one thing, the ham may not now, or at some time in the future, be the owner of the property. For example, ownership may be in the name of a landlord or spouse. For another, make sure the Board does not write that the permit will expire when the ham is no longer *domiciled* there, since domicile is a very technical word, which can sometimes involve counting the number of nights someone slept somewhere. For example, the radio amateur could become a "snow bird," living a few months each year in a warmer climate—and this is not a rational reason for the expiration of a Special Permit.

A Period of Years, Then to Coincide with License Renewal

If the Board just cannot live with itself without insisting on a renewal, it would be rational and good public policy, to make the renewal of the Special Permit coincide with the amateur's FCC license renewal. At least license renewal would prompt the ham to remember a looming renewal deadline.

A possible problem with this suggestion, but only from the perspective of the Board, is the arithmetic possibility that a ham license could be renewed and then the Special Permit granted, so that the Special Permit would not come up for review for nine years and eleven months. To the Board, this may seem like a long time before they review the situation.

From the perspective of the radio amateur, who would rather just get the Special Permit and have that end the matter, the challenge of a renewal is still presented. However, except in the case where the renewal would be presented in less than three years (which, as previously expressed, is just too short), a better solution is to agree to a renewal process in three to five years, and thereafter on renewal of the FCC license.

This would be reasonable public-policy thinking—if only licenses were stable. The problem is: "What if the ham gets a new (vanity?) call sign, or upgrades from general to extra class, and the license clock begins anew?" Ah well.

There is no doubt a compromise somewhere out there that you can make. Make a good suggestion to your Board, and include it in your suggested decision!

What if You're Stuck with a Renewal?

If, despite your best efforts, you find yourself stuck with a renewal requirement, the best thing you can do is to make it easy for the Board to renew without sliding off the rails. And how do you make it easy? You provide the Board all the information that it needs to renew. Furthermore, you do this with respect for the Board, by being formal in your request.

You should help them find your file by citing the file or case number, if one was ever assigned. You should provide, in advance, the text of the notice to be published in the local newspaper, so that when the legal notice appears your neighbors won't think you are up to something new or different. You should provide the correct language in a suggested renewal decision.

Never forget that the Board is made up of volunteers. The facts may be elusive or few may remember what you are talking about. Your permit may have been granted before the person assigned to write up your renewal grant was ever named to the Board. Mistakes are easily made, so it is your job to prevent such mistakes by doing their work for them.

The following documents appear on the CD-ROM enclosed with this book, ready for you to modify. They are presented here with commentary. See filename: **Late Request for Renewal.DOC**.

The Request for Renewal

[Comment: If a question arises, be sure to give the Secretary to the Board many different ways to get in touch with you. It can be useful to include an e-mail address, a FAX number (if possible), and your work telephone number, in case the Secretary wants to get in touch with you and ask a question.]

December 10, 1998

[Comment: Renewal requirements often include "bracket dates"; ie, no sooner than three months before expiration and no later than 30 days before expiration (to allow for advertising and scheduling on the agenda for the next available hearing).]

Board of Appeals
Town of Lincoln
Town Offices
P. O. Box 353
Lincoln, MA 01773

To the Board:

On February 22, 1984, the Massachusetts Appeals Court issued its opinion in *Fred Hopengarten v. Board of Appeals of Lincoln*, 17 Mass. App. Ct. 1006 (1984), the case involving my application for a special permit to erect a non-commercial Amateur Radio antenna-support structure at my home at Six Willarch Road. With the expiration of the appeal period occurring 20 days later, the effective date of the permit granted in this matter was March 14, 1984.

[Note: Sometimes it can be tricky to figure out exactly when the permit comes up for renewal. You cannot rely on the Board to spend the time to figure this out. This is especially true because the Board's secretary may forget to include the appeal period, yet the permit may specify that the permit is "valid for five years from the effective date" and not the date on the decision.]

The original permit granted by the Board of Appeals dated April 8, 1981, reads, in relevant part:

"Said permit shall be renewed automatically for successive three-year periods provided that a written request for renewal is made to the Board of Appeals by Petitioner for such renewal not less than three (3) months prior to the expiration of the then-existing three-year period."

Thus, I write to request the automatic renewal of the Special Permit granted in this matter for this existing antenna-support structure. No objections to automatic renewal were filed in 1986, 1990, 1993, or 1996, when on each occasion this permit was automatically renewed. I enclose a check in the appropriate amount. As a convenience to the Board, I enclose suggested wording for the decision.

*[Note: In renewal situations, keep telling everyone concerned that this is for an **existing structure**. Once on a roll, remind the Board that there is no need to get excited. Tell them, effectively, that they need not tax their brains. Don't forget any required payment, for the process and for the legal advertising.]*

Sincerely,
Fred Hopengarten

Enc: Check; suggested decision

TOWN OF LINCOLN
Middlesex County . - . Massachusetts
Town Offices
PO Box 353
Lincoln Center, MA 01773
781 259-2607

BOARD OF APPEALS

In the Matter of
      AUTOMATIC RENEWAL OF
      SPECIAL PERMIT
      FRED HOPENGARTEN
****

WHEREAS, the Petitioner has, within the required time period, requested in writing that the Special Permit granted by the Board of Appeals on April 8, 1981 (effective date March 14, 1984, the "Special Permit") be renewed automatically for a period of three (3) years pursuant to the terms of the Special Permit;

WHEREAS, public notice in connection with said request has been given as required by law;

NOW, THEREFORE, said Special Permit is hereby extended until March 14, 2002, subject to being further renewed automatically thereafter in accordance with the terms of the Special Permit.

The permit herein granted is personal to the owner and expires only if the petitioner ceases to have a substantial ownership and use interest, direct or beneficial, in his present land.

By:
Chairman
Board of Appeals

Date:

To: Nancy Zuelke, Clerk, Board of Appeals
From: Fred Hopengarten
Date: December 10, 1998

For your convenience, I found the notice you prepared in 1989 for publication, which has been used subsequently. Its wording is correct, and we agree on it.

BOARD OF APPEALS

The Board of Appeals of the Town of Lincoln hereby gives notice that the SPECIAL PERMIT TO MAINTAIN AN AMATEUR RADIO TOWER now held by FRED HOPENGARTEN, SIX WILLARCH ROAD, will be renewed for a period of three years unless an objection, in writing, citing grounds under Section 6.2(f), is received. Any such objection should be filed with the Clerk of the Board of Appeals, in writing, no later than January 6, 2001. The hearing date for renewal is February 6, 2001.

Nancy Zuelke, Clerk
Board of Appeals

Late to Renew?

Let's face it. Humans are imperfect and ham radio has its share of imperfect humans too. Let's say you somehow forget to renew a permit, if renewal is required. The usual questions in this situation are:

- Should I not bring it to their attention and just submit the application and let them worry about whether the late submission is a problem? (No.)
- Should I make a big thing of it? (Don't be an idiot.)
- Should I at least offer an excuse, such as "I was out of town"? (Yes, if it is the truth.)
- Should I ask the Board to remove the renewal requirement? (Yes. The worst thing they can do is say no, in which case you are where you were already.)
- How do I handle it?

There are likely to be several lawyers on the Board of Appeals (or whatever the Board is called). They don't know anything about antenna-support structures, but they *love* deadlines, definitions and distances. Those are things they can understand. The proper thing is to ask for "an enlargement of time to file for renewal."

In addition, since you are back in front of the dreaded Board anyway, now is your chance to ask for removal of a condition in the permit that you don't like, that being the requirement for renewal. If they don't grant it, ask again next time! Here's the gist of your application letter (on the CD-ROM, filename: **Late Renewal Request Letter.DOC**):

Ladies and Gentlemen:

This Special Permit was originally granted by decision dated _____, 2001, and was for a term of five years. By its terms, it requires renewal.

Construction began on ___date___ (or, "in the month of ___") and a Certificate of Completion dated _____, 2001 has been received. See Exhibit A.

This is a motion for an enlargement of time to file for renewal, a petition to renew the special permit, and a motion to remove the renewal requirement. *[Note to the reader: If you are convinced they will never remove the renewal requirement, ask that it be extended to 10 years, or to coincide with the renewal date of your FCC license.]*

With respect to the motion for an enlargement of time, I apologize to the Board for failure to meet the time requirement, but please note that I've been traveling for business three of the past four weeks.

With respect to the last motion, to remove the renewal requirement, please note that:

- Whereas the Board may not have had a clear idea of the appearance and visibility of the proposed antenna-support structure when the application was first, the structure has been up for more than <u>five</u> years now. The predictions and consequences envisioned by opponents have not come to pass, lessening the need for supervision.
- No change in the construction of the antenna-support structure is contemplated and, with or without a renewal process, a change in the structure would trigger a new hearing anyway.
- With respect to any questions of safety, the Building Inspector retains his right of entry to inspect for safety at any time under his police power.
- Should the antenna-support structure remain after it is no longer in use, with or without a renewal process, it puts the property at risk during any sale, since the cost of the

Town's removal of the structure would become a lien on the property — a very effective and self-enforcing protection for the town.

I ask for a hearing as soon as your calendar permits.

Respectfully submitted,

You have now created a written record, which could be useful if a nasty neighbor ever makes an issue of it. Most Boards will either grant the enlargement, or ignore the motion for enlargement because granting renewal subsumes the procedural question of the filing deadline—making the question go away.

As a convenience to the Board, and because you are a good guy, you may also wish to include the suggested wording for the renewal.

Board of Appeals
Renewal of Special Permit

In the Matter of John T. Ham

WHEREAS, the Petitioner has, within the required time period *[alternative: after a request for and the grant of grant of an enlargement of time to file]*, requested in writing that the Special Permit granted by the Board of Appeals on April 8, 1999 (effective date April 28, 1999, the "Special Permit") be renewed for a period of five (5) years or more pursuant to the terms of the Special Permit, and;

WHEREAS, no material change in the construction of the antenna-support structure is contemplated and a material change in the structure would require a hearing anyway, and;

WHEREAS, with respect to any question of safety, the Building Inspector retains a right of entry to inspect for safety at any time under the police power of that office;

NOW, THEREFORE, said Special Permit is hereby extended and shall expire when Petitioner no longer has a substantial ownership and use interest, direct or beneficial, in the land *[alternative: when it is no longer in an amateur radio use]*. Should the antenna-support structure remain thereafter, it may be removed by the Town at the expense of the landowner, with the cost of removal of the structure eligible to become a lien on the property.

By:

Chairman
Board of Appeals

Date: _____

Bond to Guarantee Removal

The same principles hold for a bond to guarantee removal. The occasional Town Planner will say: "We need a bond to protect the town and guarantee removal." There is a simple, and self-enforcing mechanism that accomplishes the same thing without much paperwork or cost.

Make the Special Permit *personal to* the amateur who applies for it, or any successor licensed amateur who lives at the property. If the property is sold and no radio amateur then living there applies for a continuation of the permit within two years, the permit will then expire. The structure is still subject to removal by the Town under police power and subject to a lien on the house and land to pay for that removal.

That is a painful and unnecessary rigmarole, but acceptable, because it really doesn't require anything more than removal someday—this is easy because there is an active market for antenna-support structures, even those that are still vertical. The usual terms are: "Take it down and it is yours."

On the other hand, I once saw a bylaw that required a cash bond to guarantee removal. While totally unnecessary for all the reasons cited above, the proper way to approach this is to suggest that the proper cash bond is $50, or just enough to place the ad in the right newspaper or *QST*. Remember too that at no cost you may put it on the Internet (TowerTalk reflector: **towertalk@contesting.com**) and ask for someone to come and haul the tower away.

12

Appeals

PROCESS: CAN YOU SPELL *REMAND*?

Many hams do not know the discouraging fact that a successful appeal from a Board of Appeals to a court normally results in a *remand* (a return) to the original forum (the Board of Appeals, for example) with instructions to that (normally hostile) Board to reconsider the matter in light of the Court's further instructions. It is a rare event for a court to grant the permit itself. For the court to grant the permit itself, you would generally have to show that a remand to the original panel would be a fruitless act, because of the demonstrated hostility of that Board to the applicant or to the application itself.

To give you an idea of just how hard it can be to convince a Court to skip over the remand step, *MacGibbon v. Board of Appeals of Duxbury*, 369 Mass. 512 (1976) (though not a ham-radio antenna case) covered 13 years and three denials on legally untenable grounds before the Court issued the permit itself. A direct issuance may be easier in your state, or in Federal court, but it is usually difficult.

APPEALS OF A GRANTED PERMIT

Many hams have been tempted to appeal the grant of a permit that contains conditions he or she does not like. Before you consider this course of action, remember that a really hostile Board could succeed in getting new information introduced by an opponent the second time around, leaving you worse off, or no better off, than you were when you started. Try to see if you can live with the permit originally granted.

If you really feel that you cannot, ask yourself if you could live with the permit as granted for a year or two. After the controversy has died down, and neighbors have discovered that the sky has not fallen, a modification totally unacceptable today may be possible in a year or two.

APPEALING A DENIED PERMIT

On the other hand, if your permit has been denied, and you cannot live with the result, you really must consider an appeal. This gets tricky, since you must now select the forum to which you will appeal. For example, according to your own local situation, you may be able to appeal to another level of land use authority (perhaps at the county or regional level), a land court, a superior court or a Federal court. Selecting the appropriate *venue* really requires the advice of a local lawyer and an analysis of your facts.

Can you handle the appeal yourself? Most lawyers would advise against it. But now and again an intrepid soul who cannot justify the legal expense, and can live with himself if he loses, tries and wins.

That's what happened to Paul Kaplan, N2FOB. He filed the case without the help of a lawyer and tried it. Here's the opinion of the court (the full finding is on the CD-ROM, filename: **Kaplan.PDF**):

In conclusion, therefore, I find that the Winslow Township Ordinance 294-107, as applied to the Applicant, is contrary to Federal Regulation PRB-1 in that it precludes amateur communications. I further find that the action of the Board does not attain the reasonable accommodation required by PRB-1 and is arbitrary and capricious.

The finding of the Winslow Township Zoning Board of Adjustment is, therefore, reversed. The matter is remanded to the Zoning Board for the purpose of issuing a permit to the Applicant for the erection of a tower and antenna for both transmission and reception, subject to such conditions and requirements that the Board imposes, including, but not limited to a reasonable height limitation, placement of the structure, appropriate installation from both the safety aspect and a grounding aspect, protection by way of fencing, if necessary, to keep children off the tower and arrangements to correct any interference with other devices which may occur.

This court decision includes an illegal condition (permitting "arrangements to correct any interference") that is blatantly contrary to Federal law. This illegal condition thoroughly and completely preempts the field of interference involving radio amateurs. Despite this, the N2FOB decision does demonstrate that with the right facts, a "do-it-yourself" appeal can work.

Before you run off to file your own appeal in court, however, you should realize just how outrageous the bylaw was in Kaplan's case. The bylaw in Winslow Township, NJ, prohibited any sort of tower in any residential district. In all other districts, a tower could not be located within 1,500 feet of a residential district. The Court found that "it would require a plot of land of a minimum 162 acres to accommodate such a tower. The practical effect is preclusive in nature and, therefore, also in violation of PRB-1."

Furthermore, the Court wrote: "I note that a television antenna for reception only of the same size, shape, configurations and visual aspects is not only permitted by the township, but a permit was subsequently issued to the applicant for such a structure." If your bylaw is not quite so outrageous—and you aren't as willing to gamble—I suggest that you seek advice of legal counsel before proceeding to file your own appeal!

In any event, whether you won or lost, do not delay in filing or responding to a complaint. The courts do not look kindly at tardiness in the filing of complaints or answers. You could lose because of a late filing and the game will be over. However, if for some good reason you simply cannot file on time, and if you can show that the other side was not prejudiced by your delay, you may petition the court for a little extra time (usually calling this a "Motion for an Enlargement of Time to File").

GENERIC APPEAL TO COURT

Here is a generic Massachusetts complaint, in the name of John T. Hamateur. A ham can save himself some money by filling in his own facts before an attorney sits down to draft the complaint. There is considerable art to drafting a complaint, as the general rule is that anything left out of the complaint cannot be raised later, because the defendant (the Town Board, in this case) was not on notice of the issue (this means that the Town didn't know that some issue was "in play"). Don't worry about paragraph numbering. That's the last thing to be done. This document appears on the CD-ROM, under filename: **MA Generic Appeal.DOC**.

Please read this generic complaint even before filing the original application for a Special Permit or Special Exception. If you haven't introduced the facts at the hearing or Board level, your state may preclude you from introducing them later. If you have not yet produced information, witnesses or forms of support for any claim you'll be making in the complaint, now (well in advance) is the time to gather what you'll need later.

COMMONWEALTH OF MASSACHUSETTS

NAME OF COUNTY, ss.

SUPERIOR COURT DEPARTMENT
OF THE TRIAL COURT
CIVIL ACTION No. 01-_____

JOHN T. HAMATEUR,

        Plaintiff

)
)
)
)

v.

) COMPLAINT

NAME OF BOARD, TOWN,

        Defendant

)
)
)
)
)

JURISDICTION

1. This is an appeal of a decision ("the decision") of the Name of Board, Town, Massachusetts ("the Board"). A copy of the Decision is attached as Exhibit B.

2. The subject matter of the Board's decision is the erection of an Amateur Radio antenna structure on Ham's property located at Address, Town, Middlesex County, Massachusetts (the "property").

3. Pursuant to M.G.L. Chapter 40A, Section 17, the Court has jurisdiction to review the Board's decision.

PARTIES

4. Plaintiff, John T. Hamateur, is an individual who resides at and is an owner (with his wife) of XXXX Road, Town, Blank County, Massachusetts. Hamateur has been a federally licensed private, noncommercial amateur (also known as "ham") radio station owner since 1975. He holds the highest class of Amateur Radio operator license (the Amateur Extra Class), and the Amateur Radio station license with the call sign W1JTH, both issued by the FCC.

5. The Board has its municipal offices at Town Hall, Address, Town, XXX County, Massachusetts.

RELEVANT PROCEDURAL HISTORY

6. On or about Date, Hamateur submitted an Application for a Building Permit to construct and use an Amateur-Radio antenna structure on his property. A copy of that Application is attached hereto as Exhibit A.

[Was it denied by the Building Inspector and forwarded to the Board for review? If there was an intermediate step in the denial, include it, and mention the date.]

7. After due notice, on Date, a hearing was held before the Board.

8. On Date, the Board's order ("the Decision") was issued and delivered by U.S. mail to Plaintiff. The Decision, bearing the date of filing, certified by the town clerk with whom the Decision was filed, is attached hereto as Exhibit B.

RELEVANT FACTS

9. Amateur-Radio operators provide an unpaid service to the community by, among other things, providing emergency and disaster related communications services. Amateur-Radio operation is strictly noncommercial. Federal law recognizes this in Public Law 103-408 (1994), a Joint Resolution of

Congress passed and signed by the President "(t)o recognize the achievements of radio amateurs, and to establish support for such amateurs as national policy."

10. Amateur Radio is also a significant conduit for the exchange of ideas and information between United States citizens and citizens world wide.

11. The Federal Government, through the Communications Act of 1934, as amended, 41 U.S.C. §151 *et seq.*, has assumed and delegated to the Federal Communications Commission ("FCC") exclusive jurisdiction over radio communications.

12. Plaintiff has been a federally licensed Amateur-Radio operator, licensed by the FCC since 19__. For over __ years, Hamateur has communicated with thousands of people from all over the world. He is an active participant in the Town's Civil Defense group, and engages in other public service and emergency communications activities.

13. In 1985, the FCC issued a declaratory order of limited federal preemption over local zoning regulations of Amateur-Radio antenna facilities and structures: Amateur Radio Preemption, 101 FCC 2d 952 (1985), 50 FR 38813, http://www.fcc.gov/wtb/amateur/prb-1.html ("PRB-1").

14. PRB-1 states in relevant part:

> 24. . . . [T]here is a strong federal interest in promoting amateur communications . . . [and] a limited preemption policy is warranted. State and local regulations that operate to preclude amateur communications in their communities are in direct conflict with federal objectives and must be preempted.

> 25. Because amateur station communications are only as effective as the antennas employed, antenna height restrictions directly affect the effectiveness of amateur communications. . . [L]ocal regulations which involve placement, screening, or height of antennas [and antenna structures] based on health, safety, or aesthetic considerations **must be crafted to accommodate reasonably amateur communications**, and to represent the **minimum practicable regulation** to accomplish the local authority's legitimate purpose. [*Emphasis added.*]

15. In 1989, the FCC codified PRB-1 in federal regulation as part of the FCC Rules, 47 CFR § 97.15(b), which states, in relevant part:

> . . . a station antenna structure may be erected at heights and dimensions sufficient to accommodate amateur service communications. State and local regulation of a station antenna structure must not preclude amateur service communications. Rather, it must reasonably accommodate such communications and must constitute the minimum practicable regulation to accomplish the state or local authority's legitimate purpose.

16. In 1999, the FCC revisited these issues and clarified Federal law by ordering:

> [T]he PRB-1 decision precisely stated the principle of "reasonable accommodation". In PRB-1, the Commission stated: "Nevertheless, local regulations which involve placement, screening, or height of antennas based on health, safety, or aesthetic considerations must be crafted to accommodate reasonably amateur communications, and to represent the minimum practicable regulation to accomplish the local authority's legitimate purpose." Given this express Commission language, it is clear that a "balancing of interests" approach is not appropriate in this context.

The Commission continued:

> [T]he very least regulation necessary for the welfare of the community must be the aim of its regulations so that such regulations will not impinge on the needs of amateur operators to engage in amateur communications.

ORDER In the Matter of RM-8763, adopted November 18, 1999, released November 19, 1999, paragraphs 7 and 9. http://www.fcc.gov/Bureaus/Wireless/Orders/1999/da992569.txt

17.   MGL, c. 40A, √3 adopts PRB-1 and 47 CFR √97.15(b) and similarly states:

> No zoning ordinance or by-law shall prohibit the construction or use of an antenna structure by a federally licensed amateur radio operator. Zoning ordinances and by-laws may reasonably regulate the location and height of such antenna structures for the purposes of health, safety, or aesthetics; provided, however, that such ordinances and by-laws reasonably allow for **sufficient height of such antenna structures so as to effectively accommodate amateur radio communications** by federally licensed amateur radio operators and constitute the **minimum practicable regulation** necessary to accomplish the legitimate purposes of the city or town enacting such ordinance or by-law. [*Emphasis added.*]

18. Radio towers and antennas are uses customarily incident to residential property. *Village of St. Louis Park v. Casey*, 16 N.W. 2d 450 (1944). Public Law 103-408 (1994), specifically establishes support for radio amateurs as national policy, recognizes that Amateur Radio promotes public safety, that Amateur Radio operations take place from residences and declares them to be a public benefit, requiring additionally that:

> (3) reasonable accommodation should be made for the effective operation of amateur radio **from residences**, private vehicles and public areas, and that regulation at all levels of government should facilitate and encourage amateur radio operation as a public benefit. [*Emphasis added.*]

19. Topography of the property, the presence of hills or other terrain features in the area, radio frequencies used, time within the sunspot cycle, desired range of communications, and other technical factors must be considered when determining sufficiency of height of an antenna for effective communication.

20. Thus, for most purposes, the higher the antenna, the higher the quality of communications for making distant, even worldwide, radio contact, where such would not be possible with a low antenna.

21. There are remote areas around the world where the only means of getting messages is by Amateur Radio. With a restricted low antenna, the radio amateur is left with no suitable alternative for communication with people in such areas.

22. Plaintiff desires to engage in long range international communications with a horizontal Yagi antenna at 14 MHz, requiring the requested height and antenna size.

23. Plaintiff desires to engage in digital communications with Town, MA at 145 MHz, also requiring the requested height.

THE DECISION

24. The Board's decision states that

[insert relevant portion of the decision, for example:
"the proposed structure would be visible from several residences in the area" and therefore the project "would have a negative effect on the amenity of the neighborhood" (Exhibit B, Decision, page 3). This holding ignores the uncontested evidence, through testimony and photographs, of solid (not "seethrough") telephone or utility poles with associated power, telephone, alarm and cable TV cabling, plus guy wires, within 300 feet of Plaintiff's house and plainly visible from the public way.]

25. Thus, for the reasons it states, the Board's objection is that the project is ____.

26. The antenna structure will not be ____.

27. Though <u>nnn</u> feet high, the proposed antenna support structure is only <u>18</u> inches wide, and see through. No additional antenna on top will be made of aluminum tubing greater than two inches in diameter. The applicant provided the Board with pictures of the proposed structure to demonstrate the negligible aesthetic impact of the structure. These pictures were taken from <u>nnn</u>, <u>nnn</u>, and <u>nnnn</u> feet away. At <u>nnn</u> feet, the antenna was barely visible to the camera. At <u>nnn</u>, <u>nnn</u> and <u>nnnn</u> feet, the antenna was not discernible.

28. No credible testimony from a reliable source was presented at the first hearing to support the Board's finding that "the structure may pose a threat to bird species, particularly migratory birds." Nor is the statement true.

29. While the Board cites "protection of wildlife habitat" as an interest adversely affected and therefore requiring denial, just the opposite is true. An antenna-support structure is a "steel tree," providing increased wildlife habitat.

30. The finding that "the structure will be visible from a wide area and is proposed to be located where no structure presently breaks the skyline" is not a proper basis for denial, as mere visibility and novelty is an inadequate reason as a matter of law.

31. Insofar as the Bylaw permits denial based on "aesthetics" without further delineation, the bylaw and regulation is impermissibly vague, and therefore void. As no standards are supplied, no applicant could ever know how to meet the requirements of the bylaw, except, perhaps, by creating an invisible structure.

32. The Board's decision to deny the Special Permit requested permitting construction is therefore arbitrary, capricious and unreasonable on its face, and exceeds the Board's authority.

33. The Board's decision to deny the issuance of an Order of Conditions and the variance requested violates its obligations under Federal and state law.

34. While the Board states that it has made its finding "after considering other alternatives which would permit the work to be undertaken without deviating from the regulations...", the facts are that the Plaintiff has attempted to obtain a Building Permit for alternatives and the Building Inspector, though willing to do so, has failed to issue the necessary Building Permit, upon instructions from Town Counsel.

35. The Town, including the members of the Board, has engaged in an illegal conspiracy, acting on several fronts, to deny the Plaintiff his right to build this antenna system, which should justify an award of damages and costs.

WHEREFORE, Plaintiff prays for judgment:

    a. Annulling the decision of the Board;

    b. Ordering the Board to issue a Special Permit;

    c. Awarding Plaintiff damages and the costs of this action;

    d. Ordering such other and further relief as the Court deems justice and equity require.

JOHN T. HAMATEUR

by his attorney

Massachusetts Bar #_____

Dated: (month, day), 2<u>00</u>

Exhibit A

[The Application]

Exhibit B

[The Decision of the Board]

Exhibit C

[The Relevant Bylaw for Antenna Support Structures]

Exhibit D

[The Relevant Bylaw for Special Permits]

VERIFICATION OF COMPLAINT

COMMONWEALTH OF MASSACHUSETTS

COUNTY, ss.   SUPERIOR COURT DEPARTMENT
                                                OF THE TRIAL COURT
                                                CIVIL ACTION No. 01-_____

_____
)
JOHN T. HAMATEUR,   )
            Plaintiff   )
)
)
v.   ) COMPLAINT
)
TOWN BOARD,   )
            Defendant   )
_____)

                                                Town, MA
                                                Date nn, 200_

    I, John T. Hamateur, of lawful age, being first duly sworn, state that I am the Plaintiff in the above captioned action, that I have read the foregoing Complaint and state that I know and believe the facts therein set forth to be true.

                                    _____
                                    John T. Hamateur

13

Tower and Antenna Regulation in Canada

By Tim S. Ellam, VE6SH

INTRODUCTION

The regulation of towers and antennas in Canada should in theory be markedly different than in the United States. However, in practise radio amateurs in Canada face many of the same problems as their colleagues south of the border. While jurisdiction over towers and antennas is legally entrenched in the powers of the Federal Government (and hence can be exercised by our regulator, Industry Canada), that has not stopped local authorities from interfering in the height and siting of support structures and demanding a greater role in the approval of such installations.

JURISDICTION FOR RADIO COMMUNICATION

Constitutional Issues

The Canadian constitution does not assign jurisdiction over telecommunications as a subject to either the Parliament of Canada (ie, the Federal Government) or the provincial legislatures (ie, the Provincial Governments, which would in turn be able to delegate certain of these powers to municipalities and local authorities). Communications is dealt with as a part of a more general scheme for the division of legislative authority for transportation and communications. Under this scheme, telecommunications, works and undertakings that are local in character are subject to provincial legislative jurisdiction, while those that are interprovincial or international in character are within the exclusive legislative jurisdiction of Parliament.

Section 92(10) of the *Constitution Act* (1867)[1] while providing that "telegraphs and other works" may be subject to laws of a province also confirms there are certain subjects that are specifically exempted from provincial jurisdiction when they are declared by the Parliament of Canada to be for the "general advantage of Canada." Further, under section 91 of the *Constitution Act* the Parliament of Canada also has the authority to make laws for the "peace, order, and good government of Canada."

The combined effect of these provisions establish the division of Federal and provincial jurisdiction for communications generally. In 1932 a decision of the Privy Council in *Re Regulation & Control of Radio Communication in Canada*[2] (the *Radio Reference* case) established that the jurisdiction of Parliament over radio communication is paramount. The essential issue in that case was the Court was asked to determine whether the Parliament of Canada had jurisdiction to "regulate and control radio communication, including the transmission and reception of signs, signals, pictures and sounds of all kinds by means of Hertzian waves, and including the right to determine the character, use and location of apparatus employed."[3]

The Privy Council determined that the Parliament of Canada had exclusive jurisdiction over radio communication, both as an emanation of its treaty making power, which is based on the "peace, order and good government clause" and by virtue of section 92(10) of the *Constitution Act*. The decision in the *Radio Reference* case still stands as good authority for the proposition that Parliament has exclusive jurisdiction in the field of international and interprovincial radio communications by virtue of section 92(10).

The basis for the decision is simply that broadcasting and communications by radio fell within the scope of the words "telegraph and undertakings," which extended beyond the limits of a province. While the provinces conceded that they likely could not regulate international radio communications, they still debated the point that the Federal Government should not be able to regulate interprovincial communication:

"The argument of the Province really depends on making, as already said, a sharp distinction between the transmitting and the receiving instrument. In their Lordships' opinion this cannot be done. Once it is conceded, as it must be, keeping in view the duties under the convention, that the transmitting instrument must be so to speak under the control of the Dominion, it follows in their Lordships' opinion that the receiving instrument must share its fate. Broadcasting as a system cannot exist without both a transmitter and a receiver. The receiver is indeed useless without a transmitter and can be reduced to nonentity if the transmitter closes. The system cannot be divided into two parts, each independent of the other."[4]

Any room for doubt concerning the scope of Federal jurisdiction in the field of radio communication has been removed by the decision of the Supreme Court of Canada in *Capital Cities Communications Inc. v. Canada* (CRTC).[5] This decision confirmed that the *Radio Reference* case had correctly decided the division of powers over communication under the terms of sections 91 and 92(10) of the *Constitution Act*.

This particular line of cases, as a matter of Canadian constitutional law, made it clear that the technical regulation of the properties and characteristics of both transmitting and receiving devices including antennas lies exclusively within the legislative authority of the Federal Government.

Power of Municipalities and Local Authorities

In a legal sense, Municipal Governments or local authorities possess only such power as is expressly delegated to them by a Provincial Government. In turn, Provincial Governments may only delegate powers in which they are lawfully vested. It should follow then that a municipality or local authority would have no power to regulate communications including the siting of antennas. However, Municipal Governments in Canada generally possess authority to regulate the health, safety and aesthetics of buildings and other structures within the confines of their boundaries. Land-use regulation is typically achieved through the use of bylaws or other rules that are legally enforceable on those who wish to develop private property within the municipality.

Starting in the 1960s, municipalities and local authorities became increasingly concerned that the siting of certain radio antennas has had a negative impact in their respective communities. Municipalities and local authorities began to lobby the Federal Government attempting to clarify exactly what authority, if any, could be delegated to them to minimize the effect caused by the siting and operation of particular antennas and their support structures.

This pressure by local authorities resulted in the Federal Department of Justice issuing a legal opinion in the mid-1970s to clarify the constitutional issues. This opinion stated in part:

"Since radio communications is a field exclusively within the legislative competence of the Federal Government, then a province or municipality does not have jurisdiction to enact legislation or pass bylaws respectively which relate directly to radio communications. However, a properly framed municipal bylaw dealing with local zoning and relating only incidently to radio communications may coexist with Federal legislation provided the bylaw neither prohibits nor unduly restricts the conduct of radio services or the operation of federally licenced radio stations."[6]

This somewhat vague definition of the division of powers really did not help matters. Municipalities and local authorities were left none-the-wiser trying to differentiate between direct or incidental relations. Municipalities and local authorities had little guidance to determine how far they could attempt to affect the siting of antennas. As a result, commencing in this time frame, many local authorities enacted bylaws to address the height and siting of antennas. These bylaws, while being of questionable legal validity, usually addressed aesthetic considerations and assigned an arbitrary height limit for antennas and their support structures. Typically, these height limits were very restrictive and did not deal with the technical considerations required for communication.

The issues of siting of antennas increased throughout the 1970s as a result of the sudden growth in interest in the General Radio Service (Citizen Band). Local authorities were suddenly faced with the erection of antennas throughout residential areas.

Municipalities continued to be quite vocal lobbying the Federal Government about regulating the height and siting of antennas through the early 1980s as the use of mobile and cellular telephones began to increase. The Federal Government clearly was willing to assert its exclusive right to regulate the area of communications, but at the same time had an interest in addressing the concerns being raised by the local authorities.

THE TOWNSEND REPORT

In July 1987, Professor David Townsend of the University of New Brunswick, Faculty of Law, prepared a careful and thoughtful legal study for the Federal Government on the question of jurisdiction over the siting of radio communication antennas. The study entitled "Canadian Municipalities and the Regulation of Radio Antenna and their Support Structures" became commonly known as the "Townsend Report."

The Report confirmed the Federal Government's exclusive authority to issue radio licences and approve antenna structures and that radio communications is a field exclusively within the legislative competence of the Federal Government. It indicated that a municipal bylaw would not be deemed to be valid should it have the direct or indirect affect of:

(a) Prohibiting the siting of an antenna structure,

(b) Expressly controlling or limiting the height or type of antenna structure for aesthetic or for any other purpose or

(c) Imposing local building codes on the structure.

However, Professor Townsend also stated that a properly framed municipal bylaw relating only incidentally to radio communications may coexist with Federal legislative authority, provided that the bylaw does not prohibit or unduly restrict the conduct of radio services. He also made it clear that the concerns of a municipality, while not having any legal standing, clearly have a pragmatic effect and should be taken into account.

The Report offered a number of general principles as guidance for municipalities drafting bylaws that attempted to affect the height and siting of antenna. These can be summarized as follows:

- Municipalities have no lawful jurisdiction to manage the use of the radio spectrum.
- Municipal bylaws may not lawfully set or police limits on the nature or duration of worker or citizen exposure to radio-frequency energy.
- Local ordinances are ineffectual to the extent that they propose to prohibit the siting of antenna.
- Municipal rules may not expressly control or limit the type or height of an antenna or support structure for aesthetic or other purposes.
- Municipal or provincial building codes have no lawful jurisdiction over the structural integrity of the antenna or its support structure.[7]
- Municipalities and local governments have full control over land in which legal title is vested with the corporation of the municipality. Controls over the health, safety or aesthetics of radio antennas situated on such land would be lawfully regarded as private controls on land.
- Antennas or antenna-support structures affixed or mounted upon a building or structure that is subject to municipal land-use control usually would require a local building permit. The municipality may set load, stress and other requirements that relate to the structure.
- A municipality may control an antenna-support structure that is used for other purposes in addition to the securing of radio antenna.
- A local authority may have the right to regulate safety issues, such as electrical power interconnections, grounding and the like with respect to the erection of the antenna-support structure. Professor Townsend also suggested that a local authority may be able to regulate security at the site of the support structure, including fences and anticlimb devices, so long as such requirements are reasonable in relation to the cost of the installation.
- Where a support structure is to be sited within or adjacent to an area where there is a "compelling local interest in the aesthetic character of the area," a local government may require "reasonable accommodations" to the siting of the antenna and support structure.

Professor Townsend suggested the creation of these principles was difficult and complicated by the fact there were no legal cases in Canada that go beyond deciding the elementary issues of jurisdictional control over radio apparatus. In other words, no court in Canada had been specifically asked to address the extent to which a municipality could make a bylaw that would have an incidental effect on radio communication. In fact, that is still the case today.

The Report concluded that the current constitutional powers of municipalities did not permit them to deny the choice of site for a radio transmitter and antenna nor would it allow them to regulate height, dimensions or structural integrity of antennas or the support structures. It then pointed out that when serious land-utilization issues arose between the user and the municipality that no mechanism existed to consider such issues. The Report suggested that accommodations to the concerns raised by local authorities would have to be addressed by the Federal Government.

The effect of the Townsend Report was to reinforce the Federal Government's authority in the area of radio communication and the height and siting of antennas and their support structure. The Report also made it clear that while municipalities could not regulate in this area, they may have valid concerns that should be addressed by the user of the radio spectrum. If necessary, the Federal Government should be prepared to respond to such concerns. This review of law made it clear that the concerns of local authorities could no longer be ignored.

LEGISLATIVE AUTHORITY FOR AMATEUR RADIO

Radio amateurs in Canada derive their authority to operate from the *Radiocommunication Act*, R.S.C. 1985, c. R-2. Section 5 of this Act provides that the Minister responsible for communication has the authority to issue radio licences for radio apparatus and spectrum licences for specified radio frequencies, and to "approve each site for radio apparatus, including where antenna systems may be located, and approve the erection of all masts, towers and other antenna supporting structures."[8] Section 6 of the Act provides that the Minister may make regulations for carrying out the purposes and provisions of the Act.

The regulation and implementation of the *Radiocommunication Act* lies with Industry Canada (formerly the Department of Communications). Industry Canada divides the users of the radio communications systems under the *Radio Communication Act* into two groups. The first is for stations that require a site-specific radio authorization (such as businesses, cellular radio companies, government agencies and utilities) and the second group being stations that do not require a site-specific authorization, such as the General Radio Service (CB), Amateur Radio and receiving earth stations. These groups are typically referred to as Type I and Type II licenses respectively.

This distinction is important for radio amateurs since Industry Canada makes it clear that the authorization process to erect an antenna and supporting structure is certainly more onerous for the first group than for the latter.

PRESENT REGULATION OF ANTENNAS AND SUPPORT STRUCTURE

As a result of the Townsend Report and the conclusions reached therein, the Federal Government attempted to implement a process whereby concerns of local authorities could be heard. This was driven by the sudden increase in cellular and PCS licences and the corresponding need for more antennas and support structures. The late 1980s witnessed a number of disputes between local authorities and cellular and PCS providers over the height and siting of antenna structures. Local authorities became very concerned that Industry Canada was simply issuing licences for cellular and PCS carriers without any thought going into the location of the antenna structures that resulted.

In 1990, the predecessor to Industry Canada implemented a compulsory consultation process for applicants whose radio systems required a "significant antenna structure." The process was designed to ensure that municipalities had early notification of proposed antenna towers in their community. More importantly, municipalities were given an opportunity to influence the location of a tower before a radio authorization was issued by Industry Canada.

This process was issued as a Client Procedure Circular entitled "Environmental Process, Radio Frequency Fields and Land-Use Consultation." The document is commonly referred to by its identification number: CPC-2-0-03.[9]

Industry Canada made it clear that when differences of opinion existed between municipalities and the users of radio-frequency spectrum, reasonable accommodations would be made. In typical Canadian fashion, Industry Canada expected the parties involved to work towards a mutually acceptable agreement.

This procedure, while designed to deal with licensees that required a site-specific radio authorization, was also applicable to radio amateurs. However, radio amateurs were specifically exempted from the reporting requirements embodied in CPC-2-0-03, but instead were subject to the following direction:

"Members of the second group [Type II stations] are not required to inform Industry Canada of their plans. However, it is the responsibility of the owner of the station to consult with the local municipality if it is felt that the installation of an antenna tower may raise community concern. Since no licence is required or one has already been issued, no licencing decision need be taken by Industry Canada. The responsibility remains with the station owner and the municipality to resolve their concerns."[10]

This direction made it clear that radio amateurs were supposed to address any municipal concerns. Somewhat helpfully, Industry Canada also noted that certain municipalities have chosen not to participate in the consultation process or consider other alternatives raised by amateurs and in some extreme cases have taken positions that effectively prohibit antenna structures within their boundaries. While not providing any clear direction to the radio

amateurs as to how to resolve such complaints, it did suggest that the licencee may "choose to proceed with the construction of the antenna structure."[11]

In theory, Industry Canada has indicated (although this is not embodied in CPC-2-0-03) that in extreme cases it will be the final arbitrator of any dispute between a radio amateur and a municipality and they are prepared to make a final determination about the height and siting of a support structure. In practice, Industry Canada is reluctant to take that approach, and instead encourages both parties to try to resolve their differences. The difficulty is that with an intransigent municipality or local authority the radio amateur is often faced with a difficult task in trying to reach a compromise. Further, many local authorities have implemented procedures for applicants to follow in obtaining municipal "approval."

The municipalities point to CPC-2-0-03 and suggest that they have a clear mandate from Industry Canada to implement procedures (which may include an application process and even a hearing) to ensure that their concerns are "addressed." Most of these procedures are designed for Type I stations and while those users of the radio spectrum usually comply with the process for public-relations reasons, the radio amateur faces a number of problems if required to follow such a process.

In general, Industry Canada encourages radio amateurs to follow whatever process a municipality or local authority has implemented in order to ensure municipal concerns are addressed. The problem is that this process can be costly and time consuming, and in many cases the radio amateur faces hostile and well-prepared positions taken by community groups. The end result can be that the radio amateur is often denied any "approval" from the municipality and the municipality may indicate to Industry Canada that it does not think the implementation of an antenna and support structure is warranted. Radio amateurs then often follow the difficult task of appealing to Industry Canada to, in essence, overrule the position taken by the municipality. In practice, the regulator is often reluctant to take that step.

In some cases, the local authorities have recognized the importance radio amateurs can play in the community (such as providing public service in emergencies) and have implemented a less onerous process for the amateur to follow in applying for an antenna and support structure. This process still requires some form of "application" and opportunity for immediate neighbours to address any concerns that they may have in an appropriately public hearing. Again, Industry Canada encourages radio amateurs to follow this process (and in practice usually indicated that they will not approve any antennas or support structure until such process has been followed), but again make it clear that Industry Canada is the final arbitrator of disputes between a radio amateur and a local authority.

THE CALGARY GUIDELINES

In 1998 the City of Calgary, Alberta, was the first municipality in Canada to work out a comprehensive set of guidelines with Industry Canada and a number of cellular and

PCS providers concerning the erection of Type I support structures. These guidelines were set as a "policy" (with the approval of Industry Canada and the Type I licensees) for applicants to follow in siting antennas and their support structures.

In that same year, Industry Canada suggested that a similar policy be developed for Type II stations. In consultation with Radio Amateurs of Canada Inc (RAC),[12] local amateurs and the City of Calgary Planning Department policy guidelines were drafted for the "Development of Amateur Radio Antenna Structures in Residential Areas."

The City Planning Department was aware that radio amateurs could not be accommodated within the maximum 10-metre height set for construction in family oriented residential land districts. It also recognized that towers set at low heights can cause RFI and other problems. Finally, it also recognized that it did not have the authority to regulate the height or siting of support structures through either municipal regulation or land-use bylaws.

The policy that was adopted by The City of Calgary, with the approval of Industry Canada, can be summarized as follows:

- Towers and antennas up to a maximum height of 13 metres (42.64 feet) may be erected in all residential areas without the need for a public consultation process.
- The City of Calgary will support erection of structures up to a height of 18 metres (59.04 feet) subject to a "public consultation process."
- The public consultation process required the amateur to notify owners of properties within 100 metres (328 feet) of the boundaries of the site for the proposed antenna.
- The amateur is also required to notify the local community association, alderman and the Federal Member of Parliament. The notification would include all information on the proposed structure including its type, height and location.
- The recipient of the letter of notification has 30 days in which to send their comments to the City administration.
- The applicant or any notified party could, if necessary, convene a public meeting to assist with the notification process.
- Within 45 days, the City administration will provide a letter to Industry Canada indicating its position on the proposed antenna structure and to confirm that the consultation process has been undertaken.

RAC did not support the 18-metre height limit. It suggested, based on a number of technical grounds, it would be prepared to support a height limit of 21 metres for residential areas. The City administration was unwilling to increase the height limited from 18 metres to 21 metres despite intense lobbying by RAC. Industry Canada took the position that an 18-metre height limit was probably acceptable to most amateurs, but they would be willing to support structures up to a height of 21 metres (or even higher) on a case-by-case basis.[13]

It was hoped that these guidelines would form a model for other municipalities to follow throughout Canada. Unfortu-nately, since RAC was unwilling to support the present height limit, many other municipalities have not adopted these guidelines.[14] RAC continues to lobby Industry Canada and the Canadian Federation of Municipalities on this point, with the hope that model policy could be developed that would automatically approve heights of up to 21 metres in urban areas.

PROCEDURES SUGGESTED BY RADIO AMATEURS OF CANADA

Radio Amateurs of Canada Inc has, for many years, suggested a procedure for radio amateurs to follow for erecting antenna structures that comply with CPC-2-0-03. This procedure is very similar to the Calgary guidelines. It includes notification to the municipality or local authority of the intended structure and notification to immediate neighbours of the intended installation in residential areas.[15]

The procedure suggested by RAC is:

(a) Existing Bylaws or Regulations

The first thing an amateur should do is determine if there are any existing bylaws or regulations that purport to limit the height or siting of antenna-support structures. In most cases, a telephone call to the planning department of the municipality or local authority (or, in some cases, checking the municipality's Web site) will usually provide you with the relevant information. It certainly does not hurt to indicate to the planning department that you are an Amateur-Radio operator and are proposing to erect a support structure and to inquire whether the local authority has a procedure already in place.

For some reason amateurs are loathe to find out if this information exists or they may take the advice of some local amateur to simply put the tower up and "avoid your neighbours for a few days." If you keep in mind the process mandated by CPC 2-0-03, then it is imperative that you find out in advance what, if any, hurdles you may face. Remember in this instance the axiom "ignorance of the law is no defense" will be applicable!

If you are unable to find this information directly from the local authority or municipality (which is unlikely), you will find that a copy of "Land Use Bylaws" can be found in most public libraries or the law library in the court house or university or college. In major urban areas, you can contact the regional or district office of Industry Canada to determine what, if any, information they may have about relevant rules and procedures.

If it appears a municipality or local authority has an unduly restrictive bylaw or regulation that seeks to restrict the height and siting of antenna-support structures, then the best course of action is to raise the jurisdictional issues with the planning department. It is also helpful to send a copy of your letter to the law department of the municipality, since issues raised in the letter will likely end up in that office in any event.[16]

It is important to stress in the letter that you fully intend to comply with CPC 2-0-03. You will find in many instances you will receive a reply from the planning department confirming that the relevant bylaw may not be valid.[17]

In the event the municipality or local authority suggests that the bylaw is applicable, then the best course of action would be to send copies of your correspondence and any reply received from the local authority to the closest regional or district office of Industry Canada. Include a covering letter explaining your position and suggesting that you will be proceeding to consult with the municipality in the erection of your antenna-support structure and that you look forward to having the assistance of Industry Canada dealing with the bylaw.[18]

(b) Notification to the Municipality

In the event you find that a municipality or local authority has a process for amateurs to follow in the erection of support structures, then you should review this process very carefully. You will find that many such processes are applicable to commercial installations or to cellular and PCS carriers and may set out a somewhat onerous notification process, complete with public hearings and the like. Again, the best course of action to follow in this instance is to alert the municipality or local authority that, as an Amateur-Radio operator, Industry Canada does not expect you to follow any formal notification procedure but to simply "consult" with them. A copy of CPC 2-0-03 sent to the local authority (and also copied to the law department) is a good first step. In the letter you should outline the process you intend to follow and suggest that by following such a process you would comply with the requirements imposed upon you by Industry Canada.[19]

In the event the municipality does not have any formal process to follow, then you can use a "standard form" document that has been developed in consultation with municipal governments and a number of amateurs. The document entitled "Notification to a Local Authority" is designed to answer Industry Canada's concern that you have met the requirements of CPC 2-0-03 and to provide the local authority with all the relevant information about your installation.[20]

(c) "Please Apply for a Development Permit"

As part of the "process," some municipalities have begun the practise of asking amateurs to apply for a "development permit." This application for a permit is handled much in the same way as a building permit, with notice of the application being published in local newspapers or other gazettes. In some cases, the municipality will hold public hearings to obtain input in the granting of the permit and, at the end of the day, may or may not grant such a permit (or even grant a modified version of the initial request) depending on the feedback, both from your immediate neighbours and others.

In most cases Industry Canada encourages amateurs to follow any requests for a development permit as part of the consultation process. However, there is an inherent problem in this approach. A municipality or local authority cannot grant a "permit" for the height and siting of an antenna-support structure. In order to have the authority to grant

such a permit, it would have to enact an appropriate land-use bylaw, which, as we have seen, is outside the scope of their jurisdiction.

RAC has always been cautious in having amateurs apply for such a permit. If the permit is denied or varied, the amateur's only recourse is to appeal the decision (usually to a Development Appeal Board) and then to a court of competent jurisdiction. There is concern that if a municipality refuses to grant a permit, whether an amateur could then raise the issue of jurisdiction. The municipality could argue that the amateur has agreed to be bound by its development process and had submitted to its jurisdiction and waived any jurisdictional issues. It is also far from clear if Industry Canada would be in a position to overrule the decision of a municipality in that case.

Where a municipality insists that amateurs apply for a development permit, the best course of action is to discuss the situation with your local Industry Canada office. If Industry Canada directs you to make such an application, then you should confirm this in writing.[21] Further, when you do make application for a development permit, it should be filed with an attached covering letter. This should make it clear that by applying for the permit, you are simply complying with CPC 2-0-03 and are following the direction of the regulator, Industry Canada. You should also confirm you are in no way submitting to, or accepting, the jurisdiction of the municipality to regulate the height or siting of antenna structures and that you are not waiving any of your rights to raise the issue of jurisdiction should it become necessary.[22]

(d) Notification to Your Neighbours

The next step will be to advise your neighbours of the proposed installation. You can use the Calgary Guideline as a starting point, but also give some thought to exactly whom you should notify. It is likely that only your most immediate neighbours will be most affected by the installation. Some of your neighbours 100 metres away may not even be able to see the antenna, but may still feel that they are somehow affected.

As an initial step, an explanatory letter should be sent to all of the neighbours you deem will be impacted by the installation. It is important to be completely candid in this letter and invite people to contact you if they have any questions. For one's most immediate neighbours, the best approach is for you to make a personal visit and discuss the installation.[23]

(e) Your Neighbours Revolt!

You will find that 90% of your neighbours will be neutral with respect to the installation, 5% will be supportive (probably on a *quid pro quo* basis) and 5% will be opposed in some fashion. In our experience, the latter group will probably be quite vocal about opposing the installation and may try to obtain support for their position by way of a petition and by lobbying the local authority.

If you gauge that there is a sufficient level of neighbour

dissatisfaction, it is usually worthwhile to suggest that you are amenable to holding some kind of public meeting to better explain your installation and deal with any concerns. It is far better to hold such a meeting in a public place. If you contact the offices of most ward aldermen or other civic politicians, you will find that they will be quite helpful finding a place for such a meeting. The local community association is also another source to contact to assist in finding a meeting place. When you hold such a meeting, it is important to send invitations to all the affected neighbours, your local ward alderman and Industry Canada. If at all possible, see if an individual from Industry Canada would be willing to attend (in most cases you will find that this can be quite helpful).

If you hold a public meeting, you must make sure it is properly run and organized. Make sure there is a written agenda that allows you to make your submissions and for the Industry Canada representative to make comments. Neighbours should then be allowed to address their concerns, and you should be allowed to have an equal opportunity to respond. It goes without saying that you will need the support of an unbiased moderator. You will find that most civic politicians are willing to take on this task. Many larger local authorities in Canada now have or use the facilities of a mediation or arbitration process and have facilitators that they are willing (usually on a no-fee basis) to try to resolve such issues. Again, your local ward alderman or community association is a good starting point.

Keep minutes of this meeting, and after the meeting send copies of the minutes to the municipality, the affected neighbours and Industry Canada.

(f) What is the Next Step?

Next, write to the local authority and Industry Canada, indicating that you have complied with CPC 2-0-03 and that you would like to proceed with your installation. Give a date when you intend to proceed with the installation and that you look forward to any further comments from the authorities. Of course, if you have followed a "process" or been asked to apply for a development permit, you will find that Industry Canada will have already been notified of the "approval."

(g) Arbitration

In some cases where there is strong neighbour concern to the proposed installation, both Industry Canada and the local authority will suggest some form of arbitration or mediation. In fact, you will find Industry Canada will encourage this process as part of the consultation structure. Arbitration is simply a process where an impartial independent person will hear both sides of a case and render a decision or suggestion without the need to resort to court process.

Arbitration can be of two types: either binding or non-binding. The amateur will obviously want to avoid binding arbitration since you will be agreeing to abide by the decision of the arbitrator (which may or may not be to your liking) and essentially usurp the authority of Industry Canada. Non-binding arbitration on the other hand simply amounts to a recommendation by the arbitrator about how matters might be resolved.

If you resort to some form of arbitration, it is vitally important to be able to educate the arbitrator. It will be necessary to prepare a "Brief" containing all of the relevant authorities to support your position, which might include:

(a) CPC 2-0-03
(b) IPC 2-0-03
(c) A copy of your Authorization Certificate
(d) A copy of your proposed "Notification to Local Authority"
(e) A copy of the Townsend Report
(f) A copy of any technical articles showing why it is necessary for an amateur antenna to be elevated to a certain level.[24,25]

(h) What if the Local Authority Maintains its Opposition to the Installation?

At the end of the consultation process, you may find that the local authority (usually under pressure from your neighbours or others in the community) may still maintain an objection to your proposed installation. In this case, it is important to remind Industry Canada that not only have you fully complied with CPC 2-0-03, but the regulator must be seen as the final decision maker in the process. As indicated previously, Industry Canada is loathe to direct the installation of an antenna-support structure without making some concessions to the concerns of the municipality. Further, Industry Canada may make several suggestions to you in an effort to accommodate municipal concerns—this might include decreasing the height of the support structure, reducing the antenna "footprint" or relocating the structure altogether.

Industry Canada may also ask you to "reconsult" with the municipality if they feel there are certain issues that have not been properly addressed. If there is any consolation in this process, I am unaware of any case where Industry Canada has disallowed an antenna-support structure and will, in almost all cases, direct the amateur to proceed with the installation of the structure, but will quite often reduce the overall height of the installation to appease the local authority.

While in theory it would be possible to appeal the decision of Industry Canada with respect to the installation of an antenna-support structure, I am unaware of any case where this has been done. I typically find that Industry Canada is accommodating to the amateur to such an extent that an appeal would be unwarranted.[26]

In practice, the level of "consultation" required of radio amateurs varies on a case-by-case basis. Amateurs in smaller communities typically face very little opposition or hostility to their proposed structure. On the other hand, amateurs in larger urban areas and in many smaller retirement communities can face problems. Industry Canada is quite content to let amateurs decide for themselves on the level of consultation required, but it is also clear that they want to see active efforts by amateurs to notify the municipality of their proposed installation and to address any concerns that neighbours may have.

As mentioned previously, Industry Canada is reluctant to become involved in disputes between amateurs and municipalities. However, Industry Canada has of late been quite clear about advising municipalities and local authorities that the ultimate jurisdiction on siting of antennas lies in their control.

RESTRICTIVE COVENANTS

It is becoming more common in many Canadian communities to find restrictive covenants. This is particularly true in new communities, so-called "gated communities" and condominium and retirement complexes. In nearly all cases, Industry Canada recognizes that such covenants restricting or limiting the erection of antennas are likely valid, since they form, in essence, part of the terms of the agreement between the vendor and purchaser of a property.

Amateurs looking to purchase any new property are then well-advised to make it a condition of any offer that they first have an opportunity to review title to the property and any covenants or restrictions that may be registered. The reader is referred to other sections of this book that deal with these issues. In some cases, prospective purchasers of properties in new areas have been able to have the covenants varied or eliminated as a condition of purchase.

CASE LAW

As Professor Townsend alluded to in his Report, there is very little substantive case law in this area. This is generally due to the fact that most litigation against amateurs takes the form of applications for injunctive relief. Decisions on interlocutory applications on such issues are usually not reported and in many cases are settled before ultimately reaching trial. Further, litigation involving antenna siting may take place in the provincial courts, where typically decisions are also not reported. Finally, given Industry Canada's direction to the amateur to try to work out problems with local authorities and their neighbours, many cases may also be decided by arbitration or mediation.

The type of litigation that an amateur may face will be, as mentioned, an application for some kind of injunctive relief from either the local authority or his or her own neighbours. In Canada, in order to be successful on an application for an injunction one must show:

- That there is a triable issue.
- The applicants will suffer irreparable harm not compensable in damages.
- And the balance of convenience will favour the applicant.

In most cases, the party facing an application for an injunction will concede the first point as there will likely be a serious issue, but the applicants will have a difficult hurdle showing that they will suffer irreparable harm.[27]

One of the few reported decisions dealing with an application for injunctive relief in the installation of amateur-support structures is found in the decision from the Supreme Court of Ontario in *Page et al. v. Mangaroo*.[28] In this decision, Mr Mangaroo, an amateur in Ontario, sought to erect a 22-metre (72-foot) tower in his backyard. Since this case predated both the Townsend Report and CPC-2-0-03, it appears that there was little, if any, consultation between the amateur and his immediate neighbours. However, the municipality in question was on record indicating that they had no jurisdiction to regulate the height and siting of the structure and Industry Canada essentially took no position on the application.

The neighbours seeking the injunction sought to tender evidence from real-estate agents suggesting that the proposed installation would cause irreparable harm by adversely affecting real-estate values. Mr Mangaroo filed his own affidavit from a real-estate appraiser who opined that the installation of the structure would not have an effect on property values.

The judge dismissed the application for an injunction and rendered very brief written reasons.[29] While the decisions are brief, the comments may be quite helpful if amateurs are faced with similar actions. The Court found that the loss or impairment of aesthetics was not a valid ground for complaint and doubted that there was a substantive issue in law. The Court also made it clear that the applicants would not suffer irreparable harm and found the evidence with respect to real-estate values as submitted by Mr Mangaroo to be compelling. As with most cases seeking injunctions, this matter never went any further. Mr Mangaroo erected his tower and his neighbours abandoned the litigation.

While this case may be helpful (being the only reported case dealing with an injunction application against an amateur structure), it is subject to a number of caveats. First, as indicated, this case predates CPC-2-0-03. The Court found that Mr Mangaroo had complied with all "Federal requirements." If in fact an amateur today did not follow the consultation requirements mandated by CPC-2-0-03, then it is likely a court could find some grounds to suggest that there is a substantive issue and be sympathetic to granting injunctive relief. Second, the evidence suggesting there would be no reduction in property values came from a radio amateur, who also happened to be an accredited real-estate appraiser.

On the latter point, one should note that there are now a number of studies undertaken by cellular and PCS carriers that address the impact support structures will have on residential property values. Accordingly, the amateur may want to rely on those studies rather than the conflicting opinions of real-estate brokers or appraisers.

A second helpful case to radio amateurs is found in the decision from the Ontario Court (General Division) in *Lafortune v. Puccini*.[30] In this decision, both the applicant and respondent were owner of certain residences that were subject to a restrictive covenant against any antenna or support structure of any kind. The respondent erected a support structure and the applicant applied to the Court for an order enforcing the restrictive covenant. In this case, the actual erection of the support structure took place prior to the implementation of CPC-2-0-03. In response to the application, the amateur submitted evidence that there had been a number of violations of other restrictive covenants by other neighbours in the complex. The Court noted that some of these violations were minor while others were quite major. The Court stated:

"Since the applicant is seeking equitable relief for enforcement of this covenant against the respondent, one must look at the equities between the parties as well as the compliance of all the neighbours to these restrictive covenants."

The Court found that the restrictive covenants had been varied by the conduct of the original purchasers of the property and by subsequent purchasers. In short, the Court found that the applicant could not try to enforce one particular restrictive covenant when over the course of time other restrictive covenants had been breached by other parties, which in effect made the restrictions ineffective. Again, the Court noted that the amateur complied with all Federal laws relating to the construction of the antenna.

Despite the dearth of case law in this area, both of these decisions are helpful in providing some precedent on the type of litigation that an amateur may face. However, it is quite clear that in order to oppose litigation commenced by the local authorities or one's neighbours, the amateur must comply with CPC-2-0-03.

SAFETY CODE 6

Amateurs are required to comply with Safety Code 6.[31] This is a code published by the Government of Canada that sets out safety requirements for the installation of and use of radio-frequency devices. Industry Canada expects amateurs not to exceed the maximum exposure levels set out in the Code. Accordingly, amateurs are now quite often being asked to address whether they meet such requirements.

The difficulty is that to try to measure maximum exposure levels for a typical amateur installation is quite difficult without the appropriate engineering software. Industry Canada recognizes that typical amateur stations operating at a nominal 100 watts in a typical urban environment are in no danger of exceeding Safety Code 6. However, it is clear that amateurs operating at the legal limit (1000 watts) may face some difficulties.

While assistance in calculating exposure limits under Safety Code 6 can be found in CPC-2-0-03 and IPC-2-0-03, one very useful way for amateurs to indicate RF radiation from the station will have no harmful health effects is to show that they do not exceed the limits set out in the American National Standards Institute C95.1-1991. This ANSI limit is often referred to in various papers dealing with the health effects of RF exposure. In addition, a number of simple programs allow amateurs to calculate their power density in watts per square metre, compared to the power density limit as a percentage of the ANSI limit.[32] (See the program *Pwr-Dens.EXE* included on the CD-ROM.)

RADIO FREQUENCY INTERFERENCE

One frequent ground that local authorities and neighbours tend to rely on to oppose antennas and support structures is the likelihood of radio-frequency interference ("RFI") to radio sensitive equipment ("RSE").[33] To address such concerns, radio amateurs can refer to Client Procedure Circular 3-14-01 "Determination of Harmful Interference With Respect to Radio-Sensitive Equipment" and its corresponding Internal Procedure Circular.[34] Industry Canada takes the position that with respect to RFI:

"Both users of the radio frequency spectrum and users of radio sensitive equipment have a right to have a reasonable expectation that they may enjoy the use of their equipment. When those rights conflict, one requires a resolution process."

Industry Canada takes its authority to make determinations on the existence of RFI pursuant to Section 5(1)(l) of the *Radiocommunication Act*.[35] However, Industry Canada makes it clear that they have no responsibility to resolve cases of RFI and will limit its own activities to the following:

(a) Recommending cooperative efforts with the radio apparatus owner.

(b) Recommending that complainants contact the manufacturer or distributor (or their service agents) of the affected equipment for assistance.

(c) Referring complainants to various self-help information products available.[36]

In addition, Industry Canada makes it clear that where RSE owners refuse to cooperate, the regulator will indicate that the RSE owner's sole recourse is to improve the immunity of their equipment or accept the consequences of the RFI. It also notes that where owners of radio transmitting apparatus are unwilling to work with the RSE owner toward the solution, Industry Canada may place limits on their authority to operate.

After all mutual avenues of resolution have been explored, Industry Canada may make a formal determination whether RFI exists and whether it is the fault of the transmitting station. Industry Canada will charge the RSE owner a fee for making such determination in the event the investigation determines that the RSE is lacking in immunity.[37]

Accordingly, radio amateurs can simply address any concerns about RFI by pointing to the requirements embodied in CPC-3-14-01 and indicating that they will cooperate fully with neighbours in the event of interference. As this is the only step Industry Canada expects radio amateurs to take, it can hardly be said that the danger of potential RFI should form the proper basis of objecting to the erection of antennas and support structures.

CONCLUSIONS

While Canadian amateurs can derive some satisfaction that the regulation of the height and siting of support structures lies exclusively within the sphere of the Federal Government, it is clear that amateurs must be in a position to consult with their local authority and to address concerns raised by that local authority and individual neighbours.

In order to obtain the support of Industry Canada for your installation, you must follow CPC-2-0-03. In some cases amateurs will find this to be a frustrating experience, since it may involve public hearings and the increased expense of having to deal directly with your neighbours. Further, municipal concerns may dictate that the amateur make some accommodation in the height of the structure. Amateurs who comply with the consultation requirements and seek approval for a reasonable structure will find that their requests are almost always granted.

FOOTNOTES

[1]U.K. (30 & 31) Vict., c.3.

[2][1932] A.C. 304 (P.C.). Until 1949, the Privy Council in the United Kingdom was the final appellate court.

[3]Ibid, at 310.

[4]Ibid, at 315.

[5][1978] 2 S.C.R. 141.

[6]See, Townsend, D. "Canadian Municipalities and the Regulation of Radio Antenna and their Support Structures" (1987) at p 5.

[7]In fact, since the Townsend Report, the Canadian National Building Code and most, if not all, of the provincial Building Codes specifically exempt freestanding antenna support structures from their requirements.

[8]*Radiocommunication Act*, R.S.C. 1985, c.R-2, S.5.(f).

[9]**http://strategis.ic.gc.ca/SSG/sf01374e.html#Client ProceduresCirculars**.

[10]IPC 2-0-03 [**http://strategis.ic.gc.ca/SSG/sf01374e.html# ClientProceduresCirculars**]. This is the Internal Procedures Circular used by Industry Canada to alert its staff to the implementation of CPC-2-0-03. While for internal use, it is a public document and provides a helpful tool to interpret the CPC.

[11]IPC-2-0-03. Presumably this would be in the face of opposition from a local authority.

[12]The national society representing radio amateurs in Canada.

[13]"Policy Guidelines for the Development of Amateur Radio Antenna Structures in Residential Areas". OE98-61.

[14]Letter from T.S. Ellam dated August 26, 1998 to City of Calgary, Planning and Building Department and Industry Canada.

[15]**www.rac.ca**.

[16]A copy of a typical letter can be found on the CD-ROM, filename: **Canada Bylaw Letter.DOC**.

[17]In practise, you will find that most major metropolitan areas across Canada have either removed such bylaws or are prepared to concede that any bylaw that attempts to deal with the height and siting of antenna-support structures may not be enforceable. However, in smaller communities, it is quite common to find bylaws that attempt to restrict the height of antenna.

[18]A copy of such a letter can be found on the enclosed CD-ROM [**Industry Canada Letter #1**]

[19]A copy of such a letter can be found on the CD-ROM, filename: **Canada Notification Letter.DOC**]

[20]A copy of such a document can be found on the CD-ROM, filename: **Canada Notification Document. DOC**.

[21]A form of such a letter can be found on the CD-ROM, filename: **Canada Industry Canada Letter #2.DOC**.

[22]Again, the appropriate form of letter can be found on the CD-ROM, filename: **Canada Confirmation Letter.DOC**.

[23]A sample form of letter can be found on the CD-ROM, filename: **Canada Neighbour Letter.DOC**.

[24]Such as Straw, R. D. and Hall, G.L. "Antenna Height and Communications Effectiveness" (1999).

[25]A draft form of Brief which can be provided to the arbitrator is on the CD-ROM, filename: **Canada Arbitration Brief.DOC**.

[26]A form of letter requesting Industry Canada make a final determination with respect to an amateur's proposed installation can be found on the CD-ROM, filename: **Canada Industry Canada Letter #3.DOC**.

[27]There is a way to guarantee to the court that there is no irreparable harm, which is to agree to a condition that the structure and antennas will be removed when the applicant or his successor in title no longer has use for them. What is guaranteed to go away may not be irreparable harm. The "harm" may be repaired by the passage of time.

[28]S.C. 883/87.

[29]Unreported, S.C. 883/87 (S.C. Ont.)

[30](1991) 2 O.R. (3d) 689.

[31]This Code is the process of being revised by Health Canada. The reader is referred to the following Website for the latest developments. [**http://strategis.ic.gc.ca/SSG/sf 01902e.html**]

[32]Website reference.

[33]RSEs are typical consumer electronics.

[34]**http://strategis.ic.gc.ca/SSG/sf01374e.html# ClientProceduresCirculars.**

[35]Ibid.

[36]IPC-3-14-01 at p 1. Industry Canada has a great number of self-help products available to the general public (including videos) to assist consumers dealing with RFI problems.

[37]In 2000, Canadian $80.00. It should be noted that Industry Canada can find that a transmitter exceeds certain levels prescribed in Electro Magnetic Compatibility Advisory Bulletin 2 ("EMCAB-2") entitled "Criteria for Resolution of Immunity Complaints Involving Fundamental Emissions of Radio Communication Transmitters" and direct the operator to take steps to reduce power levels to an acceptable level.

14

Bibliography

BOOKS

The ARRL Antenna Book, 19th Ed. (ARRL: Newington, 2000). See Chapter 23, **Radio Wave Propagation** and Chapter 3, **The Effects of Ground**.

John Devoldere, *ON4UN's Low-Band DXing* (ARRL: Newington, 1999)

ARTICLES

Ralph H. Brock, W5MV, "The Ghost in the Computer: Radio Frequency Interference and the Doctrine of Federal Preemption," *Computer Law Review and Technology Journal*, Volume 1999, No. 1, State Bar of Texas. On CD-ROM, filename: **The Ghost in the Computer.PDF**.

Wyland D. Clift, NA1L, "Land Use Regulation of Amateur Radio Towers," *1992 CQ Antenna Buyer's Guide*.

Joel L. Dryer, JD, NØGHT, "The ABCs of CC&Rs," *QST*, Oct 1996, p 47-48. On CD-ROM, filename: **The ABCs of CC&Rs.PDF**.

Richard F. Gillette, W9PE, "Latitude and Longitude the Easy Way," *QST*, Dec 99, p 55. On CD-ROM, filename: **W9PE Lat-Long the Easy Way.PDF**.

Clarke Greene, K1JX, "Station Design for DX", *QST*, Oct and Dec 1980, Jan 1981. On CD-ROM, filename: **Station Design for DX-K1JX.PDF**.

Ed Hare, W1RFI, "FCC RF-Exposure Regulations—the Station Evaluation," *QST*, Jan 1998, p 52ff. On CD-ROM, filename: **W1RFI-QST 0198.PDF**.

Chris Imlay, N3AKD (now W3KD), "But I Never Agreed to That!" *QST*, Dec 1995, p 47-48. On CD-ROM, filename: **But I Never Agreed to That.PDF**.

Al P. LaPlaca, W2WW, "Notes on the Angle of Radiation," *CQ*, Apr 1991, p 24.

James L. Lawson, W2PV, "Yagi Antenna Design: Ground or Earth Effects," *Ham Radio*, Oct 1980, p 29.

Sid Leach, Esq., K5XI, "Federal Preemption of Deed Restrictions," *The DX Magazine*, May/Jun 1993, p 36-40. On CD-ROM, filename: **Federal Preemption of Deed Restrictions.PDF**.

Albert Manville, "Introductory Remarks, Communications Towers Workshop," US Fish and Wildlife Service. On CD-ROM, filename: **FWS Forum on Bird Kills and Towers-Intro.PDF**.

Brennan Price, N4QX, "PRB-1: A Good Thing, but Still not a Panacea," *QST*, Sep 2000, p 87. On CD-ROM, filename: **N4QX-QST 0900.PDF**. (Especially interesting is material on types of Variances and Conditional-Use Permits.)

Paul D. Rockwell, W3AFM. "Station Design for DX," *QST*. On CD-ROM, filename: **Station Design for DX-W3AFM.PDF**.
Part I-September 1966, page 50
Part II-October 1966, page 48
Part III-November 1966, page 50
Part IV-December 1966, page 53

Frank Svoboda, "Study to Assess the Potential Effect of Three AM Radio Towers on Bird Migration and Local Bird Movements," for Minnesota Public Radio. On CD-ROM, filename: **Svodboda MPR Radio Tower Study.PDF**.

Karl T. Thurber, W8FX, "Reliable Communications Range", *CQ*, Mar 1986, p 90.

W. F. Utlaut, "Effect of Antenna Radiation Angles Upon HF Radio Signals Propagated Over Long Distances," *Journal of Research*, National Bureau of Standards, D. Radio Propagation, Vol 65D, No. 2, Mar-Apr 1961. On CD-ROM, filename: **Utlaut Article.PDF**.

Excerpts from "Avian Mortality at Communications Towers." On CD-ROM, filename: **Summary of Bird Kill Meeting.PDF**.

USEFUL WEB SITES

FCC, General

PRB-1: **http://www.fcc.gov/wtb/amateur/prb-1.html**
  Or **http://www.arrl.org/field/regulations/prb-1.htm**
  DA 99-2565: http:**//www.fcc.gov/Bureaus/Wireless/
  Orders/1999/da992569.txt**
Which Structures Must Be Registered with the FCC?
[Includes 200-foot rule, airport rule, and exemptions.]:
  http://www.fcc.gov/wtb/antenna.what.html
Compliance with Commission's Rules Implementing the
  National Environmental Policy Act of 1969:
  http://www.fcc.gov/wtb/siting/npaguid.html
To register for the ULS, visit:
  http://www/fcc.gov/wtb/uls
Questions Frequently Asked by FCC Licensees:
  http://www.fcc.gov/wtb/siting/npafaq.html

RF Safety

OET 65: **http://www.fcc.gov/**
Amateur Radio RF Safety Calculator:
  http://n5xu.ae.utexas.edu/rfsafety/
Average Power Estimate:
  http://n5xu.ae.utexas.edu/rfsafety/power.htm
Categorical Exemptions to Routine RF Radiation Evaluations: **http://n5xu.ae.utexas.edu/rfsafety/exemptions.
  htm**

Electrical Safety

National Fire Protection Association: *NFPA 70, National
Electrical Code* (NEC) **http://www.nfpa.org/**

RFI or Interference

FCC's Interference Handbook: **http://www.fcc.gov/
  Bureaus/Compliance/WWW/tvibook.html**.
Consumer Electronics Manufacturer's Association
  (CEMA) "What to Do If You Have An Electronics Inter-
  ference Problem."
  http://www.cemacity.org/gazette/files/whattodo.htm

Topographic or Mapping

Topographic maps on line. Purpose: To demonstrate that
  you need a straight line-of-sight over a ridge for emergency communications. **http://www.topozone.com**.
The Microsoft Network Terraserver (satellite photos):
  http://terraserver.microsoft.com/default.asp
Other satellite photos: **http://www.globexplorer.com/
  htmlclient/start.cfm**

General Construction Practices

Construction practices, as a practical matter:
  http://www.qsl.net/n1lo/tower.htm.
Screw anchors: A.B. Chance now has their "Encyclopedia
  of Anchoring" online at their web site. See: **http://
  www.hubbellpowersystems.com/powertest/chance/
  anchor_encyclopedia/anch_encyc_hom.htm** or, if you

want to see all their stuff: **http://www.hubbell.com/
  ABChance/**.
For interesting background information on antenna selection and siting, see: **http://www.alyx.org/art4.html**.
CAD programs: **http://www.cadopia.com/default.asp** and
  **http://www.turbocad.com/frame.cfm?content=
  index.cfm**.

ADDITIONAL BIOGRAPHIC INFORMATION

Tim Ellam, VE6SH
c/o McCarthy Tétrault
3300, 421 - 7th Avenue SW
Calgary, AB   T2P 4K9 Canada
e-mail: **tellam@mccarthy.ca**

Tim Ellam is a partner in McCarthy Tétrault, Canada's
national law firm, and practises international telecommunications and technology law in the firm's Calgary
office. Tim advises communications and technology related
companies, and other clients with an interest in telecommunications, throughout North America and Europe.
He has appeared as counsel in several patent, licensing and
technology related disputes and has acted for PCS carriers in
addressing municipal access issues.

A graduate of the University of Alberta Law School, Tim
is a member of the Law Society of Alberta and the Law
Society of England and Wales. He also belongs to the
Canadian Bar Association, the Federal Communications Bar
Association and the Communications Committee of the
International Bar Association. He has appeared on numerous
occasions as a speaker and panellist on technology and
communications issues, recently at the ITU Americas
Telecom 2000 in Rio de Janeiro.

Ellam has held a Canadian Advanced Amateur Licence
since 1977 and a British Amateur License since 1978 (as
G4HUA). Tim has served as counsel and in other executive
positions for Radio Amateurs of Canada Inc. (RAC) and one
of its predecessor organizations since 1990. At present he
holds the position of Vice President, Regulatory Affairs for
RAC and is also one of the International Amateur Radio
Union's group of experts, advising on legal matters that may
affect Amateur Radio.

Leonard E. Kay, K1NU (ex KB2R)
32 Bradley Rd
Andover, MA 01810
K1NU was first licensed in 1977, and has been contesting
and chasing DX and awards for the last 20+ years. He is an
active member of the Yankee Clipper Contest Club. Professionally, he holds BS and PhD degrees in Electrical Engineering, and is a Principal Engineer with Foliage Software
Systems, Burlington, MA.

He is an ARRL Volunteer Consulting Engineer, specializing in RF exposure analysis, antenna and terrain modeling
and tower permit issues. See his web site at
http://people.ne.mediaone.net/k1nu for more details.

Appendix A

The Law

This Appendix summarizes most of the types of laws you and your attorney will be dealing with in your tower-permitting adventure. Please forgive any duplications from earlier chapters, but it seemed appropriate to put as much as possible in one place for easy reference. The one major topic not included here has to do with wetlands—but the laws on wetlands vary dramatically by state.

COMMON COVENANTS AND RESTRAINTS (CC&RS)

The sad fact of life is that some developers create neighborhoods where it can be almost impossible to erect an outdoor antenna system. In certain areas of the country, such deed restrictions, known as *Common Covenants and Restraints* ("common" because they apply to all of the properties in a development) or *Covenants, Conditions and Restrictions* are ubiquitous in the suburbs of major cities. Both phrases mean just about the same thing and are abbreviated *CC&Rs*. As a result of their ubiquity, the classic theory that CC&Rs are entered into voluntarily can be false.

CC&RS CONSIDERED IN PRB-1

The CC&Rs problem was raised by amateurs and considered by the FCC in its 1985 Declaratory Ruling, FCC 85-506, widely known as PRB-1, 50 F.R. 38813 (September 25, 1985). Here's what PRB-1 says:

Restrictive Covenants

7. Amateur operators also oppose restrictions on their amateur operations which are contained in the deeds for their homes or in their apartment leases. Since these restrictive covenants are contractual agreements between private parties, they are not generally a matter of concern to the Commission. However, since some amateurs who commented in this proceeding provided us with examples of restrictive covenants, they are included for information. Mr. Eugene O. Thomas of Hollister, California included in his comments an extract of the Declaration of Covenants and Restrictions for Ridgemark Estates, County of San Benito, State of California. It provides:

No antenna for transmission or reception of radio signals shall be erected outdoors for use by any dwelling unit except upon approval of the Directors. No radio or television signals or any other form of electromagnetic radiation shall be permitted to originate from any lot which may unreasonably interfere with the reception of television or radio signals upon any other lot.

Marshall Wilson, Jr. provided a copy of the restrictive covenant contained in the deeds for the Bell Martin Addition #2, Irving, Texas. It is binding upon all of the owners or purchasers of the lots in the said addition, his or their heirs, executors, administrators or assigns.

It reads: No antenna or tower shall be erected upon any lot for the purpose of radio operations.

William J. Hamilton resides in an apartment building in Gladstone, Missouri. He cites a clause in his lease prohibiting the erection of antenna. He states that he has been forced to give up operating amateur radio equipment except a handheld 2-meter (144-148 MHz) radio transceiver. He maintains that he should not be penalized just because he lives in an apartment.

Other restrictive covenants are less global in scope than those cited above. For example, Robert Webb purchased a home in Houston, Texas. His deed restriction prohibited "transmitting or receiving antennas extended above the roof line."

8. Amateur operators generally oppose restrictive covenants for several reasons. They maintain that such restrictions limit the places that they can reside if they want to pursue their hobby of amateur radio. Some state that they impinge on First Amendment rights of free speech. Others believe that a constitutional right is being abridged because, in their view, everyone has a right to access the airwaves regardless of where they live.

9. The contrary belief held by housing subdivision communities and condominium or homeowner's associations is that amateur radio installations constitute safety hazards, cause interference to other electronic equipment which may be operated in the home (television, radio, stereos) or are eyesores that detract from the aesthetic and tasteful appearance of the housing development or apartment complex. To counteract these negative consequences, the subdivisions and associations include in their deeds, leases or by-laws, restrictions and limitations on the location and height of antennas or, in some cases, prohibit them altogether. The restrictive covenants are contained in the contractual agreement entered into at the time of the sale or lease of the property. Purchasers or lessees are free to choose whether or not they wish to reside where such restrictions on amateur antennas are in effect or settle elsewhere.

The complete text of PRB-1 may be found at: **http://www.arrl.org/field/regulations/local/prb-1.html** or **http://hamradio-online.com/library/prb1.html**. It is also on the CD-ROM, filename: **FCC PRB-1 (1985).PDF**.

Preemption in the OTARD Rule

Curiously, while the FCC took the "it's a free country" approach in PRB-1, that position may be contrasted with its later willingness to abrogate such property restrictions for Direct Broadcast Satellite (DBS), Multichannel Multipoint Distribution Service (MMDS), and Television Broadcast Antennas in the *Over-the-Air Reception Devices* (OTARD) Rule, 47 CFR §1.4000. Unlike the limited federal preemption for Amateur Radio antennas, 47 CFR §1.4000 is intended to occupy the field. An offending regulation is "prohibited."

(a) (1) Any restriction, including but not limited to any state or local law or regulation, including zoning, land-use, or building regulations, . . . that impairs the installation, maintenance, or use of: . . . an antenna that is designed to receive television broadcast signals; is prohibited, to the extent it so impairs, subject to paragraph (b) of this section.

(2) For purposes of this section, a law, regulation or restriction impairs installation, maintenance or use of an antenna if it:

(i) Unreasonably delays or prevents installation, maintenance or use,

(ii) Unreasonably increases the cost of installation, maintenance or use, or

(iii) Precludes reception of an acceptable quality signal.

Should the Town appeal to the FCC, "the burden of demonstrating that a particular . . . restriction . . . does not impair the installation, maintenance or use . . . shall be on the party that seeks to impose or maintain the restriction." 47 CFR § 1.4000 (e)."

The full text of the OTARD rule may be found at: **http://www.fcc.gov/csb/facts/otard.html**, and also on the CD-ROM, filename: **FCC-Television Broadcast Signals-OTARD.PDF**.

Rejected Again in 1999

Ham radio lawyers, believing that if the FCC would preempt antenna restrictions in the case of the OTARD Rule, hoped that the FCC, in response to an ARRL petition (RM-8763), would expand PRB-1 to include preemption of CC&Rs. Sadly, the FCC declined. Writing under delegated authority In the Matter of RM-8763, as DA-99-2569, the Deputy Chief of the Wireless Telecommunications Bureau, Kathleen O'Brien Ham (not a typo) wrote:

6. The Commission's policy with respect to restrictive covenants is clearly stated in the MO&O establishing a limited preemption of state and local regulations. In the MO&O, the Commission stated that PRB-1 does not reach restrictive covenants in private contractual agreements. The Petitioner argues that enforcement of a covenant by the court constitutes "state action," thus converting what otherwise would be a private matter into a matter of state regulation and, thus, subject to the Commission's limited preemption policy. Notwithstanding the clear policy statement that was set forth in PRB-1 excluding restrictive covenants in private contractual agreements as being outside the reach of our limited preemption, we nevertheless strongly encourage associations of homeowners and private contracting parties to follow the principle of reasonable accommodation and to apply it to any and all instances of amateur service communications where they may be involved. Although we do not hesitate to offer such encouragement, we are not persuaded by the Petition or the

comments in support thereof that specific rule provisions bringing the private restrictive covenants within the ambit of PRB-1 are necessary or appropriate at this time. Having reached this conclusion, we need not resolve the issue of whether, or under what circumstances, judicial enforcement of private covenants would constitute "state action."

Source: **http://www.fcc.gov/Bureaus/Wireless/Orders/ 1999/da992569.txt** and on the CD-ROM, filename: **FCC PRB-1 (1999).PDF**.

Arguments Available

The bottom line? The FCC is not going to provide you with the solution to your CC&R problem any time soon. This is why even lawyers who like a challenge don't like the challenge of trying to get a permit for you in a fully developed and populated development with tight CC&Rs. Nor are they too hopeful if called after you've been caught cheating on a CC&R, when you ask the lawyer to respond on your behalf after you've received a "nastygram" from the Home Owners Association (the HOA).

This does not mean, however, that a lawyer responding on your behalf would lack things to say. There are several lines of defense that could be raised on your behalf. The key element, as you read about all of the shields listed below, would be the practical one. Money. How much money does your Homeowner's Association have to spend on this matter? How much are you willing to spend before you yield or move?

This said, however, the Homeowner's Association's lack of funds doesn't always help. In California, the CC&Rs are said to run with the land by statute so even the bankruptcy of the Homeowners Association doesn't help. An individual resident may still seek to enforce.

You Still Want to Buy A Home With CC&Rs?

You've now read that Federal law is not easily going to help you (It may help, but it may require litigation.) Let's assume that you have also discovered that state law is unlikely to help you. So let's get into some serious discussion for people who are determined to go ahead anyway. Here are some tips:

1. Retain a Lawyer Early

In all likelihood, you are going to pay a lawyer to represent you in closing on the house and taking out a mortgage. So why not hire that lawyer a few months earlier and obtain advice on state law, local zoning, as well as trying in advance to avoid the impact of CC&Rs? It is a good idea.

Let's repeat that to make it really plain. Just because you feel comfortable with the CC&R situation does not mean that you've passed through the zoning hoop. You may need both. In parts of Texas, there may be no zoning—but there may be CC&Rs that will make the erection of your necessary antenna system impossible. In parts of Michigan there may be no CC&Rs, but difficult zoning issues. In parts of Pennsylvania, you may have both. Ask your lawyer to look over the entire scene.

2. Obtain the CC&Rs Before You Agree to Buy

Here is the system used by John Langdon, N5CQ:

Search for property that meets your location and terrain needs. When you find a possible piece, ask the real estate agent to fax you the CC&Rs. If they make reference to antennas or approvals by an Architectural Control Committee (ACC) or Homeowner's Association (HOA), move on to the next property. If it is a new property, or is yet to be built, where the developer still owns the house and land (and *is* the ACC) and can grant variances and/or approvals to the CC&Rs, seek and obtain such approval. Make sure there you include language assuring that this approval cannot be withdrawn or modified by a future ACC or HOA and include a drawing of the proposed tower. All this becomes a contingency in a formal offer on the property.

If there is no reference to approvals, then go down to the courthouse and get the Declaration yourself to make sure the agent didn't fax you the stuff on Horse Apple Acres Phase IV, instead of Phase V, etc.

Sometimes there are different filings for "Bozo Acres" Phase 9 than for Phases 1-8. I heard a story about a particular development that had failed to file anything for "Phase 9." The sellers, the HOA, and the realtors all assumed the Declaration was the same at the other parts of the development, but in fact there were no restrictions at all for that section! Sometimes it really pays to do your homework.

When you are satisfied, then look into whether or not a building permit is required for a tower and how successful other hams have been at getting a tower permit actually issued in that municipality or county.

If you must buy a home with an ACC and/or anti-antenna CC&Rs, subscribe to the Kachina reflector, add a second phone line and begin planning your remote station, starting with the property search above.

Sometimes you just get lucky. Larry Burke, WI5A, wrote:

This is nearly exactly the situation I found myself in when I bought the property my house sits on today. The owner had 4 adjacent parcels of land, roughly $3/4$ acre each. One of the four was already sold when I was shopping for the land. Prior to my purchase, the real estate agent provided me with the "Deed Restrictions" for my lot. I checked the county courthouse... nothing was filed. Bought the lot, built my stuff... house, towers and all.

The seller and his lawyer later conceded that my lot, indeed, had no restrictions since they had neglected to file them at the courthouse. They promptly filed them afterwards. Now the remaining two have restrictions!

In any event, here's an especially dangerous, but non-obvious deed restriction to beware of: "engaging in any loud, noxious, or offensive activities that disturb the peace and quiet" of other homeowners. The problem here is that with a law, the Federal government has completely preempted the field of TVI or RFI, but preemption may not be a valid defense in state court to a complaint by a neighbor or the HOA under the CC&Rs.

3. Make a Contingent Offer

Sometimes you've just got to ask! But before you just try filling in the blanks in the following document yourself, remember the prior instruction and hire a lawyer early. The problem with a layman using the following form is determining whether or not the signer is authorized to sign it and thereby bind the HOA or ACC.

Let's repeat that. The question of whether or not the developer, in the absence of a Homeowner's Association, can act as the agent for other owners in the subdivision is a question of fact that must be proven at trial. You'll probably want a really good recitation of facts in the developer's authorization, especially if the authorization appears to fly in the face of the express wording of the covenants. If you don't understand this paragraph, this is even more proof that you should be using a lawyer early on.

Here's some more wisdom from Jim O'Connell, W9WU, referring to a contract add-on for CC&Rs in New Construction:

> Here's my contract add-on for new construction, "builder as developer" CC&R situations. Where the builder/developer is involved, they're often agreeable to exempting your antenna tower from the "Architectural Committee" approval during the initial phase of sales. This real estate sales add-on language requires the developer to grant permission as a condition to selling you the lot/house.

> As for existing covenants in a developed area, my recommendation is to tell your real estate agent that you're not interested. If you've already purchased the XYL's dream home and just discovered the CC&Rs that prohibit any outside antenna, find another real estate agent and list your home for sale. I hate listening to a ham (who's attended one of my "Ham Radio & the Law: Getting It Up and Keeping It Up" law forums at Dayton and elsewhere) complaining about attorney's fees to defend against his neighbor's lawsuit to remove the antenna support structure.

> Remember, in most states if you're subject to CC&Rs, any other property owner subject to the same restrictions can sue you to remove the antenna. Most such restrictions provide that the owner in violation must pay attorney's fees to the winner of the lawsuit.

> A home is the most expensive thing you'll ever buy in your life. Spend a few bucks on a lawyer *before* you make that offer!

> Here's a contract (offer to purchase) add-on to help protect your tower rights when you make an offer. This version is useful when you're dealing with the Builder/Developer of a new subdivision. Often, the Builder controls the Homeowner's Association or Architectural Committee until all or most of the lots are sold. Getting the necessary approvals as a condi-

tion of your offer to purchase is key to your success. Mind the caution at the end!!

Addendum to offer to purchase between

_____, Buyers,

and _____,

Sellers, for the purchase of the property at

_____.

A. Buyer has informed Seller that Buyer is a licensed Amateur Radio operator, and Seller warrants that no covenants, conditions, restrictions of record, architectural committee or homeowner association rules or regulations presently exist or will be recorded prior to closing that would or that may be construed to restrict or prohibit Buyer, from and after closing and delivery of the premises, from installing and maintaining Amateur Radio antennae and associated supporting structure not less than _____ feet in height on the property. Seller further agrees that no such covenants, conditions or restrictions of record affecting the subject property will by imposed by Seller or his transferees or assigns in any plat of subdivision or Planned Unit Development agreement recorded prior to closing. Seller agrees to provide Buyer, within fourteen (14) days of the signing of this agreement, and again ten (10) days prior to closing, with a copy of the recorded plat of subdivision and all other documents showing all covenants, conditions or restrictions of record, homeowner association rules or regulations running with the land or affecting the property. Should such covenants, conditions, restrictions of record, homeowner association rules or regulations exist on either date such that Buyer's installation of the aforementioned antennae and support structure may be inhibited or precluded, then at Buyer's option this contract may be deemed null and void, all obligations of both parties cancelled and all deposits refunded promptly.

B. Seller further agrees that, that to the extent Seller is the owner of property located within 300 feet of the subject property, Seller will provide Buyer with a statement that Seller, as owner of adjacent properties, has no objection to the granting of a building permit for an Amateur Radio antenna support structure by the local municipality or appropriate governmental body.

C. Seller also agrees, to the extent that Seller controls any Architectural Committee, Homeowner's Association or similar committee from which permission is required for installation of Buyer's Amateur Radio antennae and support structure, that Seller will grant or cause to be promptly granted such permission upon application by Buyer.

D. The promises and covenants by the Seller contained in Paragraphs A through C hereof shall survive the closing of this transaction, notwithstanding the delivery of the deed by Seller.

_____

_____

Buyers

_____

_____

Sellers

Dated: _____, 2000

(CAUTION: This document was prepared in consideration of the laws of the State of Illinois. Real estate law varies among the states, and you should consult an attorney prior to entering into any real estate transaction. If you screw it up you'll have only yourself to blame. James C. O'Connell, W9WU, Attorney at Law.) See CD-ROM, filename: **Addendum to Real-Estate Offer-CC&R.DOC**.

Why would a developer agree to allow a radio ham to be exempt from the CC&Rs which control others? There are several scenarios:

• The developer has put a lot of money into preparing the development—in legal fees, land clearing, roads, sewers, and so forth—and really _really_ needs some income fast.

• The developer never really gave any thought to the question of antenna systems and the offending clause was put there when the lawyer for the development copied it in from a standard form. With sufficient lot size and foresting, the clause is really irrelevant.

• The developer has sold most of the lots and houses and is down to the last few. Confident that these last remaining lots can be sold with or without such protection, the developer no longer cares.

4. Prepare to Erect FAST

If you've managed to obtain permission from the developer while he comprises the entire HOA or ACC, build fast. He could sell the last house and be gone next month, leaving you in the hands of the new HOA or ACC. For this reason, you want a local attorney to be sure that your waiver will last beyond the developer's departure. Building fast adds to your legal posture. It could, for example, prevent a later purchaser from bringing suit—on the grounds he knew when he bought that your antenna system was there.

To prove when your antenna system was built, take dated photos, get a Certificate of Use or a Certificate of Completion from the local Building Inspector, and do whatever it takes to prove that your antenna system was up before the complainant bought his place. Other ideas: Take a photo of young children standing next to your structure (you can introduce a child later as evidence.). Write the date of the pour into the concrete.

Notice Of Violation Received

Against the advice you received, you bought a house with CC&Rs. Now you've received a nasty letter from a neighbor, who seeks to enforce a common covenant, or from the homeowner's association.

1. Look hard at the definitions to see if your antenna system is included. Look at the definition of "structure" (and hope that it talks about habitable space). Look at the definition of fixture (and hope that it talks about something attached to an outside wall).

2. Figure out if you have received the letter because you didn't first apply to the "architectural control committee" (generally known as an "ACC") or because you have violated a specific rule. If the covenant requires you to apply to the ACC, but there is no ACC anymore (it happens, sometimes because the last house in the development has been built), ask your lawyer if "impossibility of performance" would be a defense in your situation.

Despite stern warning from wiser heads, there will always be amateurs who, for one reason or another (common examples are divorce, disablement or retirement) find themselves living in a place with CC&Rs. For that situation, here's Attorney Phil Kane's (K2ASP) approach. This was a situation where the HOA's counsel had written to him threatening sanctions against the amateur after forcing compliance with a CC&R rule regarding antenna visibility. (See CD-ROM, filename: **Homeowners Association Counsel Letter.DOC**.)

Dear Homeowner's Association Counsel:

The Amateur Family intends to abide by all reasonable provisions of the recorded Covenants, Conditions, and Restrictions ("CC&Rs") and By-Laws of the Association.

The Amateur Family retains the right to erect any and all antennas that do not violate CC&R § [XYZ] by being "visible to the public view" with the understanding that this is interpreted in terms of the reasonable observer using reasonable means to make the observation from a place where the observer has a right to be without requesting permission from the Amateur Family to be there.

The Amateur Family retains the right to operate their licensed radio station(s) in accordance with the terms of their license(s) and applicable statutes and regulations. Said operation will, by virtue of holding a current license therefor, be presumed to be in the public interest, convenience and necessity absent a specific ruling to the contrary from the Federal Communications Commission ("FCC") [See 47 U.S.C.A. § 309(a)] and will be presumed to be in compliance with all FCC rules and regulations absent a specific determination to the contrary by the FCC.

The Amateur Family will handle issues of unwanted reception caused by improper technical operation of their equipment by bearing the responsibility to take the required steps to bring their equipment into compliance with FCC regulations and will cease operations while it is in non-compliance, with the exception of reasonable tests to determine the effectiveness of attempted adjustments, repairs, or remedial measures.

If unwanted reception is caused by conditions

beyond their control, they will assume the obligation to reasonably cooperate with the affected party or parties to determine how to prevent such unwanted reception and to make a reasonable number of tests to assist the affected party or parties in determining the effectiveness of any remedial measures, but that they have no obligation to, and will not attempt to, repair or replace any home entertainment or other electronic equipment of the affected party or parties nor are they obligated to cease operations as long as they are in compliance with FCC regulations and technical standards.

We regard any unilateral attempts by the Association to impose restrictions on the Amateur Family's operations beyond the parameters outlined above as unreasonable and an interference with the Amateur Family's own "right of enjoyment" in the use of their property, especially where the correction of the problem is in the hands of the complainant, and we are prepared to secure and defend their rights as necessary.

We trust that the situation will not come to that point. As you stated in your letter "I am hopeful that this matter has been resolved and no further action will be necessary." I echo that stance.

Sincerely,
[Name of Attorney],
Attorney for John T. Ham

As usual, use of the above approach is on the basis of "your mileage may vary." Phil Kane wishes everyone success!

Once court papers (a complaint) have actually been filed against a ham, the defense must begin. Find the right lawyer. This is *litigation* and there are many lawyers who simply do not do it—just as there are many doctors who do not do surgery. Investigate the possibility of asking your title insurance company to defend you. There is also no harm in asking your homeowner's insurance company to defend you.

Let's examine lines of argument against enforcement of a covenant or restraint. A special thanks to Sid Leach, K5XI, based in Houston, TX, where he practices with a large multi-state general practice law firm, whose article "Federal Preemption of Deed Restrictions," *The DX Magazine*, May/Jun 1993, pp 36-40, developed some of these theories. His complete article is included on the accompanying CD-ROM, under filename **Sid Leach Article.PDF** (courtesy of *The DX Magazine*). Chris Imlay, W3KD, General Counsel, ARRL, also contributed to this section.

Federal Law Prohibits Enforcement of This CC&R

Shelley v. Kraemer, 334 U.S. 1 (1948), held that a restrictive covenant against occupancy by any people of the Negro or Mongolian race could not be enforced in a state court. That famous case stands for the principle that a restriction against public policy will not be enforced by the courts.

The public policy contravened by a restrictive CC&R is found in Public Law 103-408, October 22, 1994: "[R]easonable accommodation should be made for the effective operation of amateur radio from residences, private vehicles and public areas, and that regulation at all levels of government should facilitate and encourage amateur radio operation as a public benefit." Section 1(3).

Note that this argument completely sidesteps the "problem" with PRB-1, FCC DA-99-2654 (1999), at paragraph 6: "… the clear policy statement that was set forth in PRB-1 excluding restrictive covenants in private contractual agreements as being outside the reach of our limited preemption."

The fact that the FCC declined to expand the FCC's preemption of government regulations to include CC&Rs does *not* mean that restrictive CC&Rs are good public policy. It means only that there was no majority vote of the FCC to preempt CC&Rs at this time. The FCC position is:

> [W]e nevertheless strongly encourage associations of homeowners and private contracting parties to follow the principle of reasonable accommodation and to apply it to any and all instances of amateur service communications where they may be involved. Although we do not hesitate to offer such encouragement, we are not persuaded by the Petition or the comments in support thereof that specific rule provisions bringing the private restrictive covenants within the ambit of PRB-1 are necessary or appropriate at this time. [FCC DA-99-2654 (1999), at paragraph 6.]

Thus, a Court is still free to find that a deed restriction is against public policy.

State Law May Prohibit Enforcement of This CC&R

Most state preemption laws mimic 47 CFR Section 97.15, but this is a big country. Unrelated to PRB-1, or any state law that tracks PRB-1, you can never tell what an inventive lawyer might find in your state in the way of a phrase in the state constitution or a statute that could prove useful in battling a CC&R. In addition, common law does not favor restrictions on land, and all ambiguities in restrictions are read against the drafter.

As a Matter of Equity, the Court Should Not Enforce the Covenant

A court need not enforce a deed restriction that would result in an inequity. Before considering any of the following defenses to a complaint, however, the radio amateur must recall perhaps the most famous of all equity maxims: "He who comes into equity must do so with clean hands." So it helps if you never knew about the restriction you are now accused of violating, or if you can show that the covenant was effectively terminated before you bought the land.

An inequity results in cases of:

Harm Exceeding Benefit. Enforcing the covenant would be unreasonable because the resulting harm to the homeowner is greater than the benefit produced. You can claim that the harm is to emergency communications and the benefit is ephemeral, especially where the outdoor antenna is hardly visible (for example, wires in the woods or a simple vertical), or visible only when in use (a retractable structure). *Katzman v. Anderson,* 359 Pa. 438.

Acquiescence. The CC&Rs are not being enforced against other antennas (for example, CB radio, TV, satellite TV, MMDS, or other Amateur Radio antennas). However, failure to complain about rooftop TV antennas was not sufficient to estop a complaint about a 40-foot tall freestanding CB radio antenna. *Reed v. Williamson,* 164 Neb. 99, 82 N.W. 2d 18 (1957).

Abandonment. Some lots (usually subsequent lots) are sold subject to the covenants and others are not.

Laches. Delay in enforcing a deed restriction.

Estoppel. The benefited party (in a practical sense, the developer) led you to believe that the CC&Rs would not be enforced against you with respect to an antenna system and you relied upon such a representation. Try to find something in writing that led you to believe that the covenant against antennas would not be enforced.

Changed Conditions. The amateur would have to claim that the character of the development has changed so much that it is impossible that enforcement of a restriction will yield the benefit of the restriction. Such circumstance is likely to be rare.

Clean Hands (the Other Guy's). A rewrite of "He who comes into equity must do so with clean hands" is "People who live in glass houses shouldn't throw stones." A court is not required to grant a decree in equity (briefly, a civil proceeding where someone seeks a court order, not money damages). Read *all* of your homeowner rules and regulations, in the hope that you will find one that the complaining neighbor has violated. If the neighbor who seeks to enforce a covenant against you built an illegal porch, or contravenes some other rule, learn everything you can about that violation. You can file against him and you can defend with the facts. The first strategy (file against him) may give him a reason to back off. The second strategy (claiming unclean hands) may give the Judge a reason to back off. You never know.

LOCAL ZONING BYLAWS AND ORDINANCES

The local law that applies to you is "the local law." It is *not*:

- What the real estate agent told you.
- What the homeowner now trying to sell you the house told you.
- What the counter clerk said when you dropped by Town Hall to inquire.
- What the Building Inspector told you, unless s/he looked it up almost right then.
- What another ham in town told you.
- What another ham in a neighboring town told you.

Got that? The local law is only what the local law says during your Building Permit (and if necessary, Special Permit) application process. You wouldn't be the first ham to buy a home and then apply for a tower permit, only to discover that the bylaw or ordinance is changing before your very eyes. So once you embark on the process of buying a home, acquire the entire local bylaw (all of it, not just a photocopy of what a clerk tells you is the relevant page) and

start your subscription to the local paper (reading the legal notices to see if some Board is proposing a change that will affect your ability to erect an antenna-support structure).

If, during the course of your research, interviews and reading of the local newspaper, you discover that the local bylaw is about to be changed, then you may decide that the time has come to scramble. Get that application in right away. If some portion of the process has begun, then you may need to know how to "freeze" the bylaw so that you may obtain a permit for a structure that may not be possible to obtain later, or which may be horribly more expensive later. Freezing the bylaw can usually be done two ways: *Plan Freezes* and *Non-Plan Freezes.*

In a Plan Freeze, sometimes known as an *ANR Freeze* (from the phrase "Approval Not Required), you submit a plan of some sort—to "subdivide" your property in some way (don't worry; you'll still own it all). Plan Freezes involve a highly specialized area of law and you will likely need the aid of a local real estate attorney, as well as a surveyor.

In a Non-Plan Freezes, your rights may "vest" as a result of your actions. There are many things you can do to help yourself create "vested rights," and you should start doing them immediately. Your state may have a statutory Non-Plan Freeze if you should obtain the building permit and start building but do not finish before the new bylaw takes effect. Your state may also allow a common-law Non-Plan Freeze. Here are a variety of facts that help applicants claim common law vested rights:

An Applicant can put himself in a position to apply before the effective date of the zoning change. So don't grant the seller a delay of the closing on your new house. Also, make sure you have all application requirements on hand—including a plot plan and construction plans for the structure.

An Applicant can submit as complete an application as possible, as soon as possible.

An Applicant can engage in site preparations that exceed the *barely begun* threshold. This probably means that pounding stakes into the ground to show the approximate position and laying out string is not enough. However, surveying, land clearing and obtaining delivery of construction materials (rebar, sand, gravel), plus tower lattice sections, guy anchors, the mast, rotator, as well as antennas could be useful.

An Applicant can incur and keep track of substantial expenses, such as paying for surveying, land clearing, construction materials, parts and so forth.

If there are required preliminary steps (the prerequisites for issuance) under the present bylaw, you should diligently pursue approvals required from the highway department, the police, the fire department, the health department, the conservation commission and so forth.

An Applicant can keep track of any actions by the Town that could later be considered acts of bad faith, such as requiring submission of additional information not required of other applicants, "losing" papers previously submitted, mysterious delays in site plan approval, etc.

An Applicant can demand issuance of the permit as of

right (and document the demand!) before the zoning change becomes effective. A Court may consider it critical that the Building Commissioner had the authority to issue a Building Permit before the new bylaw became effective, especially if the issuance of the permit should have been a ministerial act.

These are all actions that can lead to the creation of vested rights. For a very good discussion of the common law of vested rights or Non-Plan Freezes, interestingly enough with respect to a 460 foot tall commercial tower case, see *Franks v. DiRico*, MA Superior Court, August 26, 1997, 1997 Mass. Super. LEXIS 282. (CD-ROM, filename: **Franks v DiRico.PDF**.)

Here is another example of common-law vested rights, from a different jurisdiction, cited by Justice Susan Garsh in the Franks case. Addressing *Mattson v. City of Chicago*, 411 N.E.2d 1002, 89 Ill. App. 3d 378, 44 Ill Dec.636 (1980), she wrote: "Every division of the Department of Buildings had approved the building plans, and all processing had been completed except for the actual physical issuance of the permit, and both the approval of the applications for the building permit and demolition occurred prior to introduction of the zoning amendment... [T]he court held that a vested right arose where the plaintiff had expended substantial funds and issuance of the permit was purely ministerial."

For additional information, see *Mandelker, Land Use Law*, 4th Ed. § 6.13 (1997); *Jurgensmeyer & Roberts, Land Use Planning and Control Law*, § 5.27 (1998); and *David G. Heeter, Zoning Estoppel*: Application of the Principles of Equitable Estoppel and Vested Rights in Zoning Disputes, 1971 Urb. L.Ann.63.

Should you find yourself in one of these situations, be sure to inform your attorney that you actually obtained all the required permits and started building before the bylaw changed. There is a difference between vested rights and equitable estoppel. You may be entitled to both.

In sum, if the relevant bylaw might change, or actually does change mid-stream, you and your attorney should look at a variety of distinct responses, depending on your facts:

- A plan or statutory zoning freeze,
- A non-plan, but still statutory, zoning freeze,
- A non-plan, common-law zoning freeze (vested rights), or
- A non-plan claim of equitable estoppel, to prevent enforcement of the new bylaw.

The essence of the situation is that the local bylaw controlling your situation is the one in effect at the time your Building Permit is granted, not the law at the time you applied. There are ways to help yourself, but the message is still clear—the law is only what is on the books at the relevant moment in time, unless it is overridden in some way, or unless you and your attorney fashion a strategy to work your way through it.

BUILDING CODE

Generally, a building code is statewide. There may be places where it is rather brief, however, and subject to a great deal of interpretation by the Building Inspector or Building Commissioner as to what must be done to make the construction safe. As with local law, the building code is only what the building code says. Unlike the local zoning bylaw, however, it is probably unnecessary to buy the entire state building code. It is probably several volumes thick and it is enough to read the relevant portions at a local library, or by simply asking the Building Inspector if you can read his/her copy at the counter (and photocopy the relevant pages).

The BOCA Code

Many states have adopted the BOCA code, named after its parent organization, the Building Officers and Code Administrators, Country Club Hills, IL. In general, you need to understand only a few sections. Here they are, as they appear in the Massachusetts version (but any state building code based on the BOCA code should be similar).

Excerpts from 780 Code of Massachusetts Regulations (CMR) Sixth Edition 2/7/97 (Effective 2/28/97)
780 CMR 3108.0 RADIO AND TELEVISION TOWERS

3108.1 General: Subject to the structural provisions of 780 CMR 1611.0 for *wind loads* and the requirements of 780 CMR 1510.0 governing the fire resistance ratings of buildings for the support of roof structures, all radio and television towers shall be designed and constructed as herein provided.

3108.2 Location and access: Towers shall be located and equipped with step bolts and ladders so as to provide ready access for inspection purposes. Guy wires or other accessories shall not cross or encroach upon any street or other public space, or over any electric power lines, or encroach upon any other privately owned property without *written* consent of the owner.

3108.3 Construction: All towers shall be constructed of approved corrosion-resistant noncombustible material. The minimum type of construction of isolated radio towers not more than 100 feet (30480 mm) min height shall by Type 4.

3108.4 Loads: Towers shall be designed to resist *windloads* in accordance with EIA 222-E listed in *Appendix A*. Consideration shall be given to conditions involving *wind load* on ice-covered sections in localities subject to sustained freezing temperatures.

3108.4 Dead load: Towers shall be designed for the *dead load* plus the *ice load* in regions where ice formation occurs.

3108.4.2 Uplift: Adequate foundations and anchorage shall be provided to resist two times the calculated wind uplift.

3108.5 Grounding: All towers shall be permanently and effectively grounded.

780 CMR 3109.0 RADIO AND TELEVISION ANTENNAS

3109.1 Permits not required: A building permit is not required for roof installation of antennal structures not more than

12 feet (3658 mm) in height for private radio or television reception. Such a structure shall not be erected so as to injure the roof covering, and when removed from the roof, the roof covering shall be repaired to maintain weather and water tightness. The installation of any antenna structure mounted on the roof of a building shall not be erected nearer to the *lot line* than the total height of the antennal structure above the roof, nor shall such structure be erected near electric power lines or encroach upon any street or other public space.

3109.2 Permits required: Approval shall be secured for all roof mounted antennal structures more than 12 feet (3658 mm) in height above the roof. The application shall be accompanied by detailed drawings of the structure and methods of anchorage. All connections to the roof structure shall be properly flashed to maintain water-tightness. The design and materials of construction shall comply with the requirements of 780 CMR 3108.3 for character, quality and minimum dimension.

1611.1 Wind load zones: The locations of *wind load* zones are shown in the figures 1611.1A, 1611.1B, 1611.1C maps. Zone 1 consists of the Counties of Berkshire, Franklin, Hampshire and Hampden; Zone 2 consists of the County of Worcester; and Zone 3 consists of the Counties of Essex, Middlesex, Suffolk, Norfolk, Plymouth, Bristol, Barnstable, Dukes and Nantucket.

1611.2 Exposures: Exposure is defined as a measure of terrain roughness and is classified as follows:

Exposure A: centers of large cities and very rough, hilly terrain. Exposure A applies for downtown areas only when the terrain for at least one half mile upwind of the structure is heavily built up, with at least 50% of the buildings being in excess of four stories, and when Exposure B prevails beyond this boundary.

Exercise caution in using these reduced wind pressures for buildings and structures on high ground in the midst of cities or rough terrain.

Exposure B: suburban areas, towns, city outskirts, wooded areas, and rolling terrain. Exposure B applies only when the terrain for at least one half mile upwind is a continuous urban development, forest, wooded area, or rolling terrain.

Exposure C: open level terrain with only scattered buildings, structures, trees or miscellaneous obstructions, open water, or shorelines.

1611.4 Reference wind pressures: Reference wind pressures for the various exposures and wind zones are given in the following Table 1611.4. The tabulated pressures are combined windward and leeward pressures representing the overall effect of the wind on essentially rectangular structures, and account for typical gust effects as found in ordinary buildings. These pressures do not account for buffeting or channeling caused by positions of nearby structures, vortex shedding, or wind sensitive dynamic properties of a particular structure.

[Excerpts from Table 1611.4 for locations on or near the Massachusetts seashore]

REFERENCE WIND PRESSURE (POUNDS PER SQUARE FOOT)

Height above grade H(feet)	Zone 3 Exposure		
	A	B	C
50-100	14	21	31
100-150	18	26	37
150-200	22	30	41

Commentary: Don't worry about the fact that § 3109.1 talks about reception.

(a) The antenna is for reception.

(b) Regulation of transmission is an FCC matter, and, for these purposes, has been pre-empted.

ANSI TIA/EIA-222-F Standard

Your state building code may or may not reference, copy or mimic the ANSI standard TIA/EIA-222-F: "Structural Standards for Steel Antenna Towers and Antenna Supporting Structures." If your state building code does refer to windspeed, however, it may use a table (such as the excerpted portion from Massachusetts Table 1611.4 above) to list the windload permitted, or, putting it another way, the windspeed for which an antenna-support structure must be designed.

TIA/EIA-222-F, Annex A, § 2.3.3 B states: "The basic wind speed from Section 16, the equations for the exposure coefficient (KZ), and the gust response factor (GH) are based on wind conditions in open, level country, and grasslands." This means that if you are in a valley, protected by rolling hills, or protected by surrounding forested lands, you may not need to meet the highest windspeed standard.

If you have any doubt, seek the services of a Professional Engineer to make sure what part of which standard applies to your particular situation.

The National Electrical Code

Your jurisdiction may, or may not, have adopted the National Electrical Code (NEC), published by the National Fire Protection Association as *NFPA 70, National Electrical Code*. Whether or not it applies where you live, the NEC should never stand in the way of the grant of a permit for an Amateur Radio antenna system, so long as only low voltage (less than 36 Vdc) goes out to your antenna-support structure. You can find the NEC at the public library of most medium to large cities or you may order it from the NFPA Website: **http://www.nfpa.org/**.

STATE LAW

A growing number of states have adopted statutes that reference Amateur Radio preemption, or similarly protect Amateur Radio antenna systems. Any amateur embarking on a quest to build or protect an Amateur Radio antenna system should become familiar with his home state's statute. The latest list of state Web sites may be found at *ARRLWeb*: **http://www2.arrl.org/field/regulations/statutes.html**

SUGGESTED STATE LAW

If you have any influence when your state considers its own version of PRB-1, the draft below has much to commend it. Note that both PRB-1 and the draft below do not limit the preemption to "zoning" bylaws, so wetlands bylaws would also be preempted. Don't be horrified. Most states preempt wetlands bylaws for farming purposes, so the thought is not unprecedented. In addition, the impingement on a wetland caused by an Amateur-Radio antenna-support structure is truly minimal (a guyed support structure 12 or 18 inches on a face requires only about three cubic yards of concrete, or a block of concrete about the size of a 55 gallon drum). Unfortunately, such wetlands bylaws have been used vindictively against hams. (See the CD-ROM, filename: **Proposed State Preemption Statute.DOC**.)

PROPOSED STATE PREEMPTION STATUTE

No ordinance or bylaw, common covenant, deed restraint or restriction (collectively, "Antenna Restriction") shall prohibit the construction of or use of an antenna structure by a federally licensed Amateur Radio operator. Antenna Restrictions may reasonably regulate the location and height of such antenna structures for the purposes of health, safety or aesthetics; provided, however, that such Antenna Restrictions reasonably allow for sufficient height of such antenna structures so as to effectively accommodate Amateur Radio communications by federally licensed Amateur Radio operators and constitute the minimum practicable regulation necessary to accomplish the legitimate purposes of the city or town enacting, or the landowner(s) adopting, such Antenna Restriction.

No Antenna Restriction, nor local zoning authority may condition construction and use permits on any requirement to eliminate or remedy radio frequency interference.

This last paragraph presents no change in the law, as it merely quotes *Freeman v. Burlington Broadcasters, Inc.*, No. 97- 9141 (2d Cir. February 23, 2000). See CD-ROM, filename: **Freeman vs Burlington Broadcasters.PDF**.

If you think you really have your legislature favorably disposed to Amateur Radio, then consider adding the following, that mimics (but is not an exact copy of) FCC DA 99-2569 (1999):

The very least regulation necessary for the welfare of the community must be the aim of Antenna Restrictions so that such restrictions will not impinge on the needs of amateur operators to engage in amateur communications.

Using language such as the "least regulation necessary" could later prove to be a big winner because quite comparable language is found throughout the cases on the First Amendment with respect to "time, place and manner" restrictions on public speech. See the discussion below on the "minimum practicable" test (11.5.4).

If you are really getting bold, try adding this, from the

New York statute proposal:

No local ordinance, by-law, rule or regulation, or other local law shall: (a) restrict amateur radio support structure height to less than ninety-five feet above ground level; or (b) restrict the number of antenna support structures.

Note that the Virginia approach is dramatically different from the other statutes that largely mimic 47 CFR §97.15(b). In Virginia, the statute treats densely populated areas differently from less populated areas, and the statutes specifically mention a "safe haven" height (75'). California may adopt the Virginia approach.

FEDERAL LAW RELATING TO AMATEUR RADIO

Amateur Radio Service—Part 97—Purpose

If you ever want to look up a Federal regulation relating to ham radio, try **http://www.access.gpo.gov/cgi-bin/cfrassemble.cgi?title=199947**.

For example: If you've always wanted to know what the FCC's "200 foot" height rule may say: Just go there and enter 200 feet. Then look for any reference to 47 CFR § 97.xxxx.

Public Law 103-408
PUBLIC LAW 103-408—OCT. 22, 1994

Public Law 103-408

103d Congress

Joint Resolution

To recognize the achievements of radio amateurs, and to establish support for such amateurs as national policy.

Whereas Congress has expressed its determination in section 1 of the Communications Act of 1934 (47 U.S.C. 151) to promote safety of life and property through the use of radio communication;

Whereas Congress, in section 7 of the Communications Act of 1934 (47 U.S.C. 157), established a policy to encourage the provision of new technologies and services;

Whereas Congress, in section 3 of the Communications Act of 1934, defined radio stations to include amateur stations operated by persons interested in radio technique without pecuniary interest;

Whereas the Federal Communications Commission has created an effective regulatory framework through which the amateur radio service has been able to achieve the goals of the service;

Whereas these regulations, set forth in Part 97 of title 47 of the Code of Federal Regulations clarify and extend the purposes of the amateur radio service as a—

(1) voluntary noncommercial communication service, particularly with respect to providing emergency communications;

(2) contributing service to the advancement of the telecommunications infrastructure;

(3) service which encourages improvement of an individual's technical and operating skills;

(4) service providing a national reservoir of trained operators, technicians and electronics experts; and

(5) service enhancing international good will;

Whereas Congress finds that members of the amateur radio service community have provided invaluable emergency communications services following such disasters as Hurricanes Hugo, Andrew, and Iniki, the Mt. St. Helens Eruption, the Loma Prieta earthquake, tornadoes, floods, wild fires, and industrial accidents in great number and variety across the Nation; and

Whereas Congress finds that the amateur radio service has made a contribution to our Nation's communications by its crafting, in 1961, of the first Earth satellite licensed by the Federal Communications Commission, by its proof-of-concept for search rescue satellites, by its continued exploration of the low Earth orbit in particular pointing the way to commercial use thereof in the 1990s, by its pioneering of communications using reflections from meteor trails, a technique now used for certain government and commercial communications, and by its leading role in development of low-cost, practical data transmission by radio which increasingly is being put to extensive use in, for instance, the land mobile service: Now, therefore, be it

Resolved by the Senate and House of Representatives of the United States of America in Congress assembled,

SECTION 1. FINDINGS AND DECLARATIONS OF CONGRESS

Congress finds and declares that—

(1) radio amateurs are hereby commended for their contributions to technical progress in electronics, and for their emergency radio communications in times of disaster;

(2) the Federal Communications Commission is urged to continue and enhance the development of the amateur radio service as a public benefit by adopting rules and regulations which encourage the use of new technologies within the amateur radio service; and

(3) reasonable accommodation should be made for the effective operation of amateur radio from residences, private vehicles and public areas, and that regulation at all levels of government should facilitate and encourage amateur radio operation as a public benefit.

Approved October 22, 1994.

Public Law 100-594

SENSE OF CONGRESS

Sec. 10
(a) The Congress finds that —

(1) more than four hundred thirty-five thousand four hundred radio amateurs in the United States are licensed by the Federal Communications Commission upon examination in radio regulations, technical principles, and the international Morse code;

(2) by international treaty and the Federal Communications Commission regulation, the amateur is authorized to operate his or her station in a radio service of intercommunications and technical investigations solely with a personal aim and without pecuniary interest;

(3) among the basic purposes for the Amateur Radio Service is the provision of voluntary, noncommercial radio service, particularly emergency communications; and

(4) volunteer amateur radio emergency communications services have consistently and reliably been provided before, during, and after floods, tornadoes, forest fires, earthquakes, blizzards, train wrecks, chemical spills, and other disasters.

(b) It is the sense of Congress that —

(1) it strongly encourages and supports the Amateur Radio Service and its emergency communications efforts; and

(2) Government agencies shall take into account the valuable contributions made by amateur radio operators when considering actions affecting the Amateur Radio Service.

Federal Communications Commission Authorization Act of 1988. Pub. L. No. 100-594, 102 Stat. 3021, 3025 (November 3, 1988); see also Joint Explanatory Statement of the Committee of Conference on H.R. Conf. Rep. No. 386. 101st Cong., 1st Sess. 415, 433 (November 21, 1989), reprinted in 1990 U.S. Code Cong. & Admin. News 3018, 3037 (amateur licensees exempted from new Commission-wide fees program because "[t]he Conferees recognize that amateur licensees do not operate for profit and can play an important public safety role in times of disaster or emergency"). Joint Explanatory Statement of the Committee of Conference on H.R. Conf. Rep. No. 765, 97th Cong., 2d Sess. 18-19 (August 19, 1982), reprinted in 1982 U.S. Code Cong. & Admin. News 2261, 2262-63.

47 CFR § 97.1

Sec. 97.1 Basis and purpose.

The rules and regulations in this part are designed to provide an amateur radio service having a fundamental purpose as expressed in the following principles:

(a) Recognition and enhancement of the value of the amateur service to the public as a voluntary noncommercial communication service, particularly with respect to providing emergency communications.

(b) Continuation and extension of the amateur's proven ability to contribute to the advancement of the radio art.

(c) Encouragement and improvement of the amateur service through rules which provide for advancing skills in both the communication and technical phases of the art.

(d) Expansion of the existing reservoir within the amateur radio service of trained operators, technicians, and electronics experts.

(e) Continuation and extension of the amateur's unique ability to enhance international goodwill.

[Every section of the Code of Federal Regulations may be found by going to: **http://www.access.gpo.gov/nara/cfr/index.html**. To find every section of Part 97, governing radio amateurs, go to **http://www.access.gpo.gov/nara/cfr/waisidx_99/47cfr97_99.html**. The complete Part 97 is also located on the CD-ROM, filename: **FCC Part 97.PDF**.]

47 CFR § 97.15

Sec. 97.15 Station antenna structures.

(a) Owners of certain antenna structures more than 60.96 meters (200 feet) above ground level at the site or located near or at a public use airport must notify the Federal Aviation Administration and register with the Commission as required by part 17 of this chapter.

(b) Except as otherwise provided herein, a station antenna structure may be erected at heights and dimensions sufficient to accommodate amateur service communications. (State and local regulation of a station antenna structure must not preclude amateur service communications. Rather, it must reasonably accommodate such communications and must constitute the minimum practicable regulation to accomplish the state or local authority's legitimate purpose. See PRB-1, 101 FCC 2d 952 (1985) for details.)

[64 FR 53242, Oct. 1, 1999]

Effective Date Note: At 64 FR 53242, Oct. 1, 1999, Sec. 97.15 was revised, effective Nov. 30, 1999. For the convenience of the user, the superseded text (the text that was there before the section was divided into sub-sections (a) and (b) is set forth as follows:

Sec. 97.15 Station antenna structures.

Owners of certain antenna structures more than 60.96 meters (200 feet) above ground level at the site or located near or at a public use airport must notify the Federal Aviation Administration and register with the Commission as required by part 17 of this chapter. [63 FR 68978, Dec. 14, 1998]

PRB-1

You may find the full text of PRB-1 at **http://www.fcc.gov/wtb/amateur/prb-1.html** and the follow up in 1999, which is very helpful to amateurs, may be found at **http://www.fcc.gov/Bureaus/Wireless/Orders/1999/da992569.txt**. These are also on the CD-ROM, filenames: **FCC PRB-1 (1985).PDF** and **FCC PRB-1 (1999).PDF**.

Minimum Practicable Test

In connection with a question posed to me on an Internet reflector about the minimum practical test and how to find a way to overcome an argument that height and other similar regulations (such as setback, sideyard and number of structure limitations) are the least restrictive means available, I stated:

I'm glad you asked. Let's look at the three types of regulation you query. The key question is: "for what purpose?" I suggest that the only acceptable purposes would be health, safety or aesthetic considerations. I base this on the wording of PRB-1.

Federal Communications Commission Order PRB-1, 101 FCC 2d 952, 50 Fed. Reg. 38813 (September 25, 1985), declares in pertinent part:

"Local regulations that involve placement, screening, or height of antennas based on health, safety or aesthetic considerations must be crafted to accommodate reasonable amateur communications, and to represent the minimum practicable regulation to accomplish the local authority's legitimate purpose."

Let's take them one at a time.

Is SETBACK the least restrictive means, or minimum practicable method for health or safety? No, it isn't.

With respect to HEALTH, it would seem that the only rational issue is RF exposure, a matter that is regulated by the methods described in FCC OET 65.

SAFETY is an engineering concept and the least restrictive means with respect to the communications needs of the ham would be to require that the ham equal or exceed the building code requirements with respect to wind load. After all, this is how skyscrapers are built, with no setback. [Can you imagine a 1:1 setback requirement for a structure like the Empire State Building? Manhattan would only have a few skyscrapers dotting its skyline!—*Ed.*]

AESTHETICS is the rub. But a blanket setback rule ignores the fact that there can be placements that, for the purpose of reducing visibility (and thereby improving aesthetics) logically require that the antenna system be placed in some back corner, or along a sidelot line where trees or other buffers may block visibility. Conclusion: If the ordinance REQUIRES a certain setback, it may defeat the aesthetics purpose by forcing the antenna system out into the open, in the middle of the yard.

Does preventing antenna erection in a SIDEYARD meet the minimum practicable test? For a house on a property with 200+ feet between the house and the sidelot line, a sideyard requirement is clearly not health or safety related. So it must be aesthetics. But I recently ran into a situation where the drafting of the definition of a sideyard meant that the "best" place to put an antenna from an aesthetics perspective is in the side yard, to hide it from the neighbors. So a simple sideyard rule fails the minimum practicable test.

A Town Counsel will usually say: "But if the sideyard is the best place, our Board will just grant a variance." Yet this response fails the "regulations … must be crafted to accommodate" test. A variance is obviously available only when the regulation involving placement, screening or height fails to accommodate. The opportunity to beg for a variance, which is a matter of equity, is not "crafting to accommodate."

What about NUMBER OF STRUCTURE regulations? Let's start with the most obvious example: the ham who lives on 10 acres. Limiting him to one structure can't be for health or safety reasons. It is solely aesthetics. But the communication requirement may be a gain antenna on 12 HF bands, and a second support structure may be no more visible than the first, or perhaps they are both in the forest and not visible at all. The number of structures regulation fails the accommodation test.

Let's put this another way: an ordinance must be crafted to accommodate. If it prohibits a second, invisible structure under all circumstances, it fails the "crafted to accommodate" test.

Also think about the logic on this one. A "one tower only" ordinance forces the ham to build one taller structure, instead of two smaller structures. Whatever that is, it is NOT an ordinance crafted to accommodate communications.

What would meet the "crafted to accommodate" test? I think a town could legally require "construction and placement that minimizes aesthetic impact while reasonably accommodating the amateur's communications." A town could require monopoles, such as telephone poles, instead of lattice construction—although this would be silly because lattice towers are "see through" while a phone pole is solid. I think a town could require "placement on the lot so as to minimize visibility."

I think a town could require retractable towers that are retracted "when not in use." However this would also be silly, since many hams host repeater, digipeater or packet-node locations. Furthermore, in order to retract, retractable towers must start with a wider base to achieve the same height than could be achieved with a narrower (less visible) structure. So the town defeats the purpose of minimizing impact. Finally, a retractable requirement might fail a completely different test—the requirements of the Americans with Disabilities Act. There are many people, especially the elderly, who could not crank up or down a structure as often as would be required. These people should not be required by bylaw to spend more money for their antenna system than the "temporarily abled."

Conclusion: To craft an ordinance that meets the Federal regulation (and in the case of states that have passed state laws to echo 47 CFR § 97.15(b), local law), a municipality should craft an ordinance that is flexible. Strict setback, sideyard and number of structure regulation will always fail the minimum practicable test. Furthermore, a flexible ordinance is *better public policy*, especially if the town's permit-granting authority adopts a posture of accommodation and negotiation, rather than a quasi-judicial posture where only considers matters in an adversary context. Put another way, the best judges are always looking for ways to settle a case. Permit granting boards should show similar flexibility.

PRB-1 Case Law Summary (in chronological order):

Borowski v. City of Burbank (IL)

101 FRD 59 (ND IL, 1984). Granted class action status in an antenna case. Often has an unusual affect just attaching it to the letter pointing out that the village ordinance fails to comply with 47 CFR 97.15(e). See CD-ROM, filename: **Borowski v. City of Burbank (IL).PDF.**

Gushke v. City of Oklahoma City (OK)

763 F.2d 379 (10th Cir. 1985). Against ham, but handed down prior to PRB-1.

Bulchis v. City of Edmonds (WA)

671 F. Supp. 1270 (WD WA, 1987). Summary judgment in favor of the ham, finding ordinance (25′ height limit) as applied did not provide for reasonable accommodation. Tower: Crank-up (21′—>70′).
For ham:
* Wins summary judgment.
For Town:
* Court uses loose language about balancing.
* Court dismisses equal protection claim that satellite TV reception is treated more leniently.
Note: Town's mistake was that it failed to deal with pre-emption at the hearing level. Court takes no position on whether or not the ham established "technical necessity for a 70-foot antenna." The ordinance failed to provide a "reviewable procedure."

Bodony v. Sands Point (NY)

681 F. Supp. 1009 (ED NY, 1987). Ordinance with 25-foot height limit. Settled with $60K in legal fees to ham on Sec. 1983 claim because town was seeking ways to deny his rights (soliciting opinion of counsel on how to deny, without regard to merits). See CD-ROM, filename: **Bodony vs Sands Point.PDF.**
For ham:
* Holds 25-foot limit void, grants summary judgment.
* Acknowledges that height matters.

Izzo v. River Edge (NJ)

843 F22d 765 (3d Cir. 1988). Upholds preemptive effect of PRB-1 to 35-foot height limitation. "The effectiveness of radio communication depends on the height of antennas." p 768.

MacMillan v. Rocky River (OH)

748 F. Supp. 1241 (ND OH, 1990). Ham seeks 30-foot tower. See CD-ROM, filenames: **MacMillan v. Rocky River.PDF** and **MacMillan v. Rocky River-Fees.PDF.**
For ham:
* Commissioner's decision denying tower based on property values is wrong.

* Legal fees to the radio amateur in subsequent ORDER of November 13, 1990 (§ 1988 award).

For Town:

* Balancing test. (But see DA 99-2569)

Williams v. Columbia (SC)

906 F2d 994 (4th Cir. 1990). Applied for 65 feet, ham limited to 25 feet. Case suggests that applicant should have an emergency communications showing. Testimony of Chairman, EE Department, University of South Carolina very damaging. Ham did not put in effective technical case for need.

For ham:

* Nothing, really.

For Town:

* Balancing test. (But see DA 99-2569)
* Court wrote "plaintiff can communicate, at least at some level of effectiveness, with very low antenna." (Misreads PRB-1).

Howard v. Burlingame (CA)

937 F2d 1376 (9th Cir. 1991). Bylaw required special permit for more than 25 feet. Ham wins permit for 51-foot tower. Case started before PRB-1, ended after PRB-1. Ham erected tower without permit at first.

For ham:

* Ham got tower.
* Requires that the city "consider the application, make factual findings, and attempt to negotiate a satisfactory compromise with the applicant." At 1380.

For Town:

* Attorney's fees (§ 1983) denied. Ham radio not a civil right, not free speech.
* Court seems to accept balancing test.
* City may shift financial burden of evaluating antenna applications to applicant, if inexpensive.

Evans v. Boulder (CO)

994 F2d 755 (10th Cir., 1993). Although 35-foot absolute height limitation thrown out, towers applied for denied completely. Ham sought 125-foot tower on 1.28-acre lot, refused to accept 60-foot crank-up compromise.

For ham:

* Absolute height limit thrown out.
* Court holds that balancing under represents and mischaracterizes PRB-1. Accommodation test.

For Town:

* Bizarre conclusion that no antenna at all is a reasonable accommodation.

Pentel v. Mendota Heights (MN)

13 F3d 1261 (8th Cir., 1994). Absolute 25-foot height limit in ordinance preempted. Remand with summary judgment Pentel, applying for 68-foot antenna (crank-up 30-68 feet and two Yagis). Pentel faced no opposing technical evidence on communications when she testified that she was unable to establish reliable communications across the US, and had only one international contact. See CD-ROM, filename: **Sylvia Pentel v. City of Mendota Heights.PDF**.

For ham:

* Rejects balancing test; FCC did the balancing.
* Accepts 56.5 feet as ineffective.
* Requires "minimum practicable regulation necessary."

For town:

* Pentel's existing system was wholly ineffective; yours may not be!

FEDERAL LAW RELATING TO TV ANTENNAS

In contrast to the limited preemption for Amateur Radio antennas (known as PRB-1 or 47 CFR §97.15(b)), the FCC has issued almost a complete preemption with respect to Over-the-Air Reception Devices (known as the OTARD Rule or 47 CFR §1.4000). As a starting point, you might want to go to the FCC site and find the original FCC decision (this includes the reasoning of the Commission, and is not the regulation itself, which is 47 CFR §1.4000): **http://www.fcc.gov/csb/facts/otard.html**.

Report & Order, Memorandum & Opinion & Order, and Further Notice of Proposed Rulemaking in the matter of Preemption of Local Zoning Regulation of Satellite Earth Stations; Implementation of Section 207 of the Telecommunications Act of 1996, restrictions on Over-the Air Reception Devices: Television Broadcast Service & Multichannel Multipoint Distribution Service (IB Docket 95-59, CS Docket No. 96-83)(August 6, 1996).

The citation for the Telecommunications Act is: Telecommunications Act of 1996, Pub. L. No. 104-104, 110 Stat. 56 (1996).

One of the more interesting paragraphs from the FCC Fact Sheet reads:

> The acceptable quality signal standard is different for devices designed to receive digital signals, such as . . . digital television ("DTV") antennas. For these antennas to receive an acceptable quality signal, [they] must be installed where [they have] an unobstructed, direct view of the satellite or other device from that video programming service is received. Unlike analog antennas, digital antennas, even in the presence of sufficient over-the-air signal strength, will at times provide no picture or sound unless they are placed and oriented for optimal reception.

Here's an example of an OTARD win, though not for Amateur Radio, over a Homeowner Association. If you are getting any ideas about putting up a 2-meter beam and calling it a TV antenna, however, I'd advise against it. Instead, think about going the other way. Instead of using a ham antenna for TV reception, think about using a TV antenna for ham radio. After all, a log-periodic TV antenna should cover 144, 220 and 432 MHz quite nicely and a rotator is quite normal. Your mother told you to never lie. As Henry Kissinger has said: "The nice thing about the truth is that it is so much easier to remember." Avoid misrepresenting what you are going to put up.

However, here's a lawyer's trick. Every word is true. Question: "Aren't you really just using this TV antenna idea as a cover for putting up a ham-radio antenna?" Answer: "Actually, I've never tried mounting a TV antenna and using it for ham radio. But it sounds like a great idea. Thanks for suggesting it!"

This is a powerful rule, by the way. If you can fit under the rule, it is a complete preemption, not the limited preemption of 47 CFR § 97.15(b). It applies to both CC&Rs and zoning ordinances. Here's the FCC short description on the Potomac Ridge Homeowner Association case, and the FCC press release on the Meade, KS (municipality) case (also see CD-ROM, filename: **Star Lambert v. Meade KS.PDF**):

APPLICATION FOR REVIEW OF DECLARA-TORY RULING PREEMPTING RESTRICTIONS ON THE USE OF OVER-THE-AIR RECEPTION DEVICES IMPOSED BY HOMEOWNER ASSO-CIATION IN POTOMAC, MD. Denied Application for Review of a Declaratory Ruling (DA 97-2188), in re: Jay Lubliner and Deborah Galvin, concerning Potomac Ridge Homeowner Association antenna re-strictions. The Order affirms Cable Services Bureau's ruling that the Potomac Ridge restriction prohibiting externally mounted television broadcast antennas violates the Commission's Over-the-Air Reception Devices Rule (47 C.F.R. Section 1.4000) by impair-ing reception of acceptable quality signal. Action by the Commission. Adopted: August 18, 1998. by MO&O. (FCC No. 98-201). CSB

NEWSReport No. CS 97-20 CABLE SERVICES
ACTION   July 22, 1997

CABLE SERVICES BUREAU PREEMPTS LOCAL
RESTRICTIONS ON THE USE OF OVER-THE-AIR-
RECEPTION DEVICES IMPOSED BY
MEADE, KANSAS

The Cable Services Bureau has preempted an ordinance adopted by the City of Meade, Kansas that restricted the installation and use of satellite dishes. The Bureau found that the ordinance did not comply with the Commission's rule ("Rule") regarding over-the-air reception devices, which implements Section 207 of the 1996 Telecommuni-cations Act. The Rule prohibits governmental and private restrictions that impair the ability of antenna users to install, maintain, or use satellite dishes and wireless cable antennas that are one meter or smaller in diameter and television signal antennas unless justified by safety or historic preser-vation considerations. This is the first order issued by the Bureau under the Rule.

Star Lambert and the Satellite Broadcasting and Commu-nications Association ("SBCA") petitioned the Commis-sion for a ruling on Meade's ordinance. Star Lambert owns Stargate Enterprises, which is located in Meade. Stargate sells and installs Primestar satellite antennas, which are direct-to-home satellite antennas measuring one meter or less in diameter. SBCA is a trade association that includes among its members Primestar and other manufacturers, retailers, and distributors of satellite equipment and receiv-ing devices.

The order holds that:

The Rule prohibits the ordinance's requirement that an installer or antenna user obtain

(1) a $5.00 permit prior to installation and (2) prior City approval of the antenna's placement. These requirements conflict with the Rule's prohibition of restrictions that unreasonably delay or prevent antenna installation, mainte-nance, or use that are not required by safety or historic preservation considerations.

The "property setback regulations" in the ordinance regu-lating antenna placement violate the Rule because they are not described anywhere and therefore impermissibly delay or prevent antenna installation, maintenance and use.

The $500 per day fine provided for in the ordinance is prohibited by the Rule because penalties of this magnitude are likely to deter installation and no justification was given for the amount.

Commenting on the Meade decision, Meredith J. Jones, Chief of the Cable Services Bureau said, "This order strikes a blow for competition and for the consumer. If we cannot pre-vent unreasonable restrictions on the use of satellite dishes and other receiving antennas, competition in the market for the delivery of multichannel video will be stifled."

Action by the Chief, Cable Services Bureau, July 22, 1997, by Order (DA 97-1554).

—FCC—

Source: **http://www.fcc.gov/Bureaus/Cable/ News_Releases/1997/nrcb7019.txt**

Memorandum on Using 47 CFR § 1.4000

The texts mentioned above may be found most easily by starting with **http://www.fcc.gov/csb/facts/otard.html**. This Web page provides links to the original FCC Dockets, the OTARD (Over-the-Air-Receiving-Devices) rule, and 47 CFR § 1.4000. Note that Web links to 47 CFR § 1.4000 are to a text that was accurate as of September 4, 1996. How-ever, 47 CFR § 1.4000 has been modified twice since then. The latest version of 1.4000 is presented here, as it has existed since November 20, 1998.

The following commentary is intended to help a ham understand what is, and what is not, contained in the OTARD rule.

Commentary on Selected Elements of FCC Decisions and Orders

From FCC 96-328, paragraph 20:

20. Third, a regulation will be deemed to impair a viewer's ability to receive video programming signals if it precludes reception of an acceptable qual-ity signal. We affirm the consensus opinion of commenters who discuss this issue that the signals that are protected here are signals intended for recep-tion in the viewing area. (fn 46) Under this criterion, for example, our rule would invalidate a requirement

that an antenna be placed in a position where reception would be impossible or would be substantially degraded. However, a regulation requiring that antennas be placed to the extent feasible in locations that are not visible from the street would be permitted under our rule, if this placement would not impair reception of an acceptable signal. Requirements that antennas be set back from the street could be deemed to impair reception if compliance would mean that the antenna could not receive an acceptable signal.

Comment: What are signals intended for reception in the viewing area? An easy way to determine this is to use a map obtainable from the station by contacting the Office of the Chief Engineer, or the Sales Department showing Class B coverage, or a map from The TV and Cable Fact Book showing the station's DMA (Designated Market Area).

A viewer may also determine whether or not he is in the Class B coverage area by going to **www.getawaiver.com**, or **http://www.titantv.com**, or **www.shva.com**—sites run by Decisionmark, a database company serving TV stations subject to the Satellite Home Viewing Act (the SHVA). As a matter of strategy, picking stations that are affiliated with a major network (ABC, CBS, Fox, NBC, PAX, or WB) is likely to garner more sympathy for the cause of the potential TV watcher than a claim that the viewer wishes to watch an obscure, low power and distant station. In fact, the more distant the signal, the less likely the rule applies. However, many stations transmit signals intended for viewing 60-80 miles away. It would be difficult to maintain a claim that an antenna is necessary for Sporadic E or other forms of less-reliable propagation.

From FCC 96-328, footnote 46 to paragraph 20:

46. Thus, for example, we would not offer the same protection to consumers seeking to install, maintain, or use antennas designed to receive distant TVBS signals.

Comment: TVBS means TV Broadcast Signals. While footnotes to Opinions and Orders at the FCC do not have the same weight as a regulation in the Code of Federal Regulations, this footnote offers a hint at the response that could be expected if a matter were to be appealed to the FCC. So it is very important to frame a request for a building permit for a TV antenna system in terms of a signal or signals within the DMA (Designated Market Area), or Class B signal strength area (watch out—they can be different) of the broadcast station.

From FCC 96-328, paragraph 20:

21. In refining our rule to prohibit only restrictions that "impair" viewers' abilities to install, use or maintain devices designed for over-the-air reception, we remove from the scope of this prohibition all restrictions that may affect, but do not impair, a viewer's ability to install, use or maintain devices to receive video programming signals through over-the-air TVBS, MMDS, and DBS services. As discussed

below, we also exempt certain regulations protecting safety and historic areas, even though the regulations may impair access to over-the-air signals.

Comment: Don't get too greedy and insist that the town cannot even require a Building Permit. The inspections that accompany the building process under a Building Permit exist for safety reasons and the FCC won't support a claim that safety inspections cannot be required. Similarly, if you live in a historic district you cannot expect the FCC to help you.

From FCC 96-328, paragraph 41:

41. . . . There is general public awareness of the variations in the dimensions of TVBS antennas, and commenters have not sought to define these antennas by size or shape. Based on the lack of record showing any such desire, and on the variations in the dimensions of TVBS antennas, we decline to limit the size or shape of such antennas covered by our rule. Nonetheless, we believe that the BOCA guideline regarding the permissibility of permits for installations reaching more than 12 feet over the roofline, that we believe to be a safety guideline, may apply to TVBS antennas as well as to MMDS antennas on masts.

Comment: For the purposes of convincing a town to give you an antenna-support structure permit, add together the size and shape discussion of FCC 96-328, paragraph 41, with the height discussion in FCC 98-214, paragraph 35 (see below). When the viewer must get above the trees and erect a high-gain, multi-element Yagi or log-periodic antenna, with rotator, to avoid impairment of the reception of classic TV or digital TV signals, even though such a support and antenna may be substantial in height, size and shape, its appearance is not a valid reason for denying a permit.

However, a Building Permit may still be required for safety reasons. Thus, a wise applicant would apply for a Building Permit, submitting such reasonable plans as would ordinarily be necessary for a Building Permit for other routine accessory structures, and then it would seem that the permit could not be denied. See below.

From FCC 96-328, paragraph 37:

37. We do not believe it will be overly burdensome to require, as is provided in the BOCA code, that antenna users obtain a permit in cases in which their antennas must extend more than twelve feet above the roofline in order to receive signals. However, we would find unenforceable any restriction that establishes specific per se height limits. Similarly, we believe that the BOCA code guideline regarding permits for setbacks is safety-based, is reasonable, and does not impose an unreasonable burden.

Comment: The position that a Building Permit should not be required by a municipality for a tall antenna-support structure will apparently fail. Unless covered by the BOCA exceptions (less than 12 feet above a roof line and so forth), the applicant must obtain a Building Permit. In this case, should the Town decline to follow Federal law and grant the

Building Permit, the least expensive next step (though not the only possible next step) would be to petition the FCC. An application to the FCC would be relatively inexpensive, but can be expected to take at least six months. (Here's a hint: Include maps. The office that handles such an appeal *loves* maps.) Other possible steps—steps that would be faster (but more expensive) than an appeal to the FCC—would be to seek an injunction in Land Court, Superior Court (or whatever the local jurisdiction calls the first level of court with the power to enjoin a municipality), or a US District Court.

Nonetheless, an applicant wishing to take advantage of Section 1.4000 should not forget the impact of FCC 98-238, ¶ 35, discussed above. By effectively adopting the BOCA code even for communities that have not otherwise adopted it, the FCC permits a community to require a Building Permit, but does not mandate that a community require a Building Permit. So, if an applicant can plan his installation of, for example, an 80-foot tower so that it is at least 80 feet back from the nearest lot line, an argument can be made that, under the BOCA code and 47 CFR § 1.4000, no permit is required. Further, a careful reading of paragraph 35 may permit a claim that no permit is required when the roofline is 30 feet high, the antenna is 80 feet high and the setback is 50 feet. The footnote 101 to paragraph 37 reads: "Thus, subject to the other provisions of the code, if an antenna is no closer to the lot line than its total height above the roof, no permit will be required."

From FCC 96-328, paragraph 38:

> 38. . . .Because we believe that the model antenna height and installation restrictions in the BOCA code are safety-related, they will be enforceable under our rule. We do not believe it will be overly burdensome to require, as is provided in the BOCA code, that antenna users obtain a permit in cases in which their antennas must extend more than twelve feet above the roofline in order to receive signals. However, we would find unenforceable any restriction that establishes specific per se height limits. Similarly, we believe that the BOCA code guideline regarding permits for setbacks is safety-based, is reasonable, and does not impose an unreasonable burden. Any such permit application should be handled expeditiously. However, the antenna size restriction for satellite antennas in the BOCA code, 24 inches, is unacceptable, as the diameter or diagonal measurement of the satellite and MMDS antennas covered by our rule is one meter. . . .

Comment: This is a really nice paragraph. While you must request and get a Building Permit, a fixed-height restriction is unenforceable. Don't you just love that the town must act "expeditiously"?

From FCC 96-328, paragraph 41:

> 41. Finally, we note that there is no discussion in the record regarding a history of problems regarding local regulation of the size of TVBS antennas that would suggest the need to impose size or height limitations.

While commenters indicate that restrictions on TVBS antennas exist, especially from nongovernmental authorities, (fn omitted) these restrictions generally take the form of a total prohibition on antennas rather than limits on their size or placement. The lack of record on size or height limits on TVBS antennas may stem from the fact that TVBS is an older and more familiar technology than DBS or MMDS and thus subject to less regulation. There is general public awareness of the variations in the dimensions of TVBS antennas, and commenters have not sought to define these antennas by size or shape. Based on the lack of record showing any such desire, and on the variations in the dimensions of TVBS antennas, we decline to limit the size or shape of such antennas covered by our rule. Nonetheless, we believe that the BOCA guideline regarding the permissibility of permits for installations reaching more than 12 feet over the roofline, which we believe to be a safety guideline, may apply to TVBS antennas as well as to MMDS antennas on masts.

Comment: This paragraph sets up a wonderful scenario. Assuming that you erect a substantial TVBS Yagi, a town would be hard-pressed to subsequently argue that your tribander a few feet below would be unprecedented in height or visibility in the neighborhood. In other words, you can erect your own precedent!

From FCC 96-328, paragraph 80:

> If a governmental or nongovernmental authority wishes to enforce a safety restriction, the rule requires that the safety reasons for the restrictions be clearly defined in the legislative history, preamble or text of the restriction. Alternatively, the local entity may include a restriction on a list of safety restrictions related to antennas, that is made available to interested parties (including those who wish to install antennas). . . [**http://www.fcc.gov/Bureaus/Cable/Orders/1996_TXT/fcc96328.txt**]

Comment: A wise applicant will purchase the municipality's zoning bylaw and send a letter to the Building Inspector asking for "a list of safety restrictions related to antennas, that is made available to those who wish to install antennas." This will "fix" the municipality into a position. The object is to prevent the municipality from making up the rules as the game proceeds.

From FCC 98-214, paragraph 35:

> Regarding WCA's disagreement with our conclusion in the Report and Order that BOCA requires a permit where the height of an antenna is longer than the distance between the antenna and the lot line and WCA's argument that instead BOCA flatly forbids the installation under such circumstances, even if WCA's interpretation is correct, our rules would preempt the BOCA requirement as interpreted by WCA. In the Report and Order, we specifically stated that "we would find unenforceable any restriction that

establishes specific per se height limits." If a local authority created a per se bar to antennas over a certain height, the restriction would be prohibited. **[http://www.fcc.gov/Bureaus/Cable/Orders/1998/fcc98214.txt]**

Comment: A maximum structure height of 30 feet (or 35 feet, or whatever) is, per se, prohibited. It would appear that no municipality could justify a maximum height in all residential areas. Therefore, any letter to the Board of Appeals or Town Counsel should cite that final sentence: "If a local authority created a per se bar to antennas over a certain height, the restriction would be prohibited."

From FCC 98-214, paragraphs 51 and 52:

51. The situation is altogether different, however, for devices designed to receive digital signals, such as DBS antennas, digital MMDS antennas and digital television ("DTV") antennas. Unlike analog antennas, digital antennas, even in the presence of sufficient over-the-air signal strength, will at times provide no picture or sound unless they are placed and oriented for optimal reception. Where a DBS antenna has an unobstructed, direct view of a satellite, the antenna will produce a complete picture and sound. As the antenna is moved or oriented slightly to a position where its view of the satellite becomes less direct or partially obstructed, the antenna will continue, up to a point, to produce a complete picture and sound because digital reception devices have error correcting systems that fill in the missing data by taking into account interruptions in the digital data stream caused by the obstruction. At some point, however, as the antenna's view becomes slightly more obstructed, the obstruction will cause the picture and sound to become fragmented because the obstruction is blocking too many pieces of digital data for the antenna's error correcting system to correct. As the antenna is moved a negligible distance farther and its view of the satellite becomes more obstructed, the antenna will produce no picture or sound at all because the antenna can no longer receive sufficient data. This is the "cliff effect" that is the point at which there is a complete loss of picture and sound because the antenna can no longer receive sufficient data. At the cliff, the transition between a complete picture and no picture takes place almost immediately.

52. Obstructions are not the only causes of data disruption. Weather conditions such as severe rain can interfere with the data streams to such a degree that most antennas will be unable to produce a picture during some periods throughout the year. Manufacturers assume that satellite antennas will have an unobstructed view of the satellite and design them to keep these weather blackouts to a minimum while at the same time producing the smallest antenna possible. For antennas that have an obstructed view of the satellite, these weather blackouts will occur more frequently than for antennas that have an unobstructed view of the satellite because both the obstruction and the weather are blocking the data stream. For this reason, we conclude that, to receive an acceptable quality signal, a DBS antenna or other digital reception device covered by Section 207 must be installed where it has an unobstructed, direct view of the satellite or other device from which video programming service is received, if such a location exists on the viewer's property and the property is covered by our rules.

Comment: The thoughtful applicant will take note of the FCC's direct statement that "The situation is altogether different, however, for devices designed to receive digital signals . . ." An application should be aimed at the reception of digital television signals, and emphasize that the antenna must have an "unobstructed, direct view." Thus, it must be above the trees, and, if necessary, above nearby ridges or hills that could block reception of a DT station in a given direction. Consult USGS maps for elevations and determine the line of site directions to DT stations by using one of the relevant TV station direction and distance web sites. Try **http://bsexton.addr.com/tvdb.html**.

Thus, the applicant will:

1. Find a network station (a network station is not required, but seems strategically helpful) for desired viewing where the DMA (Designated Market Area) map clearly covers the reception site, but signals are not so strong as to be Class A (rabbit ears) reception. (See FCC 96-328, paragraph 20.)
2. Preferably find a station that is a "-DT" (digital television) station, not viewable any other way (ie, by cable TV or DBS). This is a nice touch, though not required. (See FCC 98-214, paragraphs 51 and 52.)
3. If possible, plan an antenna-support structure installation so that the support structure and antenna is no taller than the distance to the nearest property line. (See FCC 98-214, paragraph 26.)
4. Purchase a complete copy of the Town's zoning bylaw and make a written request of the Building Inspector for "a list of safety restrictions related to antennas that is made available to those who wish to install antennas." (Please use those exact words, as they mirror FCC 96-328, paragraph 80.)
5. Apply for a building permit in writing to "freeze" the town, preventing it from detrimentally changing the bylaw or adding illegitimate "safety" requirements before the applicant can obtain a Building Permit for the proposed antenna system.
6. Respectfully bring the appropriate law (both 47 CFR § 1.4000 and the clarifications available in the Reports and Orders) to the attention of the Building Inspector, the Board of Appeals and Town Counsel.
7. If the Town threatens legal action, immediately file a petition with the FCC. This can be done without the help of a lawyer by following the FCC's instructions in § 1.4000. Filing with the FCC, where the Town has the

burden of showing that its regulation outweighs the Federal interest involved, should stay local court action, if the Town tries to file against you locally. Your lawyer will smile when he realizes the strength of your position. Demand the grant of a Building Permit for the antenna-support structure and antenna. Be sure to get a Certificate of Completion when the project is done.

8. Once the TV antenna-support structure is up, with a TV antenna on top, and the Certificate of Completion has been received, no further Building Permit should be required to add an Amateur Radio antenna up to the loading capacity of the antenna-support structure.

Now for some additional tips. As an alternative to calling a station for DMA or signal-strength information, some TV stations have their own Web sites that will lead you to the sites previously mentioned and, in effect, provide all you need to know.

Should you call the station and have a problem on the phone, think about contacting a ham who works there for help in obtaining signal-coverage information. If you don't know, or wish to check up on, your latitude and longitude, or you would like to print out a map of your neighborhood, try **http://mapsonus.com/**. See the article by Richard F. Gillette ,W9PE, *QST*, Dec 1999, p 55. MapsOnUs will also help you calculate the direction and distance to your desired TV station (or repeater, or emergency management site).

OTARD Rule, 47 CFR § 1.4000

Subpart S—Preemption of Restrictions That "Impair" a Viewer's Ability To Receive Television Broadcast Signals, Direct Broadcast Satellite Services or Multichannel Multipoint Distribution Services
Sec. **1.4000:Restrictions impairing reception of television broadcast signals, direct broadcast satellite services or multichannel multipoint distribution services.**

(a) (1) Any restriction, including but not limited to any state or local law or regulation, including zoning, land-use, or building regulations, or any private covenant, contract provision, lease provision, homeowners' association rule or similar restriction, on property within the exclusive use or control of the antenna user where the user has a direct or indirect ownership or leasehold interest in the property that impairs the installation, maintenance, or use of:

(i) An antenna that is designed to receive direct broadcast satellite service, including direct-to-home satellite services, that is one meter or less in diameter or is located in Alaska;

(ii) An antenna that is designed to receive video programming services via multipoint distribution services, including multichannel multipoint distribution services, instructional television fixed services, and local multipoint distribution services, and that is one meter or less in diameter or diagonal measurement;

(iii) An antenna that is designed to receive television broadcast signals; or

(iv) A mast supporting an antenna described in paragraphs (a)(1)(i), (a)(1)(ii) or (a)(1)(iii) of this section; is prohibited to the extent it so impairs, subject to paragraph (b) of this section.

(2) For purposes of this section, a law, regulation or restriction impairs installation, maintenance or use of an antenna if it:

(i) Unreasonably delays or prevents installation, maintenance or use,

(ii) Unreasonably increases the cost of installation, maintenance or use, or

(iii) Precludes reception of an acceptable quality signal.

(3) Any fee or cost imposed on a viewer by a rule, law, regulation or restriction must be reasonable in light of the cost of the equipment or services and the rule, law, regulation or restriction's treatment of comparable devices. No civil, criminal, administrative, or other legal action of any kind shall be taken to enforce any restriction or regulation prohibited by this section except pursuant to paragraph (c) or (d) of this section. In addition, except with respect to restrictions pertaining to safety and historic preservation as described in paragraph (b) of this section, if a proceeding is initiated pursuant to paragraph (c) or (d) of this section, the entity seeking to enforce the antenna restrictions in question must suspend all enforcement efforts pending completion of review. No attorney's fees shall be collected or assessed and no fine or other penalties shall accrue against an antenna user while a proceeding is pending to determine the validity of any restriction. If a ruling is issued adverse to a viewer, the viewer shall be granted at least a 21-day grace period in which to comply with the adverse ruling; and neither a fine nor a penalty may be collected from the viewer if the viewer complies with the adverse ruling during this grace period, unless the proponent of the restriction demonstrates, in the same proceeding which resulted in the adverse ruling, that the viewer's claim in the proceeding was frivolous.

(b) Any restriction otherwise prohibited by paragraph (a) of this section is permitted if:

(1) It is necessary to accomplish a clearly defined, legitimate safety objective that is either stated in the text, preamble or legislative history of the restriction or described as applying to that restriction in a document that is readily available to antenna users, and would be applied to the extent practicable in a nondiscriminatory manner to other appurtenances, devices, or fixtures that are comparable in size and weight and pose a similar or greater safety risk as these antennas and to which local regulation would normally apply; or

(2) It is necessary to preserve a prehistoric or historic district, site, building, structure or object included in, or eligible for inclusion on, the National Register of Historic Places, as set forth in the National

Historic Preservation Act of 1966, as amended, 16 U.S.C. 470, and imposes no greater restrictions on antennas covered by this rule than are imposed on the installation, maintenance or use of other modern appurtenances, devices or fixtures that are comparable in size, weight, and appearance to these antennas; and

(3) It is no more burdensome to affected antenna users than is necessary to achieve the objectives described in paragraph (b)(1) or (b) (2) of this section.

(c) Local governments or associations may apply to the Commission for a waiver of this section under Sec. 1.3. Waiver requests must comply with the procedures in paragraphs (e) and (g) of this section and will be put on public notice. The Commission may grant a waiver upon a showing by the applicant of local concerns of a highly specialized or unusual nature. No petition for waiver shall be considered unless it specifies the restriction at issue. Waivers granted in accordance with this section shall not apply to restrictions amended or enacted after the waiver is granted. Any responsive pleadings must be served on all parties and filed within 30 days after release of a public notice that such petition has been filed. Any replies must be filed within 15 days thereafter.

(d) Parties may petition the Commission for a declaratory ruling under Sec. 1.2, or a court of competent jurisdiction, to determine whether a particular restriction is permissible or prohibited under this section. Petitions to the Commission must comply with the procedures in paragraphs (e) and (g) of this section and will be put on public notice. Any responsive pleadings in a Commission proceeding must be served on all parties and filed within 30 days after release of a public notice that such petition has been filed. Any replies in a Commission proceeding must be served on all parties and filed within 15 days thereafter.

(e) Copies of petitions for declaratory rulings and waivers must be served on interested parties, including parties against whom the petitioner seeks to enforce the restriction or parties whose restrictions the petitioner seeks to prohibit. A certificate of service stating on whom the petition was served must be filed with the petition. In addition, in a Commission proceeding brought by an association or a local government, constructive notice of the proceeding must be given to members of the association or to the citizens under the local government's jurisdiction. In a court proceeding brought by an association, an association must give constructive notice of the proceeding to its members. Where constructive notice is required, the petitioner or plaintiff must file with the Commission or the court overseeing the proceeding a copy of the constructive notice with a statement explaining where the notice was placed and why such placement was reasonable.

(f) In any proceeding regarding the scope or interpretation of any provision of this section, the burden of demonstrating that a particular governmental or nongovernmental restriction complies with this section and does not impair the installation, maintenance or use of devices designed for over-the-air reception of video programming services shall be on the party that seeks to impose or maintain the restriction.

(g) All allegations of fact contained in petitions and related pleadings before the Commission must be supported by affidavit of a person or persons with actual knowledge thereof. An original and two copies of all petitions and pleadings should be addressed to the Secretary, Federal Communications Commission, 445 12th St. S.W., Washington, D.C. 20554, Attention: Cable Services Bureau. Copies of the petitions and related pleadings will be available for public inspection in the Cable Reference Room in Washington, D.C. Copies will be available for purchase from the Commission's contract copy center, and Commission decisions will be available on the Internet.

[63 FR 71036, Dec. 23, 1998]

FEDERAL LAW RELATING TO CELLULAR TELEPHONE, PCS, PAGING, ETC.

Perhaps you were hoping that the Telecommunications Act of 1996 contained something special to help you. Perhaps you've even heard that it had very specific preemptions. The answer is that it has some very specific things to help the companies in Personal Wireless Services. Even though that sounds hopeful, it doesn't help. The definition of Personal Wireless Services is very specific and Amateur Radio is not included. Personal Wireless Services include all commercial mobile radio services (including personal communications services (PCS), cellular telephone, two way mobile radio, and paging); unlicensed wireless services; and common carrier wireless exchange access services.

Now this works two ways. Amateur Radio is not included because it does not fit within the definitions section, and therefore Amateur Radio gets no benefit from the preemption included within the Telecommunications Act. On the other hand, if a local town has drafted an ordinance to control "personal wireless service facilities" and now claims that an amateur is subject to the onerous requirements of the new bylaw controlling "wireless communications facilities," again Amateur Radio is not included.

47 USC § 332 (c)(7)(C) Definitions
For purposes of this paragraph—

(i) the term "personal wireless services" means commercial mobile services, unlicensed wireless services, and common carrier wireless exchange access services;

(ii) the term "personal wireless service facilities" means facilities for the provision of personal wireless services;

FEDERAL LAW RELATING TO FAA CLEARANCE

Now and again an author gets lucky, because someone else has written what needs to be written. This is a fragment of a question/answer session with John Hennessee, N1KB, at the Regulatory Information branch at ARRL HQ regarding tower restrictions near airports:

I plan to buy land soon and install a tower at 100 or 125 feet. The local Code Enforcement Officer said that the local ordinances did not state any prohibition on radio amateur tower height; but, he said that the local municipal airport was about 3 miles from the land I want to put the tower on...and that he thinks that the hill I will be putting the tower on is in the direct flight path. Where are the FCC rules on this?? Can you send me a copy of the pertinent FCC rules?

John Hennessee, N1KB, replied:

In November of 1995, the FCC adopted rules requiring tower owners to register with the FCC each antenna structure for which Federal Aviation Administration (FAA) notification is required. Generally, this includes all structures more than 200 feet above ground or certain towers located near or on a public use airport. The FCC has long required registration and FAA notification, but they now have specific rules that appear in Part 17 of FCC rules. FCC may assess stiff fines to tower owners who do not comply and the fines, that can range up to $10,000, appear in Section 1.80 of FCC rules. If required, all tower owners, including amateurs, must register their towers with the FCC and they are required to do so immediately. Part 17 mandates marking and lighting of non-exempt antenna structures to help protect the safety of air navigation. A copy of Part 17 is available from ARRL for an SASE with two units of postage or from the FCC Web page at **http://www.fcc.gov/wtb/rules.html**.

Fortunately, the vast majority of amateurs are exempt from the federal tower registration process, but amateurs must still abide by appropriate local government zoning ordinances...

Most antenna structures that are higher than 200 feet above ground level or that may interfere with the flight path of a nearby airport must be cleared by the Federal Aviation Administration (FAA) and registered with the FCC. Unless specifically exempted, FAA notification and FCC registration are required:

1. For any construction or alteration of more than 200 feet in height above ground level at its site.
2. When requested by the FAA if it is determined that the antenna structure might exceed an obstruction standard of the FAA.
3. For any construction or alteration of greater height than an imaginary surface extending outward and upward at one of the following slopes that represent the ratio of distance from the longest runway to the feet in height an antenna may be:

   * 100 to 1 for a horizontal distance of 20,000 feet from the nearest point of the nearest runway of each Specified Airport with at least one runway longer than 3,200 feet in actual length. If the runway is longer than 1 km (3280 feet) and the airport is within 6.1 km (3.79 miles) of your proposed installation, your antenna may be no higher than 1 meter (3.28 feet) above the airport elevation for every 100 meters (328 feet) from the nearest runway. This is a slope of 100 to 1.

   * 50 to 1 for a horizontal distance of 10,000 feet from the nearest point of the nearest runway of each Specified Airport with its longest runway shorter than 3,280 feet (6.1 km or 3.79 miles) in actual length. If the runway is shorter than 1 km (3280 feet) and the airport is within 6.1 km (3.79 miles) of your proposed installation, your antenna may be no higher than 2 meters (6.56 feet) above the airport elevation for every 100 meters (328 feet) from the nearest runway. This is a slope of 50 to 1.

   * 25 to 1 for a horizontal distance of 5,000 feet from the nearest point of the nearest landing and takeoff area of each heliport at a Specified Airport. If the installation is within 1.5 km (4920 feet) of a helipad, your antenna may be no higher than 4 meters (13.1 feet) above the airport elevation for every 100 meters (328 feet) from the nearest landing pad. That's a slope of 25 to 1.

Specified Airport

* A public use airport listed in the Airport Directory of the current Aeronautical Information Manual or in either the Alaska or Pacific Airman's Guide and Chart Supplement;
* An airport under construction, that is the subject of a notice or proposal on file with the FAA, and except for military airports, it is clearly indicated that the airport will be available for public use; or
* An airport that is operated by an armed force of the United States.

Which Towers are Exempt?

The following types of antenna structures are specifically exempted from the FAA notification requirements and FCC registration requirements by Section 17.14 of FCC rules:

1) Any antenna structure that would be shielded by existing structures of a permanent and substantial character or by natural terrain or topographic features of equal or greater height, and would be located in the congested area of a city, town or settlement where it is evident beyond all reasonable doubt that the structure so shielded will not adversely affect safety in air navigation.
2) Any antenna structure of 20 feet or less in height (except one that would increase the height of another antenna structure.)
3) An antenna which is not near an airport and is less that 200 feet tall

If you are still unsure if your tower needs to be

registered, you may call the FCC at 1-888 CALL FCC, contact them by e-mail at **mayday@fcc.gov** or you may use on line TOWAIR software that is available on the FCC's Web site at: **http://www.fcc.gov/wtb/antenna/towair.html**.

If your antenna is near an airport or over 200 feet tall, check this FCC Web site for additional information: **http://www.fcc.gov/wtb/antenna**. Owners of antenna structures required to be registered pursuant to Section 17.4 of the Commission's rules must first file FAA Form 7460-1 and obtain a final determination of "no hazard" for the structure. The FAA form is available from the Web at: **http://www.faa.gov/arp/ace/faaforms.htm**. Tower owners must file FCC Form 854 with the Commission either manually or electronically to register the antenna structure. The FCC form is available from: **http://www.fcc.gov/formpage.html**.

Provided that the owner should register the antenna structure immediately, according to the FCC, there is no cause for concern if an amateur misses the filing window deadline. The reason for this process is to provide a measure of safety in air navigation against tall structures that could cause an accident.

If an amateur who has reason to believe that the owner of a tall tower over 200 feet or near an airport is not carrying out his or her antenna structure registration responsibilities is required to (1) notify the owner; (2) notify the site management company (if applicable); and (3) notify the FCC. The FCC will provide additional instructions to the tower owner based on the specifics of the case.

If the tower owner is unable to fulfill the Part 17 requirements for painting and lighting due to negligence, bankruptcy or whatever, the tenants (amateurs, in this case) may be required to carry out these duties if specifically asked by the FCC. Amateurs who rent or are given space on tall towers should have a signed legal document addressing maintenance concerns as well as tower access. An ARRL Volunteer Counsel member can help with this. See the ARRL Web page for a list of ARRL Volunteer Counsel members, that is, hams who are also lawyers. See:

http://www.arrl.org/field/regulations/local/vci.html.

73,
John C. Hennessee, N1KB
Regulatory Information Specialist
ARRL—the national association for Amateur Radio

FEDERAL LAW RELATING TO RF EXPOSURE

Occasionally a state code-enforcement officer or health agent may inquire about whether or not an amateur is regulated by state law. There are several approaches that may be taken in such a circumstance.

If it is true, you can say "no" and take the approach that whatever the amateur does is legal, unless someone can point to a statute or regulation that makes it illegal.

Nonetheless, this is not a good approach, as it only encourages the health agent to issue some sort of order declaring that you may not transmit further until you have satisfied the agent that your operations are legal.

This approach creates great fun for your lawyer, because it may allow you to sue the agent personally for acting in bad faith "under color of law." To put it another way, except under his inherent powers to keep order, a police officer may not prevent you from doing something totally lawful, like raking the leaves on your lawn. To do so is outside of his powers as a law-enforcement officer and he would be personally liable. This puts you in court and makes the town's entire code-enforcement apparatus into enemies. Do you really want the Health Agent, Building Inspector, Dog Officer, Board of Appeals, and so forth to be on the lookout for anything you might do wrong?

Furthermore, refusing to respond reasonably can insert a needless delay into you application process. You will win your permit, or at least it will not be denied on this ground, in the long run, but being obstinate won't help either. The better approach is to find the law and share your reasoning with the health agent in a considered, temperate way.

Here follows an example, based on the Massachusetts regulations. The problem with Department of Public Health regulations in Massachusetts, by the way, is that they are not published on the Internet yet (as of 2000).

Since not all regulations from all state agencies are available on the Internet, you may need either a local law library or the cooperation of the health agent to look at his copy of the regulations in order to find the answer he wants.

Isn't this doing his homework for him? Yes. But that's life. Your lawyer will also be happy to do the work, should you be unwilling or unable. The following letter is on the accompanying CD-ROM, file name **State RF Safety Letter.DOC**.

[Date]

Mr. Joe Jones
Health Agent, Town of Friendly
Town Office Building
555 Main Street
Friendly, MA 01111   FAX: nnn/nnn-nnnn

Dear Mr. Jones:

You have asked if 105 CMR 122: NONIONIZING RADIATION LIMITS FOR THE GENERAL PUBLIC FROM NON-OCCUPATIONAL EXPOSURE TO ELECTROMAGNETIC FIELDS, EMPLOYEES FROM OCCUPATIONAL EXPOSURE TO ELECTROMAGNETIC FIELDS, AND EXPOSURE FROM MICROWAVE OVENS is applicable to the existing [a proposed] Amateur Radio tower [to be] owned and operated by Joe T. Ham, of Four Neighborly Lane, Friendly, MA 01111.

The short answer is that, as "amateur intermittent single source emitters of less than 1 kW average output" may be installed "without the approval of the Director," no filing or approval is necessary. See 105 CMR 122.021.

Mr. Ham does not propose, nor does he use [I do not propose, nor do I use], an emitter that exceeds that threshold. He is [I am] thus exempt.

In the interest of putting any concern to rest, I am pleased to explain why amateurs in Massachusetts do not make filings seeking approval of the Director of the Department of Public Health.

The maximum permissible power of an Amateur Radio station is 1500 watts output. The Massachusetts regulation (consistent with the FCC regulation) measures "average values over any 0.5 hour period" (see footnote to 105 CMR 122.015: Table 1). So if we calculate power on the basis of 50% transmitting, and 50% listening, and assume the worst case over that half hour, that would be 10 minutes on, 10 minutes off, and 10 minutes on. That would represent 67% of the time period. This is, by the way, exactly how the FCC makes such a calculation. See "Evaluating Compliance with FCC Guidelines for Human Exposure to Radiofrequency Electromagnetic Fields, Additional Information for Amateur Radio Stations," Supplement B (Edition 97-01) to OET Bulletin 65 (Edition 97-01), page 13. **www.fcc.gov/oet/info/documents/ bulletins/#65**

In addition, it is appropriate (and again the FCC also uses this technique), to calculate average power by using a duty cycle of 40-50% for single sideband voice or Morse Code CW (more properly: interrupted continuous wave) transmissions. See "Evaluating Compliance . . . ", supra, Table 2, page 14.

The calculation is: $1500 \times 0.6666666 \times 0.50 = 500$ watts.

Thus, under the Massachusetts regulation, an amateur emitter with an average of about 500 watts is clearly not required to seek approval of the Director of the Department of Public Health.

The precise answer you seek is that, like all citizens, Mr. Ham is [I am] subject to the requirements of 105 CMR 122, but the regulation does not require him [me] to make any filings, nor seek any permissions, from either the Director of the Department of Public Health or a town health agent.

Sincerely,
Fred Hopengarten
Attorney for Joe T. Ham

c: The Building Inspector

[Note: It is important to send a copy to the Building Inspector, who may be holding things up until all departments have "signed off" on the project. You don't want the paperwork to get lost on the desk of the health agent. Yes, it is more work, but you want to keep the project moving along, don't you?]

Ed Hare, W1RFI, the ARRL's expert on RFI and emissions exposure comments further on this situation:

I don't know whether you want to add, parenthetically, that in being required to comply with the FCC exposure guidelines an amateur station automatically meets the state guidelines if the state limits are higher than or equal to the Federal limits. If so, then an amateur complying with the Federal limits would be automatically in compliance with the Massachusetts limits.

This is a tough decision, because the state rules may permit a health inquiry about the station's compliance with the limits, even though an amateur is not required to seek advance permission. Nevertheless, there could be some advantage to have the health authorities understand that an Amateur Radio station is very much not likely to exceed the exposure limits.

If you'd like an idea of how much it should cost to generate such a letter to your local health authority, multiply your lawyer's hourly rate by the 2-5 hours necessary to research your state's health regulations. This kind of research has a cost, as the regulations may or may not be available on the Internet, and they are unlikely to be in the library of a small law office—so they must be obtained by FAX, by placing an order for them, by obtaining them by photocopy from a local health officer or by visiting a local law library. In addition, the state law must then be checked against Federal law. It may also take a while for a lawyer to understand the area of RF exposure, so a copy of the book *RF Exposure and You*, by Ed Hare W1RFI, ARRL (1998) would be useful. See: **http://www.arrl.org/catalog/6621/**.

In any event, the letter that appears above resulted in the following actual letter (changed only to preserve the privacy of the client involved) that was sent to the applicant by the Board of Health.

Town
Board of Health

Joe T. Ham
Town

Dear Mr. Ham:

The Town Health Department (THD) has completed its review of the building permit application for an amateur radio tower at [address]. During the review process, the THD consulted with the Massachusetts Department of Public Health (MDPH) Radiation Control Program. The guidance received on 1/14/00 was that the project, as proposed, is exempt from the filing and approval process in MDPH 105 CMR § 122 "Non-Ionizing Radiation Exposure Limit Regulation." The reason given was that typically the power density from such uses does not pose a public health concern. However, the THD was also advised that the owner/operator was not exempt from the power density limits of MDPH 105 CMR § 122.

The justification of power levels contained in the January 10, 2000 letter from Attorney Fred Hopengarten was reviewed with the MDPH Radiation Control Department and has been accepted.

The Town Health Department has signed off on the building permit application with the above guidance noted on the building permit application form. In addition, the THD noted the existing septic components are not shown as H-20 rated on the design plans. Therefore, vehicular traffic for construction of the tower should not travel over the septic components. The building permit application has been forwarded to the Building Department for their review. The building permit is issued through that department and the status of the permit may be confirmed by contacting the Building Department at Extension [nnn].

Sincerely,

Name

Health Agent

Note to the reader: Don't be afraid of the implied threat above in which the Health Agent advised "that the owner/operator was not exempt from the power density limits of MDPH 105 CMR § 122." As the FCC wrote (see the W1RFI book at page 7.12),

> The FCC is relying on the demonstrated technical skills of amateurs to comply with these rules, select an evaluation method and to conduct their own station evaluations.

If it is good enough for the Federal government, it should be good enough for the state authorities. As is mentioned elsewhere in the book, evaluations may be done by filling out the paper work in the W1RFI book, or going to the N5XU website.

FEDERAL LAW RELATING TO ENVIRONMENTAL PROTECTION

Subpart I—Procedures Implementing the National Environmental Policy Act of 1969
Source: 51 FR 15000, Apr. 22, 1986, unless otherwise noted.
Sec. 1.1301 Basis and purpose.
The provisions of this subpart implement Subchapter I of the National Environmental Policy Act of 1969, as amended, 42 U.S.C. 4321-4335.
Sec. 1.1302 Cross-reference; Regulations of the Council on Environmental Quality.
A further explanation regarding implementation of the National Environmental Policy Act is provided by the regulations issued by the Council on Environmental Quality, 40 CFR 1500-1508.28.
Sec. 1.1303 Scope.
The provisions of this subpart shall apply to all Commission actions that may or will have a significant impact on the quality of the human environment. To the extent that other provisions of the Commission's rules and regulations are inconsistent with the subpart, the provisions of this subpart shall govern.
[55 FR 20396, May 16, 1990]
Sec. 1.1304 Information and assistance.
For general information and assistance concerning the provisions of this subpart, the Office of General Counsel may be contacted, (202) 632-6990. For more specific information, the Bureau responsible for processing a specific application should be contacted.
Sec. 1.1305 Actions which normally will have a significant impact upon the environment, for which Environmental Impact Statements must be prepared.
Any Commission action deemed to have a significant effect upon the quality of the human environment requires the preparation of a Draft Environmental Impact Statement (DEIS) and Final Environmental Impact Statement (FEIS) (collectively referred to as EISs) (see Secs. 1.1314, 1.1315 and 1.1317). The Commission has reviewed representative actions and has found no common pattern which would enable it to specify actions that will thus automatically require EISs.
Note: Our current application forms refer applicants to Sec. 1.1305 to determine if their proposals are such that the submission of environmental information is required (see Sec. 1.1311). Until the application forms are revised to reflect our new environmental rules, applicants should refer to Sec. 1.1307. Section 1.1307 now delineates those actions for which applicants must submit environmental information.
Sec. 1.1306 Actions which are categorically excluded from environmental processing.
(a) Except as provided in Sec. 1.1307 (c) and (d), Commission actions not covered by Sec. 1.1307 (a) and (b) are deemed individually and cumulatively to have no significant effect on the quality of the human environment and are categorically excluded from environmental processing.
(b) Specifically, any Commission action with respect to any new application, or minor or major modifications of existing or authorized facilities or equipment, will be categorically excluded, provided such proposals do not:
(1) Involve a site location specified under Sec. 1.1307(a) (1)-(7), or
(2) Involve high intensity lighting under Sec. 1.1307(a)(8).
(3) Result in human exposure to radiofrequency radiation in excess of the applicable safety standards specified in Sec. 1.1307(b).
Note 1: The provisions of Sec. 1.1307(a) of this part requiring the preparation of EAs do not encompass the mounting of antenna(s) on an existing building or antenna tower unless Sec. 1.1307(a)(4) of this part is applicable. Such antennas are subject to Sec. 1.1307(b) of this part and require EAs if their construction would result in human exposure to radiofrequency radiation in

excess of the applicable health and safety guidelines cited in Sec. 1.1307(b) of this part. The provisions of Sec. 1.1307 (a) and (b) of this part do not encompass the installation of aerial wire or cable over existing aerial corridors of prior or permitted use or the underground installation of wire or cable along existing underground corridors of prior or permitted use, established by the applicant or others. The use of existing buildings, towers or corridors is an environmentally desirable alternative to the construction of new facilities and is encouraged. The provisions of Sec. 1.1307(a) and (b) of this part do not encompass the construction of new submarine cable systems.

Note 2: The specific height of an antenna tower or supporting structure, as well as the specific diameter of a satellite earth station, in and of itself, will not be deemed sufficient to warrant environmental processing, see Secs. 1.1307 and 1.1308.

Note 3: The construction of an antenna tower or supporting structure in an established "antenna farm": (i.e., an area in which similar antenna towers are clustered, whether or not such area has been officially designated as an antenna farm), will be categorically excluded unless one or more of the antennas to be mounted on the tower or structure are subject to the provisions of Sec. 1.1307(b) and the additional radiofrequency radiation from the antenna(s) on the new tower or structure would cause human exposure in excess of the applicable health and safety guidelines cited in Sec. 1.1307(b).

[51 FR 15000, Apr. 22, 1986, as amended at 51 FR 18889, May 23, 1986; 53 FR 28393, July 28, 1988; 56 FR 13414, Apr. 2, 1991; 64 FR 19061, Apr. 19, 1999]

Sec. 1.1307 Actions that may have a significant environmental effect, for which Environmental Assessments (EAs) must be prepared.

(a) Commission actions with respect to the following types of facilities may significantly affect the environment and thus require the preparation of EAs by the applicant (see Secs. 1.1308 and 1.1311) and may require further Commission environmental processing (see Secs. 1.1314, 1.1315 and 1.1317):

(1) Facilities that are to be located in an officially designated wilderness area.

(2) Facilities that are to be located in an officially designated wildlife preserve.

(3) Facilities that: (i) May affect listed threatened or endangered species or designated critical habitats; or (ii) are likely to jeopardize the continued existence of any proposed endangered or threatened species or likely to result in the destruction or adverse modification of proposed critical habitats, as determined by the Secretary of the Interior pursuant to the Endangered Species Act of 1973.

Note: The list of endangered and threatened species is contained in 50 CFR 17.11, 17.22, 222.23(a) and 227.4. The list of designated critical habitats is contained in

50 CFR 17.95, 17.96 and part 226. To ascertain the status of proposed species and habitats, inquiries may be directed to the Regional Director of the Fish and Wildlife Service, Department of the Interior.

(4) Facilities that may affect districts, sites, buildings, structures or objects, significant in American history, architecture, archeology, engineering or culture, that are listed, or are eligible for listing, in the National Register of Historic Places. (See 16 U.S.C. 470w(5); 36 CFR 60 and 800.)

Note: The National Register is updated and re-published in the Federal Register each year in February. To ascertain whether a proposal affects a historical property of national significance, inquiries also may be made to the appropriate State Historic Preservation Officer, see 16 U.S.C. 470a(b); 36 CFR parts 63 and 800.

(5) Facilities that may affect Indian religious sites.

(6) Facilities to be located in a flood plain (See Executive Order 11988.)

(7) Facilities whose construction will involve significant change in surface features (e.g., wetland fill, deforestation or water diversion). (In the case of wetlands on Federal property, see Executive Order 11990.)

(8) Antenna towers and/or supporting structures that are to be equipped with high intensity white lights which are to be located in residential neighborhoods, as defined by the applicable zoning law.

(b) In addition to the actions listed in paragraph (a) of this section, Commission actions granting construction permits, licenses to transmit or renewals thereof, equipment authorizations or modifications in existing facilities, require the preparation of an Environmental Assessment (EA) if the particular facility, operation or transmitter would cause human exposure to levels of radiofrequency radiation in excess of the limits in Secs. 1.1310 and 2.1093 of this chapter.

Applications to the Commission for construction permits, licenses to transmit or renewals thereof, equipment authorizations or modifications in existing facilities must contain a statement confirming compliance with the limits unless the facility, operation, or transmitter is categorically excluded, as discussed below. Technical information showing the basis for this statement must be submitted to the Commission upon request.

(1) The appropriate exposure limits in Secs. 1.1310 and 2.1093 of this chapter are generally applicable to all facilities, operations and transmitters regulated by the Commission. However, a determination of compliance with the exposure limits in Sec. 1.1310 or Sec. 2.1093 of this chapter (routine environmental evaluation), and preparation of an EA if the limits are exceeded, is necessary only for facilities, operations and transmitters that fall into the categories listed in table 1, or those specified in paragraph (b)(2) of this section. All other facilities, operations and transmitters are categorically excluded from making such studies or

preparing an EA, except as indicated in paragraphs (c) and (d) of this section. For purposes of table 1, building-mounted antennas means antennas mounted in or on a building structure that is occupied as a workplace or residence. The term power in column 2 of table 1 refers to total operating power of the transmitting operation in question in terms of effective radiated power (ERP), equivalent isotropically radiated power (EIRP), or peak envelope power (PEP), as defined in Sec. 2.1 of this chapter. For the case of the Cellular Radiotelephone Service, subpart H of part 22 of this chapter; the Personal Communications Service, part 24 of this chapter and the Specialized Mobile Radio Service, part 90 of this chapter, the phrase total power of all channels in column 2 of table 1 means the sum of the ERP or EIRP of all co-located simultaneously operating transmitters owned and operated by a single licensee. When applying the criteria of table 1, radiation in all directions should be considered. For the case of transmitting facilities using sectorized transmitting antennas, applicants and licensees should apply the criteria to all transmitting channels in a given sector, noting that for a highly directional antenna there is relatively little contribution to ERP or EIRP summation for other directions.

Table 1—Transmitters, Facilities and Operations Subject to Routine Environmental Evaluation

Service (title 47 CFR rule part)	Evaluation required if
Experimental Radio Services (part 5).	Power > 100 W ERP (164 W EIRP)
Multipoint Distribution Service (subpart K of part 21).	Non-building-mounted antennas: height above ground level to lowest point of antenna 10 m and power > 1640 W EIRP Building-mounted antennas: power > 1640 W EIRP MDS licensees are required to attach a label to subscriber transceiver or transverter antennas that: (1) provides adequate notice regarding potential radiofrequency safety hazards, e.g., information regarding the safe minimum separation distance required between users and transceiver antennas; and (2) references the applicable FCC-adopted limits for radiofrequency exposure specified in Sec. 1.1310.
Paging and Radiotelephone Service (subpart E of part 22).	Non-building-mounted antennas: height above ground level to lowest point of antenna 10 m and power > 1000 W ERP (1640 W EIRP) Building-mounted antennas: power > 1000 W ERP (1640 W EIRP)
Cellular Radiotelephone Service (subpart H of part 22).	Non-building-mounted antennas: height above ground level to lowest point of antenna 10 m and total power of all channels > 1000 W ERP (1640 W EIRP) Building-mounted antennas: total power of all channels > 1000 W ERP (1640 W EIRP)
Personal Communications Services (part 24).	(1) Narrowband PCS (subpart D): Non-building-mounted antennas: height above ground level to lowest point of antenna 10 m and total power of all channels > 1000 W ERP (1640 W EIRP) Building-mounted antennas: total power of all channels > 1000 W ERP (1640 W EIRP) (2) Broadband PCS (subpart E): Non-building-mounted antennas: height above ground level to lowest point of antenna 10 m and total power of all channels > 2000 W ERP (3280 W EIRP) Building-mounted antennas: total power of all channels > 2000 W ERP (3280 W EIRP)
Satellite Communications (part 25)	All included.
General Wireless Communications Service (part 26).	Total power of all channels > 1640 W EIRP
Wireless Communications Service (part 27).	Total power of all channels > 1640 W EIRP
Radio Broadcast Services (part 73)	All included
Experimental, auxiliary, and special broadcast and other program distributional services (part 74).	Subparts A, G, L: power > 100 W ERP Subpart I: non-building-mounted antennas: height above ground level to lowest point of antenna 10 m and power > 1640 W EIRP Building-mounted antennas: power > 1640 W EIRP

ITFS licensees are required to attach a label to subscriber transceiver or transverter antennas that:
(1) provides adequate notice regarding potential radiofrequency safety hazards, e.g., information regarding the safe minimum separation distance required between users and transceiver antennas; and
(2) references the applicable FCC-adopted limits for radiofrequency exposure specified in Sec. 1.1310.

Stations in the Maritime Services (part 80).	Ship earth stations only
Private Land Mobile Radio Services Paging Operations (part 90).	Non-building-mounted antennas: height above ground level to lowest point of antenna < 10 m and power > 1000 W ERP (1640 W EIRP) Building-mounted antennas: power > 1000 W ERP (1640 W EIRP)
Private Land Mobile Radio Services Specialized Mobile Radio (part 90).	Non-building-mounted antennas: height above ground level to lowest point of antenna <10 m and total power of all channels > 1000 W ERP (1640 W EIRP) Building-mounted antennas: Total power of all channels > 1000 W ERP (1640 W EIRP)
Amateur Radio Service (part 97)	**Transmitter output power > levels specified in Sec. 97.13(c)(1) of this chapter**
Local Multipoint Distribution Service (subpart L of part 101).	Non-building-mounted antennas: height above ground level to lowest point of antenna < 10 m and power > 1640 W EIRP Building-mounted antennas: power > 1640 W EIRP LMDS licensees are required to attach a label to subscriber transceiver antennas that: (1) provides adequate notice regarding potential radiofrequency safety hazards, e.g., information regarding the safe minimum separation distance required between users and transceiver antennas; and (2) references the applicable FCC-adopted limits for radiofrequency exposure specified in Sec. 1.1310 of this chapter

(2) Mobile and portable transmitting devices that operate in the Cellular Radiotelephone Service, the Personal Communications Services (PCS), the Satellite Communications Services, the General Wireless Communications Service, the Wireless Communications Service, the Maritime Services (ship earth stations only) and the Specialized Mobile Radio Service authorized under subpart H of parts 22, 24, 25, 26, 27, 80, and 90 of this chapter are subject to routine environmental evaluation for RF exposure prior to equipment authorization or use, as specified in Secs. 2.1091 and 2.1093 of this chapter. Unlicensed PCS, unlicensed NII and millimeter wave devices are also subject to routine environmental evaluation for RF exposure prior to equipment authorization or use, as specified in Secs. 15.253(f), 15.255(g), and 15.319(i) and 15.407(f) of this chapter. All other mobile, portable, and unlicensed transmitting devices are categorically excluded from routine environmental evaluation for RF exposure under Secs. 2.1091 and 2.1093 of this chapter except as specified in paragraphs (c) and (d) of this section.

(3) In general, when the guidelines specified in Sec. 1.1310 are exceeded in an accessible area due to the emissions from multiple fixed transmitters, actions necessary to bring the area into compliance are the shared responsibility of all licensees whose transmitters produce, at the area in question, power density levels that exceed 5% of the power density exposure limit applicable to their particular transmitter or field strength levels that, when squared, exceed 5% of the square of the electric or magnetic field strength limit applicable to their particular transmitter. Owners of transmitter sites are expected to allow applicants and licensees to take reasonable steps to comply with the requirements contained in Sec. 1.1307(b) and, where feasible, should encourage co-location of transmitters and common solutions for controlling access to areas where the RF exposure limits contained in Sec. 1.1310 might be exceeded.

(i) Applicants for proposed (not otherwise excluded) transmitters, facilities or modifications that would cause non-compliance with the limits specified in Sec. 1.1310 at an accessible area previously in compliance must submit an EA if emissions from the applicant's transmitter or facility would result, at the area in question, in a power density that exceeds 5% of the power density exposure limit applicable to that transmitter or facility or in a field strength that, when squared, exceeds 5% of the square of the electric or magnetic field strength limit applicable to that transmitter or facility.

(ii) Renewal applicants whose (not otherwise excluded) transmitters or facilities contribute to the field strength or power density at an accessible area not in compliance with the limits specified in Sec. 1.1310 must submit an EA if emissions from the applicant's transmitter or facility results, at the area in question, in a power density that exceeds 5% of the power density exposure limit applicable to that transmitter or facility or in a field strength that, when squared, exceeds 5% of the square of the electric or magnetic field strength limit applicable to that transmitter of facility.

(4) Transition Provisions. Applications filed with the Commission prior to October 15, 1997 (or January 1, 1998, for the Amateur Radio Service only), for construction permits, licenses to transmit or renewals thereof, modifications in existing facilities or other authorizations or renewals thereof require the preparation of an Environmental Assessment if the particular facility, operation or transmitter would cause human exposure to levels of radiofrequency radiation that are in excess of the requirements contained in paragraphs (b)(4)(i) through (b)(4)(iii) of this section. In accordance with Sec. 1.1312, if no new application or Commission action is required for a licensee to construct a new facility or physically modify an existing facility, e.g., geographic area licensees, and construction begins on or after October 15, 1997, the licensee will be required to prepare an Environmental Assessment if construction or modification of the facility would not comply with the provisions of paragraph (b)(1) of this section. These transition provisions do not apply to applications for equipment authorization or use for mobile, portable and unlicensed devices as specified in paragraph (b)(2) of this section.

(i) For facilities and operations licensed or authorized under parts 5, 21 (subpart K), 25, 73, 74 (subparts A, G, I, and L), and 80 of this chapter, the "Radio Frequency Protection Guides'' recommended in "American National Standard Safety Levels with Respect to Human Exposure to Radio Frequency Electromagnetic Fields, 300 kHz to 100 GHz" (ANSI C95.1-1982), issued by the American National Standards Institute (ANSI) and copyright 1982 by the Institute of Electrical and Electronics Engineers, Inc., New York, New York shall apply. With respect to subpart K of part 21 and subpart I of part 74 of this chapter, these requirements apply only to multipoint distribution service and instructional television fixed service stations transmitting with an equivalent isotropically radiated power (EIRP) in excess of 200 watts. With respect to subpart L of part 74 of this chapter, these requirements apply only to FM booster and translator stations transmitting with an effective radiated power (ERP) in excess of 100 watts. With respect to part 80 of this chapter, these requirements apply only to ship earth stations.

(ii) For facilities and operations licensed or authorized under part 24 of this chapter, licensees and manufacturers are required to ensure that their facilities and equipment comply with IEEE C95.1-1991 (ANSI/IEEE C95.1-1992), "Safety Levels With Respect to Human Exposure to Radio Frequency Electromagnetic Fields, 3 kHz to 300 GHz." Measurement methods are specified in IEEE C95.3-1991,

"Recommended Practice for the Measurement of Potentially Hazardous Electromagnetic Fields—RF and Microwave." Copies of these standards are available from IEEE Standards Board, 445 Hoes Lane, P.O. Box 1331, Piscataway, NJ 08855-1331. Telephone: 1-800-678-4333. The limits for both "controlled"' and "uncontrolled" environments, as defined by IEEE C95.1-1991, will apply to all PCS base and mobile stations, as appropriate.

(iii) Applications for all other types of facilities and operations are categorically excluded from routine RF radiation evaluation except as provided in paragraphs (c) and (d) of this section.

(5) Existing transmitting facilities, devices and operations: All existing transmitting facilities, operations and devices regulated by the Commission must be in compliance with the requirements of paragraphs (b)(1) through (b)(3) of this section by September 1, 2000, or, if not in compliance, file an Environmental Assessment as specified in Sec. 1.1311.

(c) If an interested person alleges that a particular action, otherwise categorically excluded, will have a significant environmental effect, the person shall submit to the Bureau responsible for processing that action a written petition setting forth in detail the reasons justifying or circumstances necessitating environmental consideration in the decision-making process. (See Sec. 1.1313). The Bureau shall review the petition and consider the environmental concerns that have been raised. If the Bureau determines that the action may have a significant environmental impact, the Bureau will require the applicant to prepare an EA (see Secs. 1.1308 and 1.1311), which will serve as the basis for the determination to proceed with or terminate environmental processing.

(d) If the Bureau responsible for processing a particular action, otherwise categorically excluded, determines that the proposal may have a significant environmental impact, the Bureau, on its own motion, shall require the applicant to submit an EA. The Bureau will review and consider the EA as in paragraph (c) of this section.

(e) No State or local government or instrumentality thereof may regulate the placement, construction, and modification of personal wireless service facilities on the basis of the environmental effects of radio frequency emissions to the extent that such facilities comply with the regulations contained in this chapter concerning the environmental effects of such emissions. For purposes of this paragraph:

(1) The term personal wireless service means commercial mobile services, unlicensed wireless services, and common carrier wireless exchange access services;

(2) The term personal wireless service facilities means facilities for the provision of personal wireless services;

(3) The term unlicensed wireless services means the offering of telecommunications services using duly authorized devices which do not require individual licenses, but does not mean the provision of direct-to-home satellite services; and

(4) The term direct-to-home satellite services means

the distribution or broadcasting of programming or services by satellite directly to the subscriber's premises without the use of ground receiving or distribution equipment, except at the subscriber's premises or in the uplink process to the satellite.

[51 FR 15000, Apr. 22, 1986, as amended at 52 FR 13241, Apr. 22, 1987; 53 FR 28224, July 27, 1988; 53 FR 28393, July 28, 1988; 54 FR 30548, July 21, 1989; 55 FR 2381, Jan. 24, 1990; 55 FR 50692, Dec. 10, 1990; 61 FR 41014, Aug. 7, 1996; 62 FR 3240, Jan. 22, 1997; 62 FR 4655, Jan. 31, 1997; 62 FR 9654, Mar. 3, 1997; 62 FR 23162, Apr. 29, 1997; 62 FR 47965, Sept. 12, 1997; 62 FR 61448, Nov. 18, 1997; 63 FR 65099, Nov. 25, 1998]

Effective Date Note: At 63 FR 65099, Nov. 25, 1998, Sec. 1.1307, Table 1, was amended. This section contains information collection and record-keeping requirements and will not become effective until approval has been given by the Office of Management and Budget.

Sec. 1.1308 Consideration of environmental assessments (EAs); findings of no significant impact.

(a) Applicants shall prepare EAs for actions that may have a significant environmental impact (see Sec. 1.1307). An EA is described in detail in Sec. 1.1311 of this part of the Commission rules.

(b) The EA is a document which shall explain the environmental consequences of the proposal and set forth sufficient analysis for the Bureau or the Commission to reach a determination that the proposal will or will not have a significant environmental effect. To assist in making that determination, the Bureau or the Commission may request further information from the applicant, interested persons, and agencies and authorities which have jurisdiction by law or which have relevant expertise.

Note: With respect to actions specified under Sec. 1.1307 (a)(3) and (a)(4), the Commission shall solicit and consider the comments of the Department of Interior, and the State Historic Preservation Officer and the Advisory Council on Historic Preservation, respectively, in accordance with their established procedures. See Interagency Cooperation—Endangered Species Act of 1973, as amended, 50 CFR part 402; Protection of Historic and Cultural Properties, 36 CFR part 800. In addition, when an action interferes with or adversely affects an American Indian tribe's religious site, the Commission shall solicit the views of that American Indian tribe. See Sec. 1.1307(a)(5).

(c) If the Bureau or the Commission determines, based on an independent review of the EA and any applicable mandatory consultation requirements imposed upon Federal agencies (see note above), that the proposal will have a significant environmental impact upon the quality of the human environment, it will so inform the applicant. The applicant will then have an opportunity to amend its application so as to reduce, minimize, or eliminate environmental problems. See Sec. 1.1309.

If the environmental problem is not eliminated, the Bureau will publish in the Federal Register a Notice of Intent (see Sec. 1.1314) that EISs will be prepared (see Secs. 1.1315 and 1.1317), or

(d) If the Bureau or Commission determines, based on an independent review of the EA, and any mandatory consultation requirements imposed upon Federal agencies (see the note to paragraph (b) of this section), that the proposal would not have a significant impact, it will make a finding of no significant impact. Thereafter, the application will be processed without further documentation of environmental effect.

Pursuant to CEQ regulations, see 40 CFR 1501.4 and 1501.6, the applicant must provide the community notice of the Commission's finding of no significant impact.

[51 FR 15000, Apr. 22, 1986; 51 FR 18889, May 23, 1986, as amended at 53 FR 28394, July 28, 1988]

Sec. 1.1309 Application amendments.

Applicants are permitted to amend their applications to reduce, minimize or eliminate potential environmental problems. As a routine matter, an applicant will be permitted to amend its application within thirty (30) days after the Commission or the Bureau informs the applicant that the proposal will have a significant impact upon the quality of the human environment (see Sec. 1.1308(c)). The period of thirty (30) days may be extended upon a showing of good cause.

Sec. 1.1310 Radiofrequency radiation exposure limits.

The criteria listed in table 1 shall be used to evaluate the environmental impact of human exposure to radiofrequency (RF) radiation as specified in Sec. 1.1307(b), except in the case of portable devices which shall be evaluated according to the provisions of Sec. 2.1093 of this chapter. Further information on evaluating compliance with these limits can be found in the FCC's OST/OET Bulletin Number 65, "Evaluating Compliance with FCC-Specified Guidelines for Human Exposure to Radiofrequency Radiation."

Note to Introductory Paragraph: These limits are generally based on recommended exposure guidelines published by the National Council on Radiation Protection and Measurements (NCRP) in "Biological Effects and Exposure Criteria for Radiofrequency Electromagnetic Fields," NCRP Report No. 86, Sections 17.4.1, 17.4.1.1, 17.4.2 and 17.4.3. Copyright NCRP, 1986, Bethesda, Maryland 20814. In the frequency range from 100 MHz to 1500 MHz, exposure limits for field strength and power density are also generally based on guidelines recommended by the American National Standards Institute (ANSI) in Section 4.1 of "IEEE Standard for Safety Levels with Respect to Human Exposure to Radio Frequency Electromagnetic Fields, 3 kHz to 300 GHz," ANSI/IEEE C95.1-1992, Copyright 1992 by the Institute of Electrical and Electronics Engineers, Inc., New York, New York 10017.

[61 FR 41016, Aug. 7, 1996]

Sec. 1.1311 Environmental information to be included in the environmental assessment (EA).

(a) The applicant shall submit an EA with each application that is subject to environmental processing (see Sec. 1.1307). The EA shall contain the following information:

(1) For antenna towers and satellite earth stations, a description of the facilities as well as supporting structures and appurtenances, and a description of the site as well as the surrounding area and uses. If high intensity white lighting is proposed or utilized within a residential area, the EA must also address the impact of this lighting upon the residents.

(2) A statement as to the zoning classification of the site, and communications with, or proceedings before and determinations (if any) made by zoning, planning, environmental or other local, state or Federal authorities on matters relating to environmental effect.

(3) A statement as to whether construction of the facilities has been a source of controversy on environmental grounds in the local community.

(4) A discussion of environmental and other considerations which led to the selection of the particular site and, if relevant, the particular facility; the nature and extent of any unavoidable adverse environmental effects, and any alternative sites or facilities which have been or might reasonably be considered.

(5) Any other information that may be requested by the Bureau or Commission.

(6) If endangered or threatened species or their critical habitats may be affected, the applicant's analysis must utilize the best scientific and commercial data available, see 50 CFR 402.14(c).

(b) The information submitted in the EA shall be factual (not argumentative or conclusory) and concise with sufficient detail to explain the environmental consequences and to enable the Commission or Bureau, after an independent review of the EA, to reach a determination concerning the proposal's environmental impact, if any. The EA shall deal specifically with any feature of the site which has special environmental significance (e.g., wilderness areas, wildlife preserves, natural migration paths for birds and other wildlife, and sites of historic, architectural, or archeological value). In the case of historically significant sites, it shall specify the effect of the facilities on any district, site, building, structure or object listed, or eligible for listing, in the National Register of Historic Places. It shall also detail any substantial change in the character of the land utilized (e.g., deforestation, water diversion, wetland fill, or other extensive change of surface features). In the case of wilderness areas, wildlife preserves, or other like areas, the statement shall discuss the effect of any continuing pattern of human intrusion into the area (e.g., necessitated by the operation and maintenance of the facilities).

(c) The EA shall also be accompanied with evidence of site approval which has been obtained from local or Federal land use authorities.

(d) To the extent that such information is submitted in another part of the application, it need not be duplicated in the EA, but adequate cross-reference to such information shall be supplied.

(e) An EA need not be submitted to the Commission if another agency of the Federal Government has assumed responsibility for determining whether of the facilities in

Table 2—Limits for Maximum Permissible Exposure (MPE)

Frequency range (MHz)	Electric field strength (V/m)	Magnetic field strength (A/m)	Power density (mW/cm^2)	Averaging time (minutes)
(A) Limits for Occupational/Controlled Exposures				
0.3-3.0	614	1.63	*(100)	6
3.0-30	1842/f	4.89/f	*(900/f^2)	6
30-300	61.4	0.163	1.0	6
300-1500			f/300	6
1500-100,000			5	6
(B) Limits for General Population/Uncontrolled Exposure				
0.3-1.34	614	1.63	*(100)	30
1.34-30	824/f	2.19/f	*(180/f\2\)	30
30-300	27.5	0.073	0.2	30
300-1500			f/1500	30
1500-100,000			1.0	30

f = frequency in MHz
* = Plane-wave equivalent power density
Note 1 to Table 2: Occupational/controlled limits apply in situations in which persons are exposed as a consequence of their employment provided those persons are fully aware of the potential for exposure and can exercise control over their exposure. Limits for occupational/controlled exposure also apply in situations when an individual is transient through a location where occupational/controlled limits apply provided he or she is made aware of the potential for exposure.
Note 2 to Table 2: General population/uncontrolled exposures apply in situations in which the general public may be exposed, or in which persons that are exposed as a consequence of their employment may not be fully aware of the potential for exposure or can not exercise control over their exposure.

question will have a significant effect on the quality of the human environment and, if it will, for invoking the environmental impact statement process.

[51 FR 15000, Apr. 22, 1986, as amended at 51 FR 18889, May 23, 1986; 53 FR 28394, July 28, 1988]

Sec. 1.1312 Facilities for which no pre-construction authorization is required.

(a) In the case of facilities for which no Commission authorization prior to construction is required by the Commission's rules and regulations the licensee or applicant shall initially ascertain whether the proposed facility may have a significant environmental impact as defined in Sec. 1.1307 of this part or is categorically excluded from environmental processing under Sec. 1.1306 of this part.

(b) If a facility covered by paragraph (a) of this section may have a significant environmental impact, the information required by Sec. 1.1311 of this part shall be submitted by the licensee or applicant and ruled on by the Commission, and environmental processing (if invoked) shall be completed, see Sec. 1.1308 of this part, prior to the initiation of construction of the facility.

(c) If a facility covered by paragraph (a) of this section is categorically excluded from environmental processing, the licensee or applicant may proceed with construction and operation of the facility in accordance with the applicable licensing rules and procedures.

(d) If, following the initiation of construction under this section, the licensee or applicant discovers that the proposed facility may have a significant environmental effect, it shall immediately cease construction which may have that effect, and submit the information required by Sec. 1.1311 of this part. The Commission shall rule on that submission and complete further environmental processing (if invoked), see Sec. 1.1308 of this part, before such construction is resumed.

(e) Paragraphs (a) through (d) of this section shall not apply to the construction of mobile stations.

[55 FR 20396, May 16, 1990, as amended at 56 FR 13414, Apr. 2, 1991]

Sec. 1.1313 Objections.

(a) In the case of an application to which section 309(b) of the Communications Act applies, objections based on environmental considerations shall be filed as petitions to deny.

(b) Informal objections which are based on environmental considerations must be filed prior to grant of the construction permit, or prior to authorization for facilities that do not require construction permits, or pursuant to the applicable rules governing services subject to lotteries.

Sec. 1.1314 Environmental impact statements (EISs).

(a) Draft Environmental Impact Statements (DEISs) (Sec. 1.1315) and Final Environmental Impact Statements (FEISs) (referred to collectively as EISs) (Sec. 1.1317) shall be prepared by the Bureau responsible for processing the proposal when the Commission's or the Bureau's analysis of the EA (Sec. 1.1308) indicates that the proposal will have a significant effect upon the environment and the matter has not been resolved by an amendment.

(b) As soon as practically feasible, the Bureau will publish in the Federal Register a Notice of Intent to prepare EISs. The Notice shall briefly identify the proposal, concisely describe the environmental issues and concerns presented by the subject application, and generally invite participation from affected or involved agencies, authorities and other interested persons.

(c) The EISs shall not address non-environmental considerations. To safeguard against repetitive and unnecessarily lengthy documents, the Statements, where feasible, shall incorporate by reference material set forth in previous documents, with only a brief summary of its content. In preparing the EISs, the Bureau will identify and address the significant environmental issues and eliminate the insignificant issues from analysis.

(d) To assist in the preparation of the EISs, the Bureau may request further information from the applicant, interested persons and agencies and authorities, which have jurisdiction by law or which have relevant expertise. The Bureau may direct that technical studies be made by the applicant and that the applicant obtain expert opinion concerning the potential environmental problems and costs associated with the proposed action, as well as comparative analyses of alternatives. The Bureau may also consult experts in an effort to identify measures that could be taken to minimize the adverse effects and alternatives to the proposed facilities that are not, or are less, objectionable. The Bureau may also direct that objections be raised with appropriate local, state or Federal land use agencies or authorities (if their views have not been previously sought).

(e) The Bureau responsible for processing the particular application and, thus, preparing the EISs shall draft supplements to Statements where significant new circumstances occur or information arises relevant to environmental concerns and bearing upon the application.

(f) The Application, the EA, the DEIS, and the FEIS and all related documents, including the comments filed by the public and any agency, shall be part of the administrative record and will be routinely available for public inspection.

(g) If EISs are to be prepared, the applicant must provide the community with notice of the availability of environmental documents and the scheduling of any Commission hearings in that action.

(h) The timing of agency action with respect to applications subject to EISs is set forth in 40 CFR 1506.10. No decision shall be made until ninety (90) days after the Notice of Availability of the Draft Environmental Impact Statement is published in the Federal Register, and thirty (30) days after the Notice of Availability of the Final Environmental Impact Statement is published in the Federal Register, which time period may run concurrently, See 40 CFR 1506.10(c); see also Secs. 1.1315(b) and 1.1317(b).

(i) Guidance concerning preparation of the Draft and Final Environmental Statements is set out in 40 CFR part 1502.

[51 FR 15000, Apr. 22, 1986, as amended at 53 FR 28394, July 28, 1988]

Sec. 1.1315 The Draft Environmental Impact Statement (DEIS); Comments.

(a) The DEIS shall include:

(1) A concise description of the proposal, the nature of the area affected, its uses, and any specific feature of the area that has special environmental significance;

(2) An analysis of the proposal, and reasonable alternatives exploring the important consequent advantages and/or disadvantages of the action and indicating the direct and indirect effects and their significance in terms of the short and long-term uses of the human environment.

(b) When a DEIS and supplements, if any, are prepared, the Commission shall send five copies of the Statement, or a summary, to the Office of Federal Activities, Environmental Protection Agency. Additional copies, or summaries, will be sent to the appropriate regional office of the Environmental Protection Agency. Public Notice of the availability of the DEIS will be published in the Federal Register by the Environmental Protection Agency.

(c) When copies or summaries of the DEIS are sent to the Environmental Protection Agency, the copies or summaries will be mailed with a request for comment to Federal agencies having jurisdiction by law or special expertise, to the Council on Environmental Quality, to the applicant, to individuals, groups and state and local agencies known to have an interest in the environmental consequences of a grant, and to any other person who has requested a copy.

(d) Any person or agency may comment on the DEIS and the environmental effect of the proposal described therein within 45 days after notice of the availability of the statement is published in the Federal Register. A copy of those comments shall be mailed to the applicant by the person who files them pursuant to 47 CFR 1.47. An original and one copy shall be filed with the Commission. If a person submitting comments is especially qualified in any way to comment on the environmental impact of the facilities, a statement of his or her qualifications shall be set out in the comments. In addition, comments submitted by an agency shall identify the person(s) who prepared them.

(e) The applicant may file reply comments within 15 days after the time for filing comments has expired. Reply comments shall be filed with the Commission in the same manner as comments, and shall be served by the applicant on persons or agencies which filed comments.

(f) The preparation of a DEIS and the request for comments shall not open the application to attack on other grounds.

Sec. 1.1317 The Final Environmental Impact Statement (FEIS).

(a) After receipt of comments and reply comments, the Bureau will prepare a FEIS, which shall include a summary of the comments, and a response to the comments, and an analysis of the proposal in terms of its environmental consequences, and any reasonable alternatives, and recommendations, if any, and shall cite the Commission's internal appeal procedures (See 47 CFR 1.101-1.120).

(b) The FEIS and any supplements will be distributed and published in the same manner as specified in Sec. 1.1315. Copies of the comments and reply comments, or summaries thereof where the record is voluminous, shall be attached to the FEIS.

Sec. 1.1319 Consideration of the environmental impact statements.

(a) If the action is subject to a hearing:

(1) In rendering his initial decision, the Administrative Law Judge shall utilize the FEIS in considering the environmental issues, together with all other non-environmental issues. In a comparative context, the respective parties shall be afforded the opportunity to comment on the FEIS, and the Administrative Law Judge's decision shall contain an evaluation of the respective applications based on environmental and non-environmental public interest factors.

(2) Upon review of an initial decision, the Commission will consider and assess all aspects of the FEIS and will render its decision, giving due consideration to the environmental and non-environmental issues.

(b) In all non-hearing matters, the Commission, as part of its decision-making process, will review the FEIS, along with other relevant issues, to ensure that the environmental effects are specifically assessed and given comprehensive consideration.

[51 FR 15000, Apr. 22, 1986, as amended at 62 FR 4171, Jan. 29, 1997]

Appendix B

Drafting a Bylaw, or Redrafting a Bylaw

There is a standard paragraph in the BOCA Code that deals with Amateur Radio antennas. Over the years that standard paragraph has changed. Depending on when someone cared about the issue last in your town you may find any one of several versions of the BOCA Code paragraph. Or you may find a homegrown section dealing with Amateur Radio.

To help you out, we've included several bylaws and suggestions on how they could be changed for the better. Please remember, however, that it is always better, if your town is considering amending the present bylaw, to participate rather than to not participate in the process. Participation means being there night after night as the ordinance is drafted. Do not rely on the Town Planner to represent your views.

Once again, there is some duplication of material that has been presented in earlier chapters of this book. Believe me, my motive is not to increase the number of trees killed to print this book—I want to keep arguments together so that they make sense in context.

Now, before we get serious about analyzing a bylaw, it is important to grasp, in a way that will prepare you for the inevitable question, why a radio amateur is treated differently in law, and why Amateur Radio antenna systems ought to be treated differently.

What's really being asked here is: Why are hams different?

- Hams are different because their antennas are not for a commercial use, but rather for public service.
- Hams are different because in times of emergency, they not

only provide their antennas and equipment, free of charge, but also the people trained to man the gear as well.
- Hams are different because they experiment—and change antennas all the time—at their own expense and with no revenue. This brings benefits to the public, such as the origins of satellite communications, delivery of critical data to police patrol cars on the road, television (Yes, even television!) and other new ideas.
- Hams are different because when he/she moves, the antennas move also. On the other hand, a commercial installation is there almost forever.

THE ELEMENTS OF A BYLAW

Obviously, we cannot review the thousands and thousands of bylaws from around the nation. But by describing the common elements and reviewing a few, you may find some help.

Does it Meet Federal Law Requirements?

Thanks to ARRL General Counsel W3KD for contributing much of the thinking in this section.

For Video Services

Does the proposal meet the Telecomm Act requirement of accommodation for video delivery service facilities? What is the exemption for satellite antennas? (The FCC preemption definition is broad.) Is there an exemption for television broadcast receive and MMDS antennas (as the FCC regulations require)? If you are looking to at least get this kicked back to the drawing board, where you might have an opportunity for more input, tell them that the ordinance is void as preempted by the FCC's Order of August, 1996, implementing the Telecom Act requirements for video delivery services. See Appendix A of this book and look for the discussion of the OTARD (Over-the Air Reception Devices) rule, 47 CFR 1.4000, **http://www.fcc.gov/csb/facts/otard. html**.

For Amateur Radio

This is a matter of Federal pre-emption and a Town may not ignore or overrule the Federal regulation on this issue.

47 CFR § 97.15 (b):

Except as otherwise provided herein, a station antenna structure may be erected at heights and dimensions sufficient to accommodate amateur service communications. [State and local regulations of a station antenna structure must not preclude amateur service communications. Rather, it must reasonably accommodate such communications and must constitute the minimum practicable regulations to accomplish state or local authority's legitimate purpose. See PRB-1, 101 FCC 2d 952 (1985) for details.]

In addition, the FCC has ruled:

[T]he very least regulation necessary for the welfare of the community must be the aim of its regulations so that such regulations will not impinge on the needs of amateur operators to engage in amateur communications.

ORDER In the Matter of RM-8763, adopted November 18, 1999, released November 19, 1999, paragraphs 7 and 9. [See: **http://www.fcc.gov/Bureaus/Wireless/ Orders/1999/da992569.txt**.]

Thus, any town drafting a new ordinance must have as its goal "the minimum practicable regulations to accomplish state or local authority's legitimate purpose." This is *not* "as much as we can get away with to suppress Amateur Radio antennas" but rather "the minimum, so that such regulations will not impinge on the needs of amateur operators."

The FCC has already performed the balancing test and found in favor of Amateur Radio. The Town cannot draft something that basically says: "Consider the needs of the radio amateur applicant and balance those needs against the aesthetic interests of the town." There are several Federal Appeals Court decisions that say this is not the law. See, for example, this quotation from a Federal Circuit Court in the pivotal *Pentel* case.

[W]e must discuss the extent to which this language requires municipalities to yield to amateur interests. Although some courts have evaluated whether the municipality properly balanced its interests against the Federal Government's interests in promoting amateur communications, see *Williams v. City of Columbia*, 906 F. 2d 994, 998 (4th Cir. 1990); *MacMillan*, 748 F.

Supp. at 1248, we read PRB-1 as requiring municipalities to do more—PRB-1 specifically requires the city to accommodate reasonably amateur communications.5/ See *Evans*, 994 F. 2d at 762-63. This distinction is important, because a standard that requires a city to accommodate amateur communications in a reasonable fashion is certainly more rigorous than one that simply requires a city to balance local and federal interests when deciding whether to permit a radio antenna. [Pentel v. Mendota Heights, 13 F.3d 1261 (8th Cir. 1994)]

To truly clarify this, a 1999 FCC Order reads, at Paragraph 7:

[T]he PRB-1 decision precisely stated the principle of "reasonable accommodation". In PRB-1, the Commission stated: "Nevertheless, local regulations which involve placement, screening, or height of antennas based on health, safety, or aesthetic considerations must be crafted to accommodate reasonably amateur communications, and to represent the minimum practicable regulation to accomplish the local authority's legitimate purpose." Given this express Commission language, it is clear that a "balancing of interests" approach is not appropriate in this context.

Instead, the town must draft "the minimum practicable" regulation. Or, as the Commission continued:

[T]he very least regulation necessary for the welfare of the community must be the aim of its regulations so that such regulations will not impinge on the needs of amateur operators to engage in amateur communications.

ORDER In the Matter of RM-8763, adopted November 18, 1999, released November 19, 1999, paragraph 9. [See: **http://www.fcc.gov/Bureaus/ Wireless/Orders/1999/da992569.txt**.]

In a drafting session, radio hams should never tire of asking: "Is this the minimum practicable regulation? Will it impinge?"

Exempting Amateur Radio from a Commercial Tower Bylaw

It's a small thing, but if the matter before you is the question of a definition, to ensure that a commercial or cellular tower bylaw does not, due to sloppy drafting, inadvertently control Amateur Radio antenna-support structures, watch out for one small item: the exemption. Thanks to Phil Kane, K2ASP, ARRL Pacific Division Assistant Director (Volunteer Counsel Coordinator) and Principal Attorney, Communications Law Center for pointing out the following.

If it says, "FCC licensed Amateur Radio operators are exempt from these regulations," that is very poor drafting, because US law permits Canadians (and aliens who are CEPT-nation licensees) to operate their stations here in the US without getting permission from the FCC.

Phil Kane adds:

Part of my law practice is to draft such ordinances, and in general what I do is to define what type of facility *is* regulated (commercial wireless communication facilities, specifically defined) in such a way that it cannot be "stretched" to cover amateur facilities, rather than to define what is *not* regulated.

If the client jurisdiction insists that something be mentioned about amateurs, I use a definition of "Amateur Radio Operator" that covers FCC licensees and aliens operating under reciprocal permits or blanket treaty authority, and I recommend a 75-foot height without a use permit or zoning variance, if permitted by lot size and structural considerations.

To avoid restrictions on height, location and any other mischief the town may be considering, one ARRL Volunteer Counsel likes to use this expression: "These provisions are not applicable to Federally authorized radio amateurs in any residential district."

For Radio Frequency Interference (RFI)

Zoning bylaws (or any other local bylaws, such as nuisance bylaws) may not attempt to control radio frequency interference (RFI). This subject area is *completely* preempted by the Federal Communications Commission. For an excellent discussion, and a wealth of cases, see *Southwestern Bell Wireless, Inc. v. Johnson County Board of County Commissioners*, No. 98-3264 (10th Cir. Dec. 27, 1999) **http://www.kscourt.org/ca10/cases/1999/12/98-3264.htm**.

Another well-written and thorough discussion states plainly: "We conclude that allowing local zoning authorities to condition construction and use permits on any requirement to eliminate or remedy RF interference 'stands as an obstacle to the accomplishment and execution of the full purposes and objectives of Congress.'" *Freeman v. Burlington Broadcasters, Inc.*, No. 97- 9141 (2d Cir. February 23, 2000) **http://www.tourolaw.edu/2ndCircuit/February00/97-9141.html, 2000 U.S.App. LEXIS 2672**.

Does it Meet State Law Requirements?

State Law Parallels to PRB-1(47 CFR § 97.15(b))

In at least 10 states, a state law impacts the control a town may exert over Amateur Radio antennas. To see if you are in one of those states, check out: **http://www.arrl.org/field/regulations/statutes.html**. These statutes raise the question: Does the proposal in front of you meet the requirements of your state law governing Amateur Radio? For example, if the bylaw has a flat prohibition of any antenna over 35 or 50 feet, it cannot possibly allow for accommodation in a situation where an amateur's lot slopes down from the road or is in a valley.

Fees or Costs

In evaluating an existing or proposed zoning bylaw,

consider also whether or not it may fail to meet the requirements of any state statute that limits the cost of a special permit. ARRL Volunteer Counsel Allan Yackey, WB9PKM, notes, for example that:

… an Indiana Statute prohibits towns and cities from using licenses to generate income. See I.C. 36-1-3-8 which is entitled POWERS SPECIFICALLY WITHHELD, which reads:
Sec 8 (a) *** a unit does not have the following: *** (5) The power to impose a license fee greater than that reasonably related to the administrative cost of exercising a regulatory power.
(6) The power to impose a service charge or user fee greater than that reasonably related to reasonable and just rates and charges for services.

This has been rather effective in restraining costs of permits and licenses in Indiana, where they are rather conservative when it comes to government power. You may benefit from a similar statute in your state.

Even if you don't have a similar statute, here are some additional ideas on how to deal with high fees or costs. Listed below are my comments concerning the following question:

My city will be raising the fee for a Permit for an antenna-support structure from $85 to $1,205. This is part of the city's "fee for service" or "cost recovery system" program. Ham tower permits are grouped in with licensed day care, satellite dishes over 18 inches and homes rented to 4 or more adults, all within a particular Special Use Permit Category. What do I do now?

I answered, offering some strategies for negotiating in good faith.

1. A Different Category. I would ask to be moved to a different Special Use Permit category. Why? Because the others (with the exception of 4 GHz satellite dishes, which are in fact greater than 18 inches) all involve income to the applicant as a result of the grant. Amateur radio is, on the other hand, a public service. I would submit copies of Public Law 103-408, passed October 22, 1994: "Regulation at all levels of government should facilitate and encourage amateur radio as a public benefit."

2. Waiver for Standard Installations. If they don't buy that as a general matter, then leave the price alone and ask that it be waived "upon submission by the applicant of manufacturer's specifications for installation and a showing that the Applicant can erect to those specifications."

3. Standard Installations, Standard Cost. As this is a "cost-recovery" measure, I would argue that basically ham installations are all alike, that the staff is experienced in reviewing them. If it is a standard tower and beam, the review should take all of 5 minutes. The charge is unrelated to the cost. While cost recovery may be justifiable, profit making is not. Refer to the ordinance of Brevard County, FL, where standard manufacturers specifications are on file. Use one of those structures and the review is perfunctory.

4. Waiver Below 150 Feet. If they don't buy exemption by removal to another category, *or* waiver within the same category, I'd ask to insert a definition of ham towers: "amateur radio support structures exceeding 150 feet in height." (It would be okay to compromise at 125 feet.)

5. Waiver for Large Lots. Finally, if you are in a rural area, where five-acre lots are common, try to exempt Amateur Radio antenna systems when they will be constructed on large lots, defined as five acres (you could even try for two-acre lots). An example of an exemption based on lot size is found in the exemption from certain land-use regulations for farm, where the farm exceeds five acres in size. Massachusetts General Laws, Chapter 61A, Section 3. **http:// www.state.ma.us/legis/laws/mgl/61A-3.htm**.

6. Change the Effective Date. Try arguing that while the goal may be laudable, as proposed it is presently illegal. "This section shall become effective at such time as Federal law shall no longer require the limited pre-emption of local zoning law, 47 CFR § 97.15."

With me so far? Change categories, waive the fee, make the standard fee low, define it away, make exempt for large lots or change the effective date. ARRL General Counsel Chris Imlay, W3KD, commented on the same question:

> Since those fees are high relative to the cost of the amateur antenna installation, it is arguable that the cost is either equivalent to a prohibition or at least not a reasonable accommodation, but the argument seems difficult if the fee is the same as that for other special permits.

> The larger satellite dish users have an easier time arguing that the cost of the permit is prohibitive, because in the 1986 satellite-dish pre-emption order, prohibitive permit fees or costs were specifically considered as an issue in determining whether an ordinance is valid. You might be able to work that angle.

Setback

Are the setback limitations arbitrary and self-defeating? As an example, despite a concern for safety, no one can justify an extra 6 inches of setback for one foot of height limitation (a ratio of 1.5:1). Towers don't jump if they fall.

A restriction of one foot for each foot of height above a house bracket or a set of guy wires or 36 feet, comes closer to being reasonable, though it may lead to results even planners will concede are bad. See below for the discussion of narrow lots backing up to a forest. To give you an example, if the restriction was 1:1 above 36 feet, here's a table of what that would mean:

Table 1
1:1 Setback Above 36 Feet

Distance from Structure to Lot Line (Feet)	Maximum Tower Height (Feet)
20	56
30	66
40	76
50	86
60	96
70	106
80	116

So if someone insists on inserting a 1:1 setback ratio, you might choose to agree to it (but see below for exceptions), provided that the counting begins at a reasonable height in feet (such as 36 feet), the roofline, the house bracket or the first (second? uppermost?) guy point. Remember the negotiating concept that you can always accept the other side's price, if you get to set the definitions, terms and conditions.

By the way, keep your eyes open. A common tactic is to permit Amateur Radio antenna systems in the ordinance, but require that the filing be equivalent to what would be required of the construction of a new Empire State Building (surveys, seals, traffic studies and so forth—all of which is blatantly designed to run up the cost of the applicant without serving any reasonable purpose).

Ask out loud why such impediments should apply to Amateur Radio structures when they do not apply to church construction, flagpoles, baseball backstops or an antenna-support structure out in back of a local garage so that the towing company can talk to its tow trucks? When people who are against the creation of emergency-communications capability seek to hobble the ordinance, stand up and shout these words: "minimum practicable regulation." After all, that is not just a suggestion, it is a *requirement* of the Federal regulation.

If you'd like to make someone uncomfortable in a public forum, ask this question: "Could you please explain how your proposed burden on the applicant promotes accommodation and meets the Federal law's requirement to represents 'minimum practicable regulation?'" As your opponent mumbles, split the question apart and ask it again. Does this really promote *accommodation*? Is this really *the minimum*? Then start suggesting alternatives that are even more minimal than those already "on the table." For example, if the proposed ordinance has a 1:1 setback:

1. Make the point that the best place to "hide" an antenna system may well be in the back corner, out "in the woods."
2. Make the point that these structures don't fall the length of their height, and propose that the setback begin at 50 feet (see discussion elsewhere in this chapter), and/or
3. Redefine the setback for this purpose so that it is not to the property line, but to the nearest existing inhabited building. Be sure to try for all three tests: "existing," "inhabited," and "building." The building should be an existing building, so that a spiteful neighbor cannot later

erect a tool shed, and thereby require the removal of the antenna system. It should be inhabited, to prevent an existing tool shed from holding up an otherwise worthy project just to theoretically protect a power lawnmower. (Insurance will protect the lawnmower.) And it should be a building, as opposed to a structure, so that a fence or basketball hoop or cold frame cannot bar erection of an antenna-support structure.

Good public policy requires that the ordinance must include an *escape valve* in the best interest of the neighbors. Take the example of a string of half-acre lots along the street. Each lot is 100×200 feet. (But the example would be better if each lot were 50×400 feet.) Assume all lots back up to the town dump, a state highway or a forest. Most people would argue that the spot to erect the structure where it would have the least aesthetic impact would be "way out back." Yet a ratio-based ordinance would force the structure into a *more* visible place, *closer* to the neighbors.

Conclusion: If the planners insist on a ratio, you should insist on an escape valve and add words such as: "…except where, for good reason shown, the Board decides that it is in the best interests of the neighborhood to permit construction closer to a lot line than would otherwise be permitted."

Avoid "variance" language, as the test to grant a variance is likely a higher hurdle than "for good reason shown."

Setback for Guy Wires

Watch out for the setback rule. Typically, this rule says that no structure may be erected closer to a lot line than 10-50 feet, depending on the neighborhood or lot size. Normally there is an absolute minimum.

However, public policy already recognizes some exceptions. Examples of exceptions are: basketball backboards and nets, fences, post boxes, stonewalls, and a shed for the children to keep them dry while waiting for the school bus. Sometimes the setback rule includes an exception by height (for example, nothing greater than 10 feet in height within the setback area). Sometimes the setback rule includes an exception by use (such as some of the uses listed above). Sometimes the setback rule is set out as an exception for construction that is expressed in Latin: *de minimis*.

Here are a few approaches that can work in the face of such a setback rule. If you are dealing specifically with an Amateur Radio antenna-support structure, you could specify that: "No anchor for guy wires may be located closer to a boundary line than three (3) feet." If there is an exception for construction under ten (10) feet in height, you might try: "For the purposes of the exception for structures less than ten (10) feet in height, the height of sloping guy wires entering the setback area shall be the average height of the wires in the setback area."

Furthermore, "Amateur Radio antennas or guys, if made of wire, shall be considered *de minimis* construction to which the setback shall not apply." The public policy reason that supports this approach is that if it is not applied, the amateur will be forced to erect a tall pole to intercept the sloping antenna, or a steel I-beam to "shorten" the guy wires,

and the pole or I-beam will be far less aesthetically pleasing than allowing the antenna or guy wires to come all the way to the ground anchor. Furthermore, you can hide the guy wires more easily with shrubbery planted to block the view of the wires gathering at the anchor's equalizer plate.

For the purposes of the bylaw, horizontal elements of an antenna should be permitted. "The horizontal elements of an amateur radio antenna may encroach upon the setback area, but in no event may such an element intrude into the air space of an abutting lot, as if a plane were drawn vertically on the lot line." The public policy argument here is that no one ever requires that a flag may not encroach on the setback, and therefore a Yagi antenna turning radius should similarly be irrelevant.

Vertical antennas are antennas, not antenna-support structures, typically round and unobtrusive, generally less visible than a solid flagpole. For this reason, they should not be prohibited within the setback. "For the purposes of the bylaw, vertical antennas no greater than five inches in equivalent diameter shall be considered *de minimis* construction to which the setback shall not apply." The term "five inches in equivalent diameter" covers a vertical antenna made with triangular tower section up to 18 inches on each face, such as Rohn 45 tower.

DEFINITIONS

A wise lawyer once told me that he would allow a client to agree to anything, as long as he got to draft the definitions and starting dates. So spend a great deal of time working on the definitions section. First, ask yourself if the bylaw you are looking at presently has a silly definition, perhaps one that would theoretically require a permit for a crystal radio set with a wire out the window, or that would prohibit a short wave listener's all-band dipole antenna. In one Massachusetts town, if you read the definition closely and have a dipole in a tree higher than 50 feet, you'd have to chop off any portion of the tree above 50 feet—because the support of any antenna whatsoever cannot exceed 50 feet.

Tip: Think about a blanket exemption for accessory antenna support structures less than 75-150 feet in height for Amateur Radio antennas. In other words, leave the ordinance alone but exempt short towers in the definitions section, not the height section. Then add: "For the purposes of this ordinance, an antenna or mast extending less than 12 feet above any support structure shall not require a permit of any kind."

Think this is impossible? Go read the Virginia statute at **http://leg1.state.va.us/cgi-bin/legp504.exe?000+cod +15.2-2293.1**.

Another possible exemption to a height limit (or a requirement for a Special Permit) could be "If a supporting structure adjoins and is securely attached to a building (not including a chimney) or is integral to the building, the additional height above such point of secure attachment shall not exceed one foot for each one foot in horizontal distance from the point of secure attachment to the nearest property line." Under such a definition, if you have a 36-foot house and 40 feet to the side lot line, you get a 76-foot structure without a special permit.

But you knew this from the earlier discussion about ratios. The reason to review the subject is that this time it is approached from the *definitions* section, and not in the *height* section. With respect to wire antennas, verticals, and other less substantial construction, consider proposing an exception for antenna systems that cost less than $500.

For antenna-support structures, consider dividing them in the definitions section into structures greater than 100 feet and less than 100 feet high. Perhaps a compromise can be reached between people of good will such that structures under 100 feet can be erected, providing other conditions are met, by a Building Permit process, while structures over 100 feet would require a Special Permit. This can be very important where Special Permit applications have substantial fees.

In any event, the Amateur Radio negotiator should insist that the height limit applies to the support structure, and not the repeater antenna or VHF/UHF vertical at the top, since that is the most important antenna for local public-safety purposes. If possible, ask the local RACES/ARES/Civil Defense officer who may be participating directly (or participating by writing a letter) to emphasize that communications to handi-talkies during emergencies is highly dependent on the height of the VHF/UHF vertical at the top of the structure.

HEIGHT-TO-LOT-LINE RATIOS

These are dangerous for the ham and unwise for the town. They are usually expressed as a maximum of one foot of height for each foot of distance to the nearest lot line (a 1:1 ratio), or the like. Imagine a ham on a lot 100-feet wide. The maximum height tower would be 50 feet and you would be forced to build at the mid-line of the property. The real purpose behind such ratios is to control height, since the building code controls safety.

However, if the Town's purpose is to minimize aesthetic impact, the Town really would want the tower put along a tree line, or in that portion of the yard where it would have the least impact—not in the most visible place, out in the open in the middle of the grassy area. Where such language is an absolute control on height, it may also violate 47 CFR § 97.15(b).

BACK LOT ONLY

An ordinance provision against placement in a side lot or front lot also reduces flexibility and could prevent a ham from placing an antenna in the least visible spot. Some examples: a long driveway from the street (perhaps through an unbuildable area, sometimes called a *flag lot* because the lot resembles a flag pole with flag) with a house that is actually closer to the backdoor neighbors than the street. In this case, the neighbors might prefer a "front" yard placement. Similarly, a side lot may also have the least aesthetic impact. It depends on the characteristics of the lot. The bylaw should not take that flexibility away by assuming that all lots are tidy squares. Suggested language if you are backed into a corner: "Except where visibility to neighbors would be less-ened by placement in a front or sidelot location, . . ."

STRUCTURE TYPE

The type of antenna support you use is really not the business of the Town—just as it cannot dictate that all houses must be colonials or ranches. In any event, be sure to preserve the possibility of using a utility pole, as well as a guyed lattice, unguyed monopoles, crank up/tilt-over and straight crank-up types of antenna supports.

As long as the discussion is theoretical, as it is when discussing the draft of a new bylaw, tell the Planning Board that requiring crank-up antenna-support structures only could be a violation of the Americans with Disabilities Act, for failure to accommodate a citizen who cannot—by reason of a disability—"crank" the structure up or down. When someone suggests that such structures could be motorized, the bylaw is quickly moving away from "the minimum practicable regulation," since only hams—not public safety, commercial or cellular communications—would have such a requirement.

GRANDFATHERING

Make sure that the new bylaw doesn't make some existing towers illegal!

COST

You don't want the process to be costly. Keep asking this question: "Sure, it would be nice to have all that additional information—such as a survey with contour lines drawn every three feet of elevation—but is it necessary?" Everything that adds cost and delay is:

1. Bad government, since it tacitly encourages some people to flout the law
2. A burden on the volunteers who serve on Boards
3. A burden on the traditional public service role of Amateur Radio.
4. Most important of all, it is illegal, because it fails the "minimum practicable regulation" test required of ordinances under 47 CFR § 97.15(b).

Suggested language: "In no event shall submission and documentation requirements result in costs that exceed a reasonable proportion of the proposed construction cost." If you have the votes, make it 10%, or $200, whichever is greater.

WIND

It is possible for a town to think that increasing the wind speed requirement may discourage Amateur Radio antenna-support structures. Here's how a response to just such a suggestion was fashioned, along with some other proposed changes to the town bylaw. This letter was created after the first draft, and before the required hearing on the proposed bylaw change. If your town is thinking of changing a bylaw, a respectful letter that says what is wrong—and why it is wrong and that suggests substitute language—can go a long way.

January 10, 2002

Mr. Mao Tse Tung
Chairman, Friendlyville Planning Board
Town of Friendlyville
Town Office Building
Main Street
Friendlyville, MA 01111 BY FAX 555/111-1111

Dear Chairman Mao:

I write to comment on the proposed Town of Friendlyville zoning bylaw amendment, Section 164-39.1 Amateur Radio Towers. I understand that a public hearing on the matter is scheduled for January 11, 2002. I ask that you read these remarks at the hearing, as I shall be unable to attend.

I represent Mr Joe T. Ham, a Federally licensed Amateur Radio operator, residing at 6 Friendly Street, Friendlyville, MA.

The proposed bylaw, as currently drafted, fails to meet several standards of Federal and/or state law. I hope that my remarks will aid the Board in its drafting efforts.

Federal Law

An analysis of Federal law bearing on proposals such as 164-39.1 begins with Public Law 103-408, October 22, 1994:

[R]easonable accommodation should be made for the effective operation of amateur radio from residences, private vehicles and public areas, and that regulation at all levels of government should facilitate and encourage Amateur Radio operation as a public benefit. Section 1 (3).

As drafted, it is hard to find "encouragement" in many parts of the proposed 164-39.1. This federal policy was originated by the Federal Communications Commission, in FCC Order PRB-1, 101 FCC 2d 952, 50 Fed. Reg. 38813 (September 25, 1985), which declares in pertinent part:

[L]ocal regulations which involve placement, screening, or height of antennas based on health, safety or aesthetic considerations must be crafted to accommodate reasonably amateur communications, and to represent the minimum practicable regulation to accomplish the local authority's legitimate purpose.

Since 1985, some courts and communities have mistakenly taken the position that the FCC rule in this matter permits a balancing of the amateur's interests with those of the community. In this regard, it is important to note the FCC's 1999 comments:

[T]he PRB-1 decision precisely stated the principle of "reasonable accommodation". In PRB-1,

the Commission stated: "Nevertheless, local regulations which involve placement, screening, or height of antennas based on health, safety, or aesthetic considerations must be crafted to accommodate reasonably amateur communications, and to represent the minimum practicable regulation to accomplish the local authority's legitimate [purpose." Given this express Commission language, it is clear that a "balancing of interests" approach is not appropriate in this context.

The Commission continued:

[T]he very least regulation necessary for the welfare of the community must be the aim of its regulations so that such regulations will not impinge on the needs of amateur operators to engage in amateur communications.

ORDER In the Matter of RM-8763, adopted November 18, 1999, released November 19, 1999, paragraphs 7 and 9.

The 1985 order subsequently became a federal regulation, as 47 C.F.R. § 97.15(b):

Except as otherwise provided herein [This refers to antenna systems near an airport.], a station antenna structure may be erected at heights and dimensions sufficient to accommodate amateur service communications. State and local regulation of a station antenna structure must not preclude amateur service communications. Rather, it must reasonably accommodate such communications and must constitute the minimum practicable regulation to accomplish the state or local authority's legitimate purpose.

Note especially that 47 CFR § 97.15(b) is not limited to "regulations which involve placement, screening, or height." Don't get the Town into a situation where wetlands bylaws, which are certainly regulations, but not "zoning" regulations or bylaws, could hurt the radio amateur.

Massachusetts State Law

In addition to the federal law on this issue, the Massachusetts General Laws, Chapter 40A, Section 3, state:

No zoning ordinance or by-law shall prohibit the construction of or use of an antenna structure by a federally licensed Amateur Radio operator. Zoning ordinances and by-laws may reasonably regulate the location and height of such antenna structures for the purposes of health, safety, or aesthetics; provided, however, that such ordinances and by-laws reasonably allow for sufficient height of such antenna structures so as to effectively accommodate Amateur Radio communications by federally licensed Amateur

Radio operators and constitute the minimum practicable regulation necessary to accomplish the legitimate purposes of the city or town enacting such ordinance or by-law.

Conflicts with Federal and State Law

Two sections of the proposed Friendlyville by-law fail to meet the tests of "accommodation" (or "will not impinge"), "minimum practicable regulation" and reasonableness. A discussion of each follows.

(1) Category-5 Hurricane Design

Proposed Section 164-39.1, Amateur Radio Towers, Section B. Requirements, sub-section (2) Safety, requires that antenna support structures "shall be designed to withstand sustained winds and gusts of a Category-5 hurricane."

Suggestion: This section should be deleted entirely. It is superfluous, because all construction must meet the requirements of Federal, State and local law. It should also be deleted for the additional reasons specified below. In the alternative, it should be shortened to read:

"Amateur Radio towers shall be installed, maintained, and operated in accordance with applicable Federal, State and local codes, standards and regulations."

(a) As proposed, B. (2) fails the test of "minimum practicable regulation."

I refer you to the Massachusetts State Building Code, 780 CMR § 3108.0 "Radio and Television Towers."

3108.1 General: Subject to the structural provisions of 780 CMR 1611.0 for *wind loads* and the requirements of 780 CMR 1510.0 governing the fire resistance ratings of buildings for the support of roof structures, all radio and television towers shall be designed and constructed as herein provided.

At 780 CMR § 1611.0, for tower structures in Barnstable County, the design standard required (the reference wind velocity) at Table 1611.3 is 90 miles per hour for the "fastest-mile" wind velocity (780 CMR 1611.3). Where the exposure (a measure of terrain roughness) includes wooded areas and rolling terrain, and is at least one half mile upwind, the design requirement is actually reduced in accordance with Table 1611.4a. In other words, the wind speed requirement in wooded areas and rolling terrain at least one half-mile from the water in Friendlyville is less than 90 mph.

There being no rational reason to distinguish Friendlyville winds from similar winds in other Barnstable County towns, the State Building Code is "practicable," and meets the requirements of both federal and state law. By contrast, a Category-5 requirement is not the minimum practicable standard.

In the past I have inquired about such things from the Office of the State Climatologist. I recall that a Category-5 wind speed has never been recorded in Barnstable County. Therefore, such a requirement would fail Federal and State requirements of reasonableness. See also the discussion below, reflecting the position of the American Society of Civil Engineers.

By applying a Category-5 construction standard to amateur radio towers, in a court action the town would face the questions: "Why is a wind speed requirement applied to Amateur Radio towers that is not applied to other structures, for which a lower wind speed requirement—the State Building Code—applies? What distinguishes an Amateur Radio use at any height, from a house, church steeple and so forth at the same height?"

Incidentally, a Category-5 requirement would also exceed ANSI EIA/TIA 222-F, the standard of the American National Standards Institute, the Electronic Industries Association, and the Telecommunications Industries Association, demonstrably causing the proposed 164-39.1 (2) design standard to fail the "minimum practicable regulation" test. If the Town includes the Category-5 standard in its bylaw, it would be hard-pressed to argue that the bylaw was passed in good faith.

(b) This section involves a subject which zoning may not regulate.

I refer you to MGL Chapter 40A: Section 3 Subjects which zoning may not regulate .

"No zoning ordinance or by-law shall regulate or restrict the use of materials, or methods of construction of structures regulated by the state building code."

The Category-5 wind survival requirement in the proposed amateur tower bylaw dramatically exceeds the Massachusetts Building Code requirement. By specifying a standard of construction currently regulated by the State Building Code, the Town would exceed its power and violate Chapter 40A, Section 3.

(c) This section represents bad engineering.

I refer you to the American Society of Civil Engineers, ANSI/ASCE 7-95, Section 6.5.2.1 Special wind regions.

. . . The authority having jurisdiction shall, if necessary, adjust the values given in Fig. 6-1 [the basic wind speed chart] to account for higher local wind speeds. Such adjustment shall be based on meteorological information and an estimate of the basic wind speed obtained in accordance with the provisions of 6.5.2.2

6.5.2.2 Estimation of basic winds speeds from regional climactic data. Regional climactic data shall only be used in lieu of the basic wind speeds given in Fig. 6-1 when: (1) Approved extreme-value statistical analysis procedures have been employed in reducing the data; (2) and the length of record, sampling error, averaging time, anemometer height, data quality, and terrain exposure have been taken into account.

Even if it were legal to change the State Building Code basic wind speeds uniquely for Friendlyville, and legal to single out Amateur Radio uses (as contrasted with all other uses) for a higher wind speed standard, I am unaware that the data required by ANSI/ASCE 6.5.2.1 and 6.5.2.2 is in front of the Planning Board. I doubt the existence of such data.

(d) This Category-5 standard conflicts with the expressed aesthetic concern.

A Category-5 design standard is clearly in conflict with an underlying intent of this bylaw; *ie*, aesthetic impact. Section B. (6) states "Amateur Radio towers shall be designed to minimize visual impact." The imposition of a Category-5 standard will **maximize visual impact**. The resulting mass of a tower designed to meet such a requirement will be a far more imposing structure than a typical Amateur Radio antenna-support structure.

If in doubt, examine the two towers on Friendly Hill Road in Friendlyville. The original tower was designed to meet either the State Building Code or the ANSI standard, and is far less obvious to the casual passerby than its twin "Category-5" design located to its south. The more massive tower was designed to meet the more stringent requirements of the 1997 commercial communications tower bylaw.

Stepping aside from the conflicts with Federal and State law, surely this Board does not wish to create a situation where more massive structures will result.

Given 47 CFR § 97.15(b), the safest haven from litigation for the Town of Friendlyville is to reflect the language of Public Law 103-408 in the bylaw and then to act in an even-handed manner with respect to amateur permit requests, which may arise at heights greater than 35 feet. As the FCC has made plain on several occasions (documents are available), amateur communications are only as reliable as the effectiveness of the antenna employed at a given station.

(2) Fencing

May I suggest:

> (4) Access Control. Fencing, an anti-climbing device, or other form of access control determined by the building commissioner to be adequate to protect public safety shall be provided.

Discussion:

As presently written, this section requires fencing, and fencing only. While sub-section (4) is not in conflict

with either Federal or State law, it should be reworded to promote the reduction of visual impact. Anti-climbing devices that blend in with the surroundings may be more pleasing and less industrial than chainlink fence.

Conclusion

Thank for you for reviewing these suggestions and comments. If I can answer any questions this letter has raised, or if I can help in any way to review possible revisions that may be made to the text of this proposed bylaw, please do not hesitate to contact me.

Sincerely,
Fred Hopengarten

The result? As a result of this letter, the 125-mile-per-hour wind requirement was dropped entirely and the suggested change to fencing language was adopted.

EXAMPLES

I am not including the following examples of bylaws because they are perfect. Nor do I include them because they are even less than perfect but still admirable! I include these bylaws to demonstrate a variety of approaches that towns use and to stimulate thinking.

Where a bylaw is not a blanket prohibition of antennas over a fixed height such as 35 feet (obviously illegal because it allows no room for accommodation), it may still be illegal for failure to meet the "minimum practicable regulation" test.

Uxbridge, MA

This example came from Randy Thompson, K5ZD, for his town of Uxbridge, MA. Randy says: "Here is the text of the Uxbridge zoning as it relates to antenna height. The zoning is very clear that there is a 35-foot height limit in town. It lists a number of exceptions as follows (quoted exactly and in full):"

> c. In all districts, spires, domes, steeples, radio towers, chimneys, broadcasting and television antennae, bulkheads, cooling towers, ventilators, flag poles, and other appendages customarily carried above the roof; ie, farm buildings, churches, municipal or institutional buildings, may have any height.

This is an example of a good exemption from a bylaw that would otherwise be illegal for amateur antenna supports.

Walnut Creek, CA

See **http://www.ci.walnut-creek.ca.us/muni** and search on "Amateur Radio" to pick up all the chapters that have provisions related. Section 10-2.3.120(B)(4) is the guts of it, found under "Zoning Part 3." This ordinance allows an amateur to install a 45-foot high structure under a specific exemption (after getting a permit and a safety review by the Planning Division). Higher antennas are allowed, but a Conditional Use Permit is required.

Sec. 10-2.3.120. Wireless Communication Facilities.

A. **Purpose and Intent**. The purpose and intent of this section is to establish development standards to regulate the placement and design of wireless communication transmission facilities so as to preserve the visual character of the City; to establish development standards which are consistent with federal law related to the development of wireless communication transmission facilities; to acknowledge the community benefit associated with the provision of wireless communication services within the City and to provide incentives for well designed and well placed facilities; and, to pursue additional benefit from the facilities to the public by encouraging the leasing of publicly owned properties where feasible for the development of wireless communication facilities.

B. **Exemptions**. The following wireless communication facilities shall be exempt from the requirements of this section and will not require Design Review Approval pursuant to **Section 10-2.4.1202** et. seq. or a conditional use permit pursuant to **Sec. 10-2.4.601** et. seq.:

1. A wireless communication facility shall be exempt from the provisions of this section if and to the extent that a permit issued by the California Public Utilities Commission (CPUC) or the rules and regulations of the Federal Communications Commission (FCC) specifically provides the antenna is exempt from local regulation.

2. Direct Broadcast Satellite (DBS) antennas and Multipoint Distribution Services (MDS) antennas which are 1 meter or less in diameter or diagonal measurement and Television Broadcast Service (TVBS) antennas so long as they are located entirely on-site and are not located within the required front yard setback area. This locational requirement is necessary to ensure that such antenna installations do not become attractive nuisances and/or result in accidental tripping hazards if located adjacent to a street or other public right of way. Wireless communications facilities which are exempted in this provision shall also not require approval of a building permit.

3. Satellite Earth Station (SES) antennas which are two meters or less in diameter or in diagonal measurement located in a Commercial or Industrial zoning district. However, such antennas shall require building permit approval and review of placement by the Planning Division to ensure maximum safety is maintained. In order to avoid the creation of an attractive nuisance, reduce accidental tripping hazards and maximize stability of the structure, such antennas shall be placed whenever possible on the top of buildings and as far away as possible from the edges of rooftops.

4. Amateur Radio Antenna structures which meet the following standards shall be exempt from regulation under this section. However, such antennas shall require building permit approval and review of place-

ment by the Planning Division to ensure maximum safety is maintained.

a. No antenna structure, when fully extended, shall exceed forty-five (45) feet in height from grade level.

b. The antenna support structure shall not exceed a width or diameter of twenty-four (24) inches.

c. No portion of the antenna shall overhang any property line.

d. No antenna boom shall exceed twenty (20) feet in length. No antenna element shall exceed thirty-two (32) feet in length. The diameter of any boom shall not exceed three (3) inches and the diameter of any antenna element shall not exceed two (2) inches; or,

The turning radius of any antenna shall not exceed twenty-six (26) feet.

C. **Review and Approval**.

1. **Type of Approval Required**. No wireless communication facility shall be permitted unless it is first approved as follows:

a. **Conditional Use Permit**. The following wireless communication facilities require approval of a conditional use permit: (I) wireless communications facilities located in or within 600 feet of a Residential Zoning District (as defined in Section **10-2.1.303(100)**; (ii) wireless communications facilities located within the Open Space/Recreation Zoning District; (iii) any monopole; and (iv) an Amateur Radio Antenna structure which, when fully extended, exceeds sixty (60) feet in height.

b. **Design Review Approval**. The following wireless communications facilities require Design Review approval: (I) wireless communications facilities located anywhere other than in or within 600 feet of a Residential Zoning District or the Open Space/Recreation zoning district; (ii) any monopole; and (iii) an Amateur Radio Antenna structure which, when fully extended, is between forty-five (45) and sixty (60) feet in height or less, and which have a turning radius which does not exceed twenty-six (26) feet.

Maricopa County, AZ

Note: This ordinance pertains to Maricopa County, Arizona outside of the incorporated cities of Phoenix, Tempe, Mesa, Chandler, etc. Don't you wish all cities and towns allowed hams to put up two towers, to a maximum height up to 120 feet, as a matter of right?!

Section 2308A (NEW) Amateur Radio Antennas and Antenna Support Structures.

1) Amateur Radio antennas and Amateur Radio support structures shall not exceed a maximum height of 120 feet (inclusive of both the support structure and any attached antennas) in any district.

2) Amateur Radio antennas and support structures shall be located in the rear yard, except in rural zoning districts on sites of 5 acres or larger where such

antennas and support structures may be located any-where on the buildable area of the lot.

3) Amateur Radio antennas and Amateur Radio support structures must meet the yard requirements of primary buildings or structures of the zoning district in which they are located, such setbacks shall be measured from the lot line to the closest horizontal extension of the antenna support structure or any attachment, including antennas.

4) Amateur Radio antennas and Amateur Radio support structures shall be set back an additional one foot (in addition to the yard requirements noted in subsection 3 above) for every one foot in height which the antenna or support structure exceeds the height limitation of the zoning district in which it is located. Such additional setback shall be measured from the lot line to the closest point of the base of the antenna or support structure.

5) Guy wire anchors may be installed within a required setback, but shall not be placed within three feet of any lot line, or within any easement, sight distance triangle, runway or landing strip.

6) Nothing in this section shall preclude the installation of two Amateur Radio antenna support structures on any lot in the rural zoning districts provided the standards of this section are met and there is at least twenty thousand square feet of lot for each antenna support structure.

7) No variances to the standards of this section shall be considered, and any Amateur Radio antenna or Amateur Radio antenna support structure requiring a deviation from the standards of this section shall require a special use permit.

Concord, MA

Section 5.3.2 Radio, television and other communication towers and structures:

In all districts, the Board by special permit may authorize the erection and maintenance of a radio, television and other communication tower(s), antennas and related structures. In the case of privately owned "dish-type" satellite receiving antennas larger than twenty-four (24) inches in diameter, such antennas may be required to be located behind buildings and/or screened by solid fences or landscaping material so as not to be visible from abutting streets and houses. Such towers, antennas and related structures in connection with the operation of an amateur radio station may not be denied unless the safety of the public will be endangered. Roof-mounted television antennas not exceeding ten (10) feet in height and dish-type satellite receiving antennas not exceeding twenty-four (24) inches in diameter are exempted from the requirements of this provision and are allowed as of right.

Passed by two-thirds vote at Town Meeting, May 5, 1997

Bloomington, MN

This comes from Bloomington, MN. It's not by any means a perfect document for the cause of Amateur Radio, but it says a lot of very good things in our favor. See CD-ROM, filename: **Bloomington Tower Ordinance.PDF** or: **http://www.ci.bloomington.mn.us/cityhall/dept/commdev/planning/regs/tower/towerord.htm**.

(E) in accordance with the Federal Communications Commission's preemptive ruling PRB-1, towers erected for the primary purpose of supporting Amateur Radio antennas may exceed 30 feet in height provided that a determination is made by the Planning Manager that the proposed tower height is technically necessary to successfully engage in Amateur Radio communications.

Other Good Examples

Check this URL to see how hams belonging to the Massanutten Amateur Radio Association, Inc, in the central Shenandoah Valley in Virginia successfully helped change an ordinance to become more amateur-friendly: **http://cob.jmu.edu/fordhadr/MARA/backissue/mon9710.htm**.

See the file on the CD-ROM (filename: **Grand Rapids MI Local Ordinance.PDF**) for how locals hams in Grand Rapids, MI, managed to influence positively their ordinance dealing with Amateur Radio antennas and antenna-support structures.

DRAFTING A STATE STATUTE

DO NOT CITE PRB-1

If you have anything to say about it, do not cite PRB-1. PRB-1 may be modified by subsequent FCC language (it was certainly clarified in 2000, by the so-called "Ham" order—named after the FCC attorney who wrote the opinion). It may also be effectively modified by subsequent court decisions. You do not want to freeze the state protections of Amateur Radio with what was available to radio hams in 1985, before subsequent writing and court decisions that proved more favorable. Leave it more general.

The first draft of the Maine law protecting Amateur-Radio antennas contained a direct reference to PRB-1. The law as passed did not and that was good.

PLACEMENT, SCREENING OR HEIGHT?

Do not limit your protections to zoning ordinances that impact the placement, screening or height of an antenna system. There are other municipal ordinances that are not zoning ordinances. This category includes such additional ordinances as "general bylaws," but hams should be most particularly concerned about wetland ordinances and historic-district ordinances.

Just be sure that the statute applies generally and to more than just *zoning* ordinances. For example, re-read the Massachusetts preemption statute earlier in this Appendix and you will notice that it is *less extensive* than the Federal preemption, because it is limited to "zoning" bylaws. Try not to get caught on that one. If you are drafting a state law, there is no logical reason that it should be less extensive than the Federal law, which will control anyway.

Nonetheless, don't spend your goodwill fighting for an exemption from historic-district regulation, unless the local authority has attempted to put the entire town and not just the town green or commons with surrounding houses into the historic district.

GO FOR A MINIMUM?

When the first California drafts were circulated, they contained language paralleling Virginia's statute. Antenna supports less than 75 feet high in more populous areas would not require more than a building permit. This drew vocal opposition from some hams, who held the opinion that the mere presence of a height number in the statute would result in local ordinances making that the maximum.

On the "greatest good for the greatest number" theory, however, many ham lawyers prefer this tactic, because so many hams do not have a need for a height above 75 feet. The really important thing is to keep open the path for hams to apply for—and have a reasonable chance of being granted—heights over 75 feet. Such heights can also be quite necessary for the purposes of a substantial number of other hams.

THINK REAL HARD ABOUT HOW TO EXCEED ANY HEIGHT MENTIONED

Do not allow the method to exceed any mentioned height to be by *variance*, since a variance presents substantially different tests when compared to a Site Review or a Special Permit, for example. Deciding what will work in your jurisdiction is the province of lawyers. Get some drafting help.

LINE UP LOBBYING HELP

Get the regional office of FEMA (the Federal Emergency Management Agency), the Red Cross and your state emergency management agency lined up to support your position. It may take some doing to find a person authorized to write a letter or to testify, and it may take additional doing to convince that person to actually do it!

A final word: Lobbying does not require Armani suits and Gucci shoes, despite the fact that it is frequently practiced that way. It does, however, require persistence, patience and politeness. Good luck!

Appendix

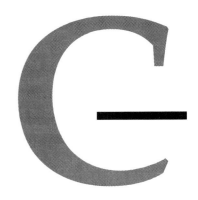

Lawsuits

This is going to be a short chapter, because the questions and answers are really an entire civics course—or a brief orientation. We'll stick to the brief orientation.

CAN I BE SUED?

Of course! You can be sued every step of the way and for the silliest of reasons. The more detailed questions are: "Is anyone likely to sue me? Is anyone likely to win?"

It generally costs money to sue someone else. When your neighbor takes her complaint to a lawyer, her lawyer will discuss the likelihood of success and the cost. Most of the time your neighbor will stop right there. However, you can never tell.

My all-time-favorite true story came from my own antenna Special Permit, right here in the little town of Lincoln, MA. Since it is instructive, I'll tell the story here. If you want to, you can find the case under: *Anderson v. Barker*, Middlesex Superior Court Civil Action No. 81-2494 (Massachusetts, 1981). Since it is a local court case, you cannot find it on the Internet or in any publication. You'll have to go to the courthouse to see the original decision.

Here's the story. After I bought my house, I sought a Special Permit under the local bylaw to erect and maintain an Amateur Radio antenna-support structure. The permit was granted to erect an antenna system totaling 100 feet in height. Within the appeal period (20 days), my neighbors to the east (the Andersons) sued the Board of Appeals (Barbara Barker was the first name on the list of Board members) to annul the grant of the permit. I was later named as a party

defendant. Here's the critical wording from the complaint, reprinted as written, for it is worthy of examination:

"One should not under estimate the force of Mother Nature and should not rule out the possibility that either the tower could fall or the 26 ft antenna on top of it could fall, depending upon the prevailing wind, on the abutters properties."

Of course, a lawyer did not draft this. Mr. Anderson drafted it himself. As I understand it, he subsequently tried to hire a lawyer to prosecute the complaint, but could not find one who would sign a pleading. He did find eventually an attorney who helped draft the wording of documents filed in the court, but that attorney would not sign any of the documents.

Readers should understand that when a lawyer signs pleadings in a lawsuit, the lawyer takes on the responsibility of seeing to it that a claim is legitimate (ie, it is not a *vexatious* claim) and that there is no fraud on the court. In addition, by signing it the attorney affirms that the pleading is not interposed for the purpose of delay.

In any event, I responded with interrogatories (a series of questions in writing to which a party must reply in good faith, after reasonable inquiry) and requests for admission of facts. These are standard procedures in litigation aimed at narrowing the issues—by requiring the parties to agree on certain basic facts such as names, addresses, ages and so forth.

As soon as it became possible, I requested a pretrial conference, which was scheduled in due course. At the appointed date and time, I was asked to come into the Judge's chambers, accompanied by the neighbors' lawyer. He entered an appearance for the limited purpose of representing them in the pre-trial conference. Since his clients were the Plaintiffs, the Judge asked him the usual Judge's question: "What's this all about?"

My neighbors' lawyer replied that his clients thought that what I intended to do was dangerous, and that they should have their day in court to make the complaint. Then the Judge turned to me. Here's the approach I took.

"Your Honor, as you can see from the complaint itself, the heart of the complaint is that one should not underestimate the force of Mother Nature. However, the good mother is unavailable for testimony, and safety is always a responsibility of the Building Inspector—who acts on her behalf. In response to my interrogatories, the Plaintiffs basically replied that there was no height or site at which I could erect an antenna system on my property that would, in their opinion, be safe. While they clearly have issues, none of them are genuine. You can't call Mother Nature as a witness."

Returning to the lawyer for my neighbors, the Judge asked for a reply. He stated that his clients would be affected by the antenna system and should have their day in court. The Judge then returned to me and I said:

"Your Honor, I've prepared a Motion for Summary Judgment for you. Here it is." I then handed the following to opposing counsel and to the Judge.

COMMONWEALTH OF MASSACHUSETTS

MIDDLESEX, ss.

**SUPERIOR COURT
Civil Action No. 81-2494**

RONALD F. ANDERSON, *et al,* **Plaintiffs**)
)
)   **MOTION FOR
)   SUMMARY JUDGMENT**
v.   )
)
BARBARA BARKER, *et al,* **Defendants**)

1. Fred Hopengarten, Party Defendant, is the applicant for a permit to erect and maintain a mast and antenna structure for his hobby of Amateur Radio. He has applied under Lincoln Town By-law Section 6.2.f., which states that a permit for such a structure "shall not be denied unless the safety of the public will be endangered by such erection or maintenance."

2. The Party Defendant, holder of the highest class of license issued by the FCC (the Amateur Extra Class), has introduced information to the record intending to show the safety of the proposed installation.

3. The Party Defendant has also produced information for the record by the manufacturer of the proposed mast, signed by a Registered Professional Engineer, and further information on various issues of safety to respond to questions raised by the Board of Appeals and at previous stages of this application, again signed by another Registered Professional Engineer.

4. Under the ordinance, the burden is upon a party opposing the grant of a permit to show danger. Yet, in almost one year's time since the filing of the suit by Plaintiff, and in all of the time since the filing of the Party Defendant's original petition on November 18, 1980, Plaintiffs have never done more than claim danger exists. No facts tending to show danger have been produced.

Under Rule 56, there being no genuine issue as to any material fact, the Party Defendant now therefore moves this Court:

To grant a motion for summary judgment for the defendants.

(signature, address, telephone)

March 16, 1982

Without going into the courtroom (you've often heard the phrase "in open court"), Judge William Garbose granted the Motion right then and there, in his chambers. The neighbors' lawyer sputtered a bit, but it was over.

So what lessons can be learned from my story?

1. I originally filed for the permit on November 18, 1980, and the neighbors' lawsuit was not dismissed until March 16, 1982, a period of almost 16 months. Litigation can take less time, or more time. But anyone can be sued for even the flimsiest of reasons and it can still take up a considerable amount of time before you may put up your antenna. It might go faster today, as some courts have gotten a little speedier. It might have taken longer, if the neighbors had been willing to spend more money

on a lawyer to prosecute their case.

2. There are some things even lawyers won't do. My neighbors never got a lawyer to sign a pleading.
3. There are judges who, when the proper paperwork is in front of them, will make decisions promptly.

In recent years, I have represented two hams who applied for Special Permits and were opposed at the Public Hearing by lawyers who were neighbors. In each case, the lawyers did not file suit after the Special Permit was granted. So there you have an interesting contrast: non-lawyer neighbors who did file suit and lawyer neighbors who did not. Such things are not predictable.

Was it a question of money? There is a joke of long standing among lawyers, "Whenever you hear a client say: 'It's not the money, it's the principle.' You can bet it's the money." In some respects, the opposite is also true. If there is no money at stake, even a lawyer who could do his own lawyering is unlikely to file suit where the likelihood of success is low. Most lawyers understand the idea of spending time on a fruitless endeavor, especially one for which they are not being paid.

The flip side of all of this is also true. If you proceed to apply for a permit for an antenna system and somehow wind up in a lawsuit, remember this line from a recent movie: "Remember that money you've been squirreling away for a rainy day? It's *raining*."

Walter Reuther, while president of the United Auto Workers, used to say: "If you can't get up from the table, you have no right to sit down at the table." In other words, if you aren't prepared to strike, you had no right to threaten a strike. In our context, you must decide just how far you will carry a disappointment, should you lose along the way or be sued after winning. You don't really have to make this decision before you start, but once a lawsuit pops up—it is a decision you get to face at every step along the way.

STRESS

In the course of my years of representing hams, I've found that being in a lawsuit can be very stressful. When I went through it 20 years ago—as a lawyer who knew that he'd win—it was stressful. There will always be questions (questions you ask yourself, questions from a spouse) that amount to: "Are you sure you want to go through with all this just for an Amateur Radio antenna?" It is a legitimate question. Fortunately, well-represented hams win a lot of these cases.

However, you should know that I think that litigation over an antenna system may have once contributed to a divorce, and I know that litigation once convinced a ham that he'd rather switch than fight. He moved to another town.

So, even though your likelihood of success may be good, prepare yourself for the stress of it all and for the possibility that it will cost something to litigate.

CAN I SUE TO RECOVER MY LEGAL FEES?

Yes. See above. Anyone can sue for anything. The real question must be: What is the likelihood of recovering my legal fees? Frankly, the answer is that your likelihood of recovering your legal fees is not good, at least not in the United States. The tradition here is that each side in a controversy pays its own legal fees, absent special circumstances.

The Kaplan, N2FOB, Case

Nonetheless, since you asked, there are some situations in which you can recover something. Paul Kaplan, N2FOB, successfully sued the town to which he moved for expenses associated with finally receiving a variance to put up his antenna system. I had some interesting e-mail correspondence with him. I started out by asking:

Subject: Re: Out-of-Pocket Expenses
I'm an ARRL Volunteer Counsel and routinely represent radio hams in tower matters. I was rereading an old *QST* the other day and ran across a note that in your case you were able to recover out-of-pocket expenses. I wonder if you'd care to tell me: HOW DID YOU DO THAT?

Seriously, did you file a motion to the court? (If so, could I have a copy? Or could you e-mail the text of the motion to me in ASCII?) Did the expenses include lawyer's fees? What was the actual amount of the award?

Paul replied, in part:

I did several strange things in my case. For example, I changed the tower to a TV receiving tower so construction could begin. [This bylaw permitted TV receiving towers as a matter of right—*Fred Hopengarten.*]

After my case was heard by Judge Fratto it was returned to the Zoning Board for them to issue the variance. After everything was all said-and-done I decided to ask for my expenses. Actually I planned it that way.

The township had me apply to their liability insurance company, which denied the claim, as expected. I wrote a letter to the township advising them that if I was not reimbursed I would sue them in Small Claims Court. I said in my letter that the township KNOWINGLY AND WILLINGLY disregarded two Federal laws and an Act of Congress. I could prove that the township knew ahead of time they were in violation of the law. The township told me that they were sorry, but they had immunity. I told them to tell the judge about their immunity.

The township finally decided it was cheaper to pay me off than to go back to court again. I was paid $882.75. I was not paid lawyer fees, because I did not use a lawyer at any time relating to this matter. I believe having a lawyer would have been a mistake. I would have had to pay several hundred dollars for the time it would take me to educate the lawyer. Several other cases in my area were lost because they had lawyers involved.

In fact my township sent two lawyers to the hearing. They wanted a postponement because they had not been able to discuss the matter between themselves. I told the judge they had 92 days since the notice of the hearing. It was not my fault they could not talk within those 92 days. The postponement was denied. If I had had a lawyer, there probably would have been a postponement, more legal fees, more wages lost, etc. They might have even settled during the postponement time, which in hindsight would have been real bad.

The $882.75 included many expenses. The ones that come to mind are $315 for a transcript of the zoning hearing; $250 for Zoning appeal application fee; $75 for the court filling fee, plus postage for the notification to the neighbors. Now the best one was $150 for "engineering fees." A friend of mine attended the hearing. He just happens to be an engineer for RCA. The township solicitor denied me loss of wages, but OFFERED me engineering costs!

We both know there are lots of hams who are engineers. This engineer was with me just for support, not for engineering reasons. He is an engineer of defense systems, not towers! I donated the $150 engineering fees to the ARRL legal defense fund.

I replied:

Aha! Small Claims Court. Brilliant! Black mail. I love it. Very clever of you to claim "knowing and deliberate" activities to blast your way through municipal immunity.

Some other questions:
1. Did you get the permit for the TV antenna tower?
2. How could you prove knowing and deliberate violation of PRB-1? Did you tell them about it at the start?
3. Am I correct that there were two courts involved here? An appeal from the Town to one court, and then Small Claims Court for expenses? Is that right?

Paul replied:

1) After a three-plus hour hearing with all the neighbors, builder, etc, I was denied. The town ordinance required a 1500 foot buffer to the next residence for a transmit antenna. A case of discrimination was now on my mind. It was October and getting cold. I knew I would win, but the ground would be too hard to dig if I did not get started soon.

So I revised my paperwork for a receiving TV antenna and it was approved within a day or two without issue (and without the zoning board). I put the yellow building permit in the window for all the neighbors to see. The builder who was still working on the street went nuts at the zoning office. One day it was denied, the next day he sees tower parts in my truck and a permit card in the window.

My inspection of the TV tower failed because there was no antenna on top. So I tie-wrapped a pair of rabbit ears on top of the tower and called the inspector back. As you will read in the judge's remarks the TV tower was a good idea on my part.

2) Deliberate violation of PRB-1: I had put all my PRB-1 documents in a binder with dividers and gave it to the zoning officer even before I made settlement on the house. The zoning officer sent me a letter telling me he gave the book to the Zoning solicitor. The solicitor also wrote me and told me that PRB-1 did not apply. I had several phone calls and letters with these two men about PRB-1. I tried to do their jobs for them because they were so incompetent. This is why I said they knew about it ahead of time. Then the zoning board had also put their noses in the air about my binder; so they knew too.

Later the judge's remarks say I would have needed a plot of land of 162 acres to comply with the 1500 ft setback. A clear violation of PRB-1.

When I lost at the zoning hearing I told them I was going to sue them. They laughed at me out loud. Less than a week later they had a summons. By the way, today I still have friendly neighbors. I still attend all township meetings and have since been appointed to the Planning Board. Some people say I've come full circle.

3) About the courts: Same court house, different court system. The zoning appeal was heard by a judge who normally hears criminal appeals. In fact the form I was given to file was a criminal form. The first question was, "What is the crime you were charged with?_____." I forget what I filled in for that blank, but it was kinda strange.

I never had to go to the Small Claims Court to collect the money. I just threatened that I would. However, it would have been a separate court and separate set of procedures. I've been there several times before. I sued the two largest banks in the world in Small Claims Court and the Goodyear Tire Company twice. I'm a regular there and was ready to go back to claim my costs.

Also: The zoning hearing is not a court. They think it is. It is just in the town hall!

The Bottom Line: N2FOB had a valid, but highly unusual, point. Where a town knowingly and willfully violates Federal law, expenses are indeed recoverable. N2FOB got back his filing fees by threatening to go to Small Claims Court.

The Bodony, K2LE, Case

K2LE (*Andrew B. Bodony v. Incorporated Village of Sands Point et al (NY)*) got even more, but again the circumstances were very unusual. In fact, fraudulent activity by his opponents swung the case K2LE's way. See CD-ROM, filename: **Bodony vs Sands Point.PDF**.

The Borowski Case

You or your lawyer might also be able to use the case of *Borowski v. City of Burbank (IL)*, 101 F.R.D. 59 (1984), in which ARRL Volunteer Counsel Jim O'Connell, W9WU, was absolutely brilliant. (See CD-ROM, filename: **Borowski v. City of Burbank.PDF**.) O'Connell convinced the Federal District Court that radio amateurs (approximately 52) and citizens band radio operators (approximately 200) in Burbank, IL, constituted a class of persons affected by a common question of law—the local zoning ordinance, which on its face appeared to violate Federal law. This created a "class action." A good class action should make any defendant town very worried, since it can be the basis for a claim for a fee by the ham's lawyer.

The Barrett Case

Another strategy is to claim fees under a state statute that permits a court to award fees where the position of a Municipality, Board or Commission (or even a neighbor!) is "wholly insubstantial, frivolous and not advanced in good faith." Just such an example where fees were awarded to someone abused by the Falmouth (MA) Conservation Commission occurred in *Barrett and Barrett v. Conservation Commission of Falmouth*, Mass. Ap. Ct. (1996) (see CD-ROM, filename: **Barrett.PDF**) under Massachusetts General laws Chapter 231, §6F. **http://www.state.ma.us/legis/laws/mgl/231%2D6f.htm**. Your state may have a similar statute. Here's the wording of the Massachusetts statute.

Chapter 231: Section 6F. Costs, expenses and interest for insubstantial, frivolous or bad faith claims or defenses.

Section 6F. Upon motion of any party in any civil action in which a finding, verdict, decision, award, order or judgment has been made by a judge or justice or by a jury, auditor, master or other finder of fact, the court may determine, after a hearing, as a separate and distinct finding, that all or substantially all of the claims, defenses, setoffs or counterclaims, whether of a factual, legal or mixed nature, made by any party who was represented by counsel during most or all of the proceeding, were wholly insubstantial, frivolous and not advanced in good faith. The court shall include in such finding the specific facts and reasons on which the finding is based.

If such a finding is made with respect to a party's claims, the court shall award to each party against whom such claims were asserted an amount representing the reasonable counsel fees and other costs and expenses incurred in defending against such claims. If the party against whom such claims were asserted was not represented by counsel, the court shall award to such party an amount representing his reasonable costs, expenses and effort in defending against such claims. If such a finding is made with respect to a party's defenses, setoffs or counterclaims, the court shall award to each party against whom such defenses, setoffs or counterclaims were asserted (1) interest on the unpaid portion of the monetary claim at issue in such defense, setoff or counterclaim at one hundred and fifty per cent of the rate set in section six C from the date when the claim was due to the claimant pursuant to the substantive rules of law pertaining thereto, which date shall be stated in the award, until the claim is paid in full; and (2) an amount representing the reasonable counsel fees, costs and expenses of the claimant in prosecuting his claims or in defending against those

setoffs or counterclaims found to have been wholly insubstantial, frivolous and not advanced in good faith.

Apart from any award made pursuant to the preceding paragraph, if the court finds that all or substantially all of the defenses, setoffs or counterclaims to any portion of a monetary claim made by any party who was represented by counsel during most or all of the proceeding were wholly insubstantial, frivolous and not advanced in good faith, the court shall award interest to the claimant on that portion of the claim according to the provisions of the preceding paragraph.

In any award made pursuant to either of the preceding paragraphs, the court shall specify in reasonable detail the method by which the amount of the award was computed and the calculation thereof.

No finding shall be made that any claim, defense, setoff or counterclaim was wholly insubstantial, frivolous and not advanced in good faith solely because a novel or unusual argument or principle of law was advanced in support thereof. No such finding shall be made in any action in which judgment was entered by default without an appearance having been entered by the defendant. The authority granted to a court by this section shall be in addition to, and not in limitation of, that already established by law.

If any parties to a civil action shall settle the dispute which was the subject thereof and shall file in the appropriate court documents setting forth such settlement, the court shall not make any finding or award pursuant to this section with respect to such parties. If an award had previously been made pursuant to this section, such award shall be vacated unless the parties shall agree otherwise. [**http://www.state.ma.us/legis/laws/mgl/231%2D6f.htm**]

The MacMillan and AT&T Wireless Cases

Finally, you could be awarded fees under a Civil Rights statute. This is what happened in the case of *MacMillan v. Rocky River, OH*, 748 F. Supp. 1241, N.D. Ohio 1990. See CD-ROM, filename: **MacMillan v. Rocky River.PDF**.

If you don't think you quite qualify as a person whose civil rights have been violated, take a look at the award of fees in (are you ready for this?) *AT&T Wireless PCS, Inc. v City of Atlanta*, CA 11 Cir., No. 99-12261, April 26, 2000, Lawyers Weekly USA No. 9918123. **http://www.law.emory.edu/11circuit/apr2000/99-12261.man.html**. (See CD-ROM, filename: **AT&T Wireless PCS v. City of Atlanta.PDF**.) In this matter AT&T successfully complained that its rights under 42 U.S.C. § 1983 had been violated when a cell tower permit was denied. This opened the gate for attorneys' fees. In that case, Circuit Judge Carnes wrote:

I concur in Judge Wilson's opinion for the Court, because he has laid out the controlling law and applied it to this case in the way required by precedent. I write separately only to note in passing how far we have come from the original purposes of the attorney fee shifting provision that is 42 U.S.C. § 1988. In discussing the policy considerations underlying that provision, we have observed that its "primary function is to shift the costs of civil rights litigation from civil rights victims to civil rights violators." *Jonas v. Stack,* 758 F.2d 567, 569 (11th Cir.1985). We have explained that the legislative history behind § 1988 shows two justifications for it: "First, the mechanism affords civil rights victims effective access to the courts by making it financially feasible for them to challenge civil rights violations. Second, it provides an incentive for both citizens and members of the bar to act as 'private attorneys general' to ensure effective enforcement of the civil rights law." *Id.* [Citations omitted.]

AT&T Wireless is no civil rights victim, at least not in the traditional sense of that term. Nor do corporations like AT&T Wireless need reimbursement of attorney fees to make it financially feasible for them to challenge in court regulatory denials that cost them money. Their financial self-interest and the vast sums at stake make them more than happy to serve as "private attorneys general" to enforce the legislative measures that they have lobbied through Congress, without the need for taxpayers to pay their litigation costs. Section 1988 was intended to help the civil rights Davids of the world do battle with the governmental Goliaths. AT&T Wireless is a seven-billion dollar subsidiary of a sixty-two billion dollar multi-national corporation. [Footnote omitted.] My, how the Davids have grown.

At first blush, your attorney may think that recovery of legal fees in that case was possible because Atlanta failed to make "specific findings" and thereby failed a required test in the Telecommunications Act. There is no such parallel requirement in the wording of 47 CFR §97.15(b).

Attorney Harry L. Styron, K6HS, of Walnut Creek, CA, also an ARRL VC, has crafted the following very tight argument.

> While *Howard v. Burlingame,* 937 F.2d 1376 (9th Circuit, 1991) was a "right to operate" case, and did not permit the recovery of legal fees, *AT&T Wireless v. Atlanta* is about the right to a process of administrative adjudication that requires specific findings for denial. You can't have "minimum practicable regulation to achieve legitimate objectives" without articulating the objectives and considering the alternatives, and the <u>Pentel v. Mendota Heights</u> court explicitly supported this concept when it wrote: "The city informed Pentel that her application had been denied via **a bare-bones letter that did not list any bases for denial**. Because the city council failed to make any factual findings [footnote and cites omitted] we need not consider whether, if it had, such findings would be afforded preclusive effect here." [Emphasis added.]

Clearly one of the best strategies is to get into Federal Court right away. Be sure your lawyer is aware of both the *Borowski* and *MacMillan* cases and understands what happened in each. All of the above said and done, don't count on getting a court to award you your legal fees. Most towns are too smart to be so blatant that a court will award fees. But it does happen.

Index

A

Accessory structure: 5.4, 6.7
Accommodation: 5.4, 8.5
Ad hominem: 6.12
Addenda to Real-Estate Offer.DOC: 2.4
Addendum to Real-Estate Offer-CC&R.DOC: A.5
Additional loss per hop: 7.28
Advertising: 8.1
Aesthetic impact: 6.3
Airspace safety: 6.2
Airspace Safety Analysis Corp: 6.3
Allies: 2.8
Alligator: 7.40
Alternative technologies: 6.15
Altman, Jim, W4UK, Letter.DOC: 11.4, 11.5
Aluminum tubing: 7.46
Anderson v. Barker: C.1
Angle:
  of incidence: 7.27
  of radiation: 7.38
  of reflection: 7.27
ANSI TIA/EIA-222-F standard: 7.5, A.9
Answer Cards:
  .DOC: 8.3
  .PDF: 6.1, 6.9, 8.3
Antenna:
  Height: 7.38
  Height and Communications Effectiveness:.........6.5, 7.7ff,
                                   7.23, 7.25, 8.6
  Nomenclature.PDF: 8.6, 8.8
  Rotator: 6.19
  Support structure: 8.1
  Support structure type: B.6
Antennas are not specified: 6.17
Anti-climbing devices: 6.3, 6.4, 10.2, 11.3
Appeals: 2.8, 12.1
  Generic to court: 12.2
  Of denied permit: 12.1
  Of granted permit: 12.1
Applicant's assurance: 6.9
Appurtenance: 6.8
Architectural review board: 5.8
ARES Letter.DOC: 7.20
Argue the law: 6.18
ARRL:
  ARRLWeb: 8.13
  Continuing Legal Education: 8.4
  SEC Letter.DOC: 7.21
  Volunteer Counsel: 2.2, 3.2
Assessor's map: 4.2
AT&T Wireless PCS v. City of Atlanta.PDF: C.5, C.6
Attorney Fees Letter of Understanding.DOC: 3.2
Attorney Fees recovery (see also Barrett, Kaplan, Bodony,
  MacMillan) A.13
Attractive nuisance: 6.3
Audubon Letter.PDF: 8.7
Average height: 6.8

Awkward post-permit situations: 11.1

B

Back lot only: B.6
Balancing: 8.5
Balloon testing: 6.6
Barrett:
  .PDF: C.5
  and Barrett v. Conservation Commission: C.5
Basic preparations: 4.1
Basketball nets: 5.5
Be:
  Nice: 1.5, 5.7
  Respectful: 8.7
Beam antenna: 7.24, 7.31
Becker, Greg, JD, PhD, NA2N: 11.5, 11.13
Bellows, Jay, KØQB: 6.21
BellSouth Mobility-Summary.PDF: 6.10
Bibliography: 14.1ff
Bioeffects: 8.6
Birds: 6.19ff
Black hat: 1.2
Bloomington, MN: B.11
Board:
  of appeals: 2.5, 2.8, 5.1, 5.5
  of health: 5.4
  of selectmen: 5.7
BOCA code: A.8
Bodony, Andrew, K2LE, v. Sands Point: ..7.10, 8.1, A.13, C.4
Bond to guarantee removal: 11.18
Borowski:
  Case: 2.4
  v. City of Burbank (IL).PDF: A.13, C.4, C.6
Bound notebook: 4.1
Briggs, Jeff, K1ZM: 6.3
Bring to the hearing: 8.4
Broyde:
  v. Gotham Tower: 6.8ff, 7.43, 11.10, 11.13
  v. Gotham Tower.PDF: 3.6, 6.9, 7.43, 8.5
Building:
  Code: 4.5, A.8
  Code, state: 6.2
  Commissioner: 2.5, 2.8, 5.3, 5.7, 10.3
  Department: 1.4
  Inspector: 1.4, 2.4ff, 3.7, 4.5, 5.3ff, 6.2, 6.17, 7.1, 10.1
  Inspector Form Letters: 10.3
  Permit: 2.5, 2.6, 7.1, 10.1
Burke, Larry, WI5A: A.3
Buying a home: 2.1
Bylaws: 6.6ff, B.1ff
By right: 1.2

C

Calgary Guidelines: 13.4
Camera: 4.3

Digital: 4.4
Canada:
  Case law: 13.8ff
  Constitutional issues: 13.1ff
  Legislative authority to amateur radio: 13.3
  Present regulation of antennas and support structure: 13.4
  Procedures, Radio Amateurs of Canada: 13.5ff
  Radio frequency interference: 13.9
  Safety Code 6: 13.9
  Tower and antenna regulation: 13.1ff
Capital Cities Communications Inc. v. Canada: 13.2
Captain Louis Renault: 2
Carman, Jan, K5MA: 7.35
Casablanca: 2
Caselaw.DOC: 8.7
Cause celebre: 8.12
CB inteference statute: 11.14
CC&Rs: 6.5, A.1
Certificate of completion: 10.2, 10.3
Child safety: 6.3
City council: 5.7
Civil:
  Air Patrol: 8.3, 8.4
  Defense: 2.8
  Defense Letter.DOC: 7.20
Closely spaced antennas: 7.33
Code enforcement officers: 5.7
Color photography: 4.4
Commit yourself to win: 1.1
Communications:
  Act of 1934: 6.6
  Act of 1996: 1, 4.5
  Local area: 7.37
Complaint, generic: 12.2
Computer: 4.6
Concord, MA: B.11
Concrete: 10.2
Cone of protection.PDF: 6.18
Construction tips: 10.2
Consumer Electronics Manufacturers Association: 6.9
Continuance: 8.1, 8.9
Conveyancing work: 2.4
Cover page: 4.3, 7.3
Crank-up towers: 6.6
Curvature of the earth: 7.26

D

DA 99-2569: 7.10, 8.5, 8.9, A.2, A.12
Danger: 11.4
  to birds: 6.19
De minimus: 6.7, 6.8, B.5
Definitions: B.5
Degradation of performance: 7.33
Deliberations and decisions: 2.8, 9.1
Delorme: 6.16
Dinman:
  No Noise Letter.PDF: 6.19, 7.45
  Saul, PE, W1SBD: 6.19
Disclose all distances: 1.2
Documents you may need: 4.1, 4.2
Don't gloat: 9.1
Drafting:
  a bylaw: B.1
  a state statute: B.11
  Drawing software: 4.7
Drive by and photograph: 6.11

Dry seals: 3.6

E

EHS: 6.17
  Guys: 5.5
Eiffel Tower: 2.7
Electric Power Study.PDF: 8.6
Elements of a bylaw: B.1
EMF: 3.6, 4.3, 7.44, 8.6
Emissions safety: 6.14
Environment: 6.6, 7.44
  Protection: A.24ff
Escape valve: B.5
Eschew a commercial use: 1.2
Evaluating home/antenna sites: 2.2
Evans v. Board of County Commissioners: 7.17, A.14
Ex parte communications: 8.2
Exposure to electromagnetic fields: 7.24

F

F layer: 7.25
FAA: 6.2
  No Hazard K1ZM: 6.3
Fair representation: 4.4
Fairfax Bird Letter.DOC: 6.20
Family, your: 5.3
Favorable letters: 2.7, 2.8
FCC:
  & National Environmental Policy.PDF: 8.5
  Amateur Radio Information.PDF: 7.12
  Amateur Radio license: 4.2, 4.7
  DA 99-2569: 7.10, 8.5, 8.9, A.2, A.12
  FAA Antenna Form.PDF: 6.3
  Interference Handbook: 7.44
  Interference Handbook.PDF: 7.44
  Local Government Guide to RF Safety.PDF: 6.14
  OET-65 Supplement B.PDF: 6.14, 8.6
  OET-65.PDF: 6.14, 8.6
  Part 97.PDF: 6.2, A.12
  Phone RFI.PDF: 7.44
  PRB-1 (1985).PDF: 7.10, 8.4, A.2, A.12
  PRB-1 (1999).PDF: 7.10, 8.5, 8.9, A.2, A.3, A.12
  Registering Antennas.PDF: 6.2, 6.3
  Television Broadcast Signals-OTARD.PDF: A.2
Federal:
  Law: 8.4ff
  Preemption: 8.4
  47 CFR: 4.5
FEMA: B.12
  Letter.DOC: 7.21
Film is cheap: 4.3
Filters: 6.9
Fire department: 5.4
Fix any TVI/RFI first: 2.5
Flat ground: 7.28, 7.35
Flying setback: 6.7, 6.8
Footprint: 7.42
Fourth estate: 8.11
Fraasch:
  Bird Letter.DOC: 6.20
  Steve, KØSF: 6.21
Franks v DiRico.PDF: A.8
Free lawyering: 5.8
Freeman:
  v. Burlington Broadcasters: 6.8ff, 7.43, 11.10
  vs Burlington Broadcasters.PDF: 6.9, 7.43, 8.5, A.10

Front row: 8.2
Fundamentals of Physics: 7.46

G

G-2 on the neighbors: 2.7
Gain: 7.31
Gartenberg.DOC: 6.17
Garwood, Bob, NØBG: 6.21
General liability insurance: 4.2
Generic complaint: 12.2
Getting to know the players: 2.5
Gillette, Richard F., W9PE: A.19
Good engineering practice: 7.7
Grand Rapids MI Local Ordinance.PDF: B.11
Grandfathering: B.6
Gray: 6.6
Great:
   Decisions: 4.3
   Impressions: 4.3
Greene, Clarke, K1JX: 2.2
Ground rods: 10.2
Gushke v. City of Oklahoma City: A.13
Guy:
   Guards: 6.3, 10.2
   Wire: 6.3, 6.7, 6.8, 6.19, 7.46

H

Hall, Gerald L., K1TD: 6.5, 7.25
Handheld compass: 4.5
Hare, Ed, W1RFI: 6.14
Harker (University of Texas): 3.6, 7.44, 8.6
Height: 6.15ff, 7.6ff
Heights Tower Systems Specs.PDF: 4.5, 7.6ff
Hennessee, John, N1KB: A.21
HF: 7.25
Higher is better: 7.38
Holes in the ground: 11.2
Home electronics devices: 7.38
Homeowner's:
   Association: 5.7, 5.8
   Association Counsel Letter.DOC: A.5
   Insurance: 6.2
Hop: 7.27
Hopengarten:
   Attorney Fees Letter.DOC: 3.2
   Fred, K1VR: 2
   Fred Hopengarten v. Board of Appeals of Lincoln: 11.16
   Maxim: 6.13
   Retainer Letter.DOC: 3.4
Horizontal half-wave dipole: 7.28
House Hunting Guidelines.DOC: 2.2
How:
   Long will this take?: 2.9
   Much will this cost?: 2.9
Howard v. Burlingame: 7.17, C.6
Humor: 6.2

I

Idelson:
   Jim, K1IR: 4.4, 8.7, 8.8
   Sander, KB1FPU: 4.4
Images: 4.7
Imlay, Chris, W3KD: 6.6
Inclinometer: 4.5, 4.6
Index map: 6.11
Informal discussions: 5.2

Information sheet: 7.2
Inkjet printer: 4.6
Insurance:
   Agency letter: 6.18
   Company Coverage Letter.DOC: 7.8, 7.14
   General liability: 4.2
   Homeowner's: 6.2
Interaction: 7.33
   Electrically: 7.33
Interference, RFI or TVI: 6.8ff
Interview, the: 8.11
Ionosphere: 7.25
Ionospheric propagation: 7.25
Isotropic antenna: 7.31
Izzo v. River Edge: 7.4, A.13

J

Jolly Green Giant: 4.4, 8.12
Just a hobby: 6.16, 8.4

K

KØQB: 6.21
K1HT: 6.4, 11.3
   Anti-climb shield: 6.3
   Anti-Climb.PDF: 7.7, 7.14
K1IR:
   Assessments.PDF: 7.9
   Assessments.XLS: 7.9
K1NU: 6.13, 6.15, 7.8
   Assessments.PDF: 6.10, 6.11, 7.8
   Assessments.XLS: 7.8
   Professional Engineer-RF Safety.PDF: 6.15
K1TD: 6.5, 7.25, 8.6
K1TR: 6.14, 7.44, 7.45
K1VR: 2, 2.3, 7.1, 8.7
   Lawyer to Cop RFI Letter.DOC: 11.8
   Lawyer to Lawyer RFI Letter.DOC: 11.9
K1ZM: 6.4, 11.3
   Anti-climb shield: 6.3
   Anti-Climb.PDF: 7.7, 7.14
   Dartantra Dr Study.PDF: 6.10
K2ASP RFI Letter.DOC: 11.7
K2LE: 7.10, 8.1, A.13, C.4
K5ZD: B.9
KA9FOX RFI Letter.DOC: 11.6
Kachina: A.3
Kane:
   Phil, K2ASP: 11.7
   Retainer Letter.DOC: 3.2
Kaplan:
   Kaplan.PDF: 12.1
   Paul, N2FOB: 12.1, C.3
KC4AAA Letter of Thanks.DOC: 6.17
Kleinhaus:
   et al v. Cortlandt: 1, 6.21
   Kleinhaus, JP, W2XX: 1, 6.21
Know:
   Exactly what you want: 1.2
   The law: 1.4
   The players: 1.5, 5.1
   The process: 1.2

L

Land use ordinance: 4.5
Langdon, John, N5CQ: A.3
Landscape view: 4.3

Laser: 4.6
Laser printer: 4.6
Late Renewal Request Letter.DOC: 11.17
Lawsuits: 2.9, C.1
Lazaroff, Mike, K3AIR: 8.8
Legal fees: C.3ff
Legal notices: 8.1
Lessons from the past: A.13
Letter:
    from a Police Chief.DOC: 7.22
    from Another Ham in Town.DOC: 7.22
    Ham's lawyer to neighbor's lawyer: 11.9
    Ham's lawyer to town counsel: 11.11
    Hams Lawyer to Policeman Neighbor: 11.8
    Hams's Lawyer to a neighbor: 11.7
    to the Editor: 8.12
    TVI/RFI Complaint by neighbor with gun: ... 11.13
Letters of support: 4.2
    from Neighbors: 7.19
Lightning: 6.18
Local:
    Clubs: 3.2
    Contractors: 5.4
    Health: 6.14
    Newspaper: 9.1
    TVI committee: 6.9ff
    Zoning bylaw: 4.5
Lowell, Mark, N1LO: 6.18

M

MacMillan:
    v. City of Rocky River: 7.17
    v. Rocky River-Fees.PDF: A.13
    v. Rocky River.PDF: A.13, C.5
Making an offer on a home: 2.4
Manufacturer's specifications: 4.5
Maricopa County, AZ: B.10
Mass Attorney General Letter.PDF: 7.14, 8.5
Matched pairs: 6.12
Matter of right: 5.4
Mayor: 5.7
Memorandum of Law.PDF: 6.9
Memphis PCS Towers-Summary.PDF: 8.7
Microsoft Word: 7.1
Minimum practicable test: A.12
Minnesota Public Radio (MPR): 6.21
MN Ornithologist Union: 6.21
Modem: 4.6
Momentum: 2.7
Multihop propagation: 7.28

N

N1LO: 6.18
N2FOB: C.3
N5XU: 3.6, 4.3, 7.44, 8.6
N6BV: 2, 6.5, 7.25, 8.6
Nancy Reagan posture: 1.2
National Electrical Code: A.9
National Environmental Policy Act of 1969: . 6.6, 7.5, 7.6, 8.5
Neader, Scott, KA9FOX: 11.6
Need: 2.3, 6.15, 7.7, 7.23ff
Neighbor with a gun: 11.13
Neighboring town: 8.4
Neighbors:
    Who Were Not Home.DOC: 7.12, 7.19

Your: 5.3
NIMBY: 8.9
No hazard letter: 6.3
Noise: 6.18
Nomenclature: 8.6
Non-plan freeze: A.7
Not licensed for this location: 6.18
NOTAM: 6.3
Notebook: 4.1, 5.6
Notice to Airmen: 6.3
NQ0I:
    Boulder CO Assessment: 6.10
    Boulder CO Assessment.PDF: 8.7

O

O'Connell, Jim, W9WU: 2.4, 2.5, 6.6, 11.11, A.4
O'Neil, Thomas P. (Tip): 2.6
Objections, specific: 5.6
Objector:
    Effective strategies: 5.2
    Type A: 5.1
    Type B: 5.2
Old technology: 8.3
Opportunity for argument: 8.11
Opposition: 5.6
Optical horizon: 7.26
Ordinances, see Bylaws
Ordinary accessory use: 7.4, 7.5, 7.15, 12.5
OTARD: A.2, A.14
Other hams in town: 5.3
Owner Permission Letter.DOC: 7.13

P

Packet radio: 8.4
Paint: 6.6
Painting and lighting: 6.2
Parise, Jim, W1UK: 8.2
Parsons, Ed, K1TR: 6.14, 7.44, 7.45
Path profiles: 7.7
Pentel v. Mendota Heights: 7.4, 8.5, B.2, C.6
Performance degradation: 7.33
Permission from owner: 7.13
Petit-Haller-MacNamara Letters.PDF: 8.5
Petitions: 2.7
Phillystran: 11.4
Photos: 4.7, 6.5, 8.12
    Perspective: 4.3
PL103-408.PDF: 7.5, 7.10, 8.4
Plan freeze: A.7
Planning:
    and zoning commission: 2.5, 2.8
    Board: 1.2, 5.1, 5.5, 5.7, 7.1
    Commission: 7.1
Plot plan: 4.3
Polar plots: 7.29
Political correctness: 1.2
Possible objections: 6.1
Post-permit situations: 11.1
Posting: 8.1, 10.1
Potential:
    for RF Interference Sample.DOC: 7.43
    Participants: 8.2
Power density computations: 7.45
Practice communication skills: 8.3
PRB-1: 6.10, 7.9, A.1, A.6, A.12
Predator birds: 6.20

Preemption: 7.9ff
Prejudice: 2
Preparation: 2.1
   Is everything: 1.2
Preparing the permit application: 7.1
Presentation:
   from outline: 8.3
   Your: 8.2ff
Press: 8.11
Presumption of regularity: 6.11, 6.12
Principle structure: 6.7
Prior existing structure: 10.3
Professional engineer: 3.7, 4.2
Property value: 6.10, 7.8ff, 8.6
   Create values study, Hopengarten technique: 6.11
   Create values study, real estate agent: 6.10
Propose in the alternative: 6.7
Proposed:
   Decision and order: 8.10
   State Preemption Statute.DOC: A.10
Protractor: 7.29
Proving a negative: 6.14
Proximity of transmitter: 7.38
Public:
   File: 8.1
   Hearing: 2.8, 6.17, 8.1, 8.2, 9.1, 10.1
   Law 100-594: A.11
   Law 103-408: 8.4, ... A.10
   Law 103-408.PDF: 7.5
   Law and Amateur Radio.PDF: 6.16, 7.15
   -service hobby: 8.4
   -service resume: 7.12
Purchase-and-sale contract: 2.3
Pwr_dens.EXE: 3.6, 6.14, 7.44

R

Radiation: 6.14
Radio frequency interference: 8.5
Radio Mobile Deluxe: 6.16
Ratios, height-to-lot-line: B.6
Real Estate:
   Agency Assessment.DOC: 3.8
   Agent: 3.8
   Buyer's agent: 2.2
   Selecting: 2.1
Reception: 7.37
Recover my legal fees?: C.3
Red Cross: 8.4
Refracted: 7.26
Registered professional engineer: 3.6, 3.7
Remand: 12.1
Renewal: 11.14ff
   Frequency: 11.15
   Request for: 11.16
   Stuck with?: 11.16
Reporters: 8.11
Respect: 5.7
RF exposure: A.22ff
RF Exposure and You: 6.14
RFI: 6.8ff, 7.43, 8.5, 11.4
Rockwell, Paul D., W3AFM: 2.2
Rohn: 8.12
   SSV: 7.5
   25G Specs.PDF: 7.13
   45G: 4.5, 7.5
   45G Specs.PDF: 7.13

Ruin our nice neighborhood: 8.3

S

Safety:
   Airspace: 6.2
   Building: 6.2
   Emissions: 6.14
   Regulations: 6.14
   Structural: 6.1
   Turnbuckle wires: 10.2
Sails on a sailboat: 6.17
Sample:
   Bylaws: B.9ff
   Permit application: 7.2
   RFI letters: 11.6
Scanning: 4.6
Scatter: 7.28
Schroeder v. The Municipal Court of Los Cerritos: 7.15
Screening: 8.6
Seals: 3.6, 5.4
   Dry: 3.6
   In-state: 3.7
   Out-of-state: 3.7
   Wet: 3.6
Second structure (see Kleinhaus)
Secretary:
   To the Board of Appeals: 1.5
   To the Planning Board: 1.5, 5.5
   Zoning Authority: 5.6
Section dividers: 4.1
Setback: 5.4, 6.6ff, B.4
   Area: 6.7
   Example: 7.46
   Flying: 6.7, 6.8
   Guy wires: B.5
Sid Leach Article.PDF: A.6
Signal hopping: 7.28
Simple RFI Booklet.PDF: 7.44
Slash: 8.11, 10.2
Sohl, Bill, K2UNK: 8.8
Southwestern Bell Wireless: 6.8ff, 7.43, 8.5, 11.10, B.3
Spaghetti defense: 6.8
Special:
   Exception: 4.5
   Permit: 2.5, 5.4, 6.2, 8.3, 10.1, 11.15
   -use permit: 4.5, 7.1
Specific objections: 5.6
Spreadsheets: 4.7
SSV: 8.12
Star Lambert v. Meade KS.PDF: A.15
State:
   Building code: 6.2
   RF Safety Letter.DOC: 6.14
   Statute on municipal hearings: 8.3
Station Design for DX: 2.2
Steamroller effect: 2.8
Straw, R. Dean, N6BV: 2, 6.5, 7.25, 8.6
Stress: C.3
Structure:
   Accessory: 6.7
   Principal: 6.7
   Safety: 6.1
Stuck with a renewal?: 11.16
Sunspot: 7.34
Supporters: 5.6
Surveyor: 3.7

Svoboda: 6.21
    MPR Radio Tower Study.PDF: 6.20
SW Bell Wireless: 6.8ff, 7.43, 8.5, 11.10, B.3
    .PDF: 6.9, 7.43
Swartz, John, WA9AQN: 2.4
Sylvia Pentel v City of Mendota Heights.PDF: 7.15, A.14

T

Table of contents: 4.3, 7.3
Tape measure: 4.5
Tax map: 4.2
Telecommunications Act of 1996: A.20
The:
    ARRL Antenna Book: 2.2
    DX Magazine: A.6
    Interview: 8.11
    Law: A.1
    Press: 8.11
    Process: 2.1
    Viewing: 8.10
Thernes v. City of Lakeside Park: 7.10, 7.17
Thompson, Randy, K5ZD: B.9
TIA/EIA-222-F: 7.5, A.9
TIMELINE.DOC: 4.7
Too high: 7.30
Topozone: 2.3, 7.7
Tower, crank-up: 6.6
Town:
    Assessor: 6.11, 6.12
    Background: 2.7
    Planner: 1.5, 5.5
Townsend report: 13.2
Transmitting antenna: 7.37
Tree:
    Height: 4.6
    Removal: 11.2
    Screen: 6.4
    Screening.PDF: 6.5, 8.6
Tri-Ex: 8.12
Turnbuckles: 10.2
Turning radius: 1.2
TV: 7.38
    Antennas: A.14
TVI: 6.8ff, 7.43, 8.5
TVI/RFI complaint: 11.4
    by a neighbor: 11.4
Two or more towers: 7.33
Types of players: 5.1

U

US Geological Survey topographic map: 4.2, 7.39
US Tower HDX-555: 7.5
USGS DEM: 6.16
Utlaut Article.PDF: 7.7
Uxbridge, MA: B.9

V

Variance: 2.5, 2.6, 4.5, 10.1
VCR: 7.38
VE2DBE: 6.16
Vertically stacked: 7.33
View shed: 1

Viewing: 2.8, 8.10
Violations, zoning: 6.6ff
Visit the assessor: 6.11
Volunteer counsel: 2.2, 3.2

W

W1RFI: 3.6, 6.14
W1SBD: 6.19, 7.45
W1UK: 6.12, 6.16
    Assessments.PDF: 6.10, 6.11, 7.9
W3AFM: 2.2
W3KD: 6.6, B.1
W9WU: 2.4, 2.5
Walnut Creek, CA: B.9
Wavelengths: 7.29
Wear the white hat: 1.2
Wester, Dave, KØIEA: 6.21
Western Civilization: 2.7, 2.8
Wet seals: 3.6
Wetlands: 4.2
White hat: 1.2
Why this height?: 7.6ff
Wild Bird Center Letter.PDF: 8.7
Williams v. City of Columbia: B.2
Wilson, Marv, VE7BJ: 6.1
Wind: B.6
Winning team: 1.2
Wireless communications facilities: 4.5
WN1NJL: 2
Wood-stove: 5.3
Word processing software: 4.6, 4.7
Work:
    Fast: 11.1
    Neatly: 11.1, 11.2
    Safely: 11.1
    Thoughtfully: 11.1, 11.2

Y

Yagi: 7.31
Yale: 3.7
Yards: 6.6ff
You misled me: 8.3
Your:
    Building-permit application: 2.6
    Family: 5.3
    Neighbors: 5.3
    Own skills: 3.1
    Winning team: 3.1
YT: 2.2, 2.3

Z

ZIP code data: 6.11
Zoning:
    Authorities: 5.6
    Board: 1.2
    Board of Appeals: 1.2, 7.1, 8.8
    Boards: 1.1, 5.7
    Violations: 6.6ff

14 CFR: 6.3
47 CFR: 6.2, 6.10, 8.4, A.11

Navigating the CD-ROM

Antenna Zoning for the Radio Amateur

The CD-ROM included with this book contains a large assortment of files that you can use in your own presentations. There are three types of files, organized into three different subdirectories, plus a subdirectory for the latest *Adobe Acrobat Reader* 4.0 files.

The subdirectories on the CD-ROM are:
- \Document Forms — containing Microsoft *Word* *.DOC files.
- \PDFs — containing *Adobe Acrobat Reader* *.PDF files.
- \Spreadsheet — containing Microsoft *Excel* *.XLS files.

To navigate around the almost 300 files on the CD-ROM, you may want to use an *Adobe Acrobat Reader* file in the root directory called **"Navigating the CD.PDF."** This file uses a menu system and hyperlinks to allow you to easily find the file you want. Shown below (left) is a graphic showing the listings you'll see.

As indicated in the directions at the bottom of the screen below, you navigate by placing the mouse cursor over the listing you want to investigate and then clicking the left-hand mouse button. This will link you to a new menu. For example, let's say you want to look at the ARRL Files on the menu below. Here's what you'll see (below right) when you click on that selection.

Note that the cursor has turned into a link icon pointing to the file **"ARRL SEC Letter.DOC."** If you click on this link you will be asked whether or not you wish to allow Microsoft *Word* to open the file—but this will only happen if you have Microsoft *Word* installed on your computer. If you don't have Microsoft *Word* installed an error message will appear, telling you that *Acrobat Reader* can't find *Word*. (This same sort of problem will occur if you try to access an *Excel* file without having the *Excel* program installed on your computer.)

You will still be able to read any *Adobe Acrobat Reader* PDF file using this navigation scheme, but you won't be able to directly access the *Word* DOC files. Later versions of *Windows* included the *WordPad* program, which can read files created by *Word*. Use *WordPad* to open a file in the CD-ROM subdirectory **\Document Forms** and then customize it and save it to your hard disk.

If you do have Microsoft Word installed, go ahead and click the "Yes" or "All" button. Then you may examine the file, edit or customize it and then save it to your hard disk to become part of your permit application.

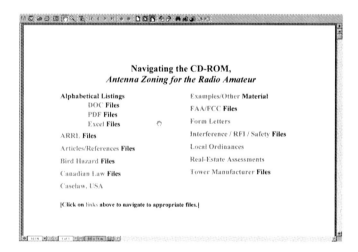

Navigating the CD-ROM,
Antenna Zoning for the Radio Amateur

Alphabetical Listings	Examples/Other **Material**
DOC **Files**	FAA/FCC **Files**
PDF **Files**	Form Letters
Excel **Files**	Interference / RFI / Safety **Files**
ARRL **Files**	Local Ordinances
Articles/References **Files**	Real-Estate Assessments
Bird Hazard **Files**	Tower Manufacturer **Files**
Canadian Law **Files**	
Caselaw, USA	

[Click on links above to navigate to appropriate files.]

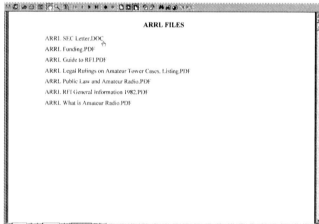

ARRL FILES

ARRL SEC Letter.DOC
ARRL Funding.PDF
ARRL Guide to RFI.PDF
ARRL Legal Rulings on Amateur Tower Cases, Listing.PDF
ARRL Public Law and Amateur Radio.PDF
ARRL RFI General Information 1982.PDF
ARRL What is Amateur Radio.PDF

Notes

Notes

Notes